THE PUZZLE MURDERS

igloobooks

Contents

Detective Sergeant Katie McCrawley has a hunch.

She's convinced that the recent spate of murders in the small town of Graven End were all committed by one person: the notorious Puzzle Piece Killer, a serial killer who taunts the police by leaving unsolvable puzzles at the scene of each murder.

The problem is, no one else in the Homicide Division agrees with her theory, especially not her long-suffering boss, Detective Chief Inspector Charlie Turner, who has ordered her to drop it and: "get on with some actual police work, McCrawley, instead of wasting my time and patience."

Still, McCrawley is convinced, and decides to secretly pull all the evidence, revisit each of the six crime scenes and put together the clues in order to catch the serial killer that she *knows* is hiding somewhere in Graven End.

However, she can't do it alone. She needs you to help her work through the puzzles one by one and work out who has been committing these vile murders. Then, she can finally make an arrest and prove Inspector Turner wrong.

You will need considerable crime-solving knowledge and extensive puzzle-solving skills to tackle the case. Nothing you read from here on should be discounted. Everything you find in the following files is a clue and everyone should be considered a suspect until you prove them otherwise.

Everything you need to crack the case can be found in the following six files. There is a space on pages 232-233 to record any notes you feel are needed about the case.

So, are you in?

Meet the Team

Detective Sergeant Katie McCrawley

McCrawley has worked for the Police for 12 years, since leaving university. She started in community policing but quickly rose through the ranks after her superiors noticed her ability to put clues together quickly. She became the youngest female detective in the force. She can be a bit abrasive, and will often irritate her colleagues without realising.

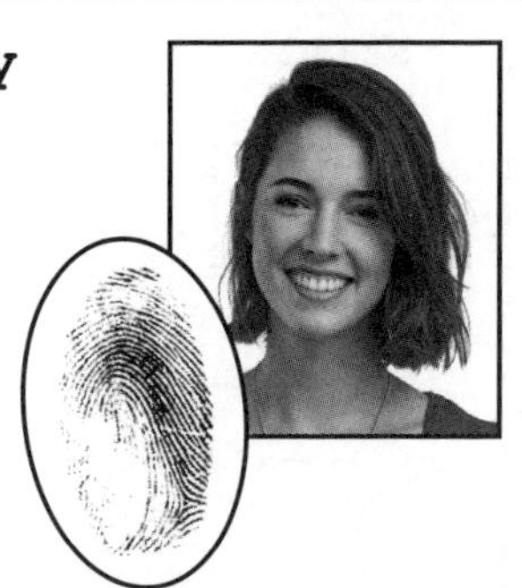

Detective Chief Inspector Charlie Turner

DCI Turner has very little time for time-wasters. He is a no-nonsense boss, who terrifies new members of the team with his loud voice and big stature. He is, however, secretly rather fond of his team, sincerely believing them to be the best of the best. Before he joined the police force, he worked in the Graven End Crime Laboratory.

Coroner Doctor Alan Easton

As the local coroner for Graven End, Dr Easton has attended each of the six crime scenes. The Crime Scene Technicians spend their time finding ways to work around his forgetfulness. He is an amateur magician, entertaining the officers at crime scenes instead of working. At university he specialised in methods used to determine the time of death.

Detective Constable Alex Summers

Summers is accidentally good at his job, often stumbling across clues and unintentionally solving crimes that would take others a lot of hard work and overtime. It's given him the reputation in the department as a whizz kid, a crime-solving savant. Really, he has absolutely no idea what is going on most of the time, and he is fine with that.

This is the team you'll be working with. Use everything they tell you to help solve the case and catch the killer.

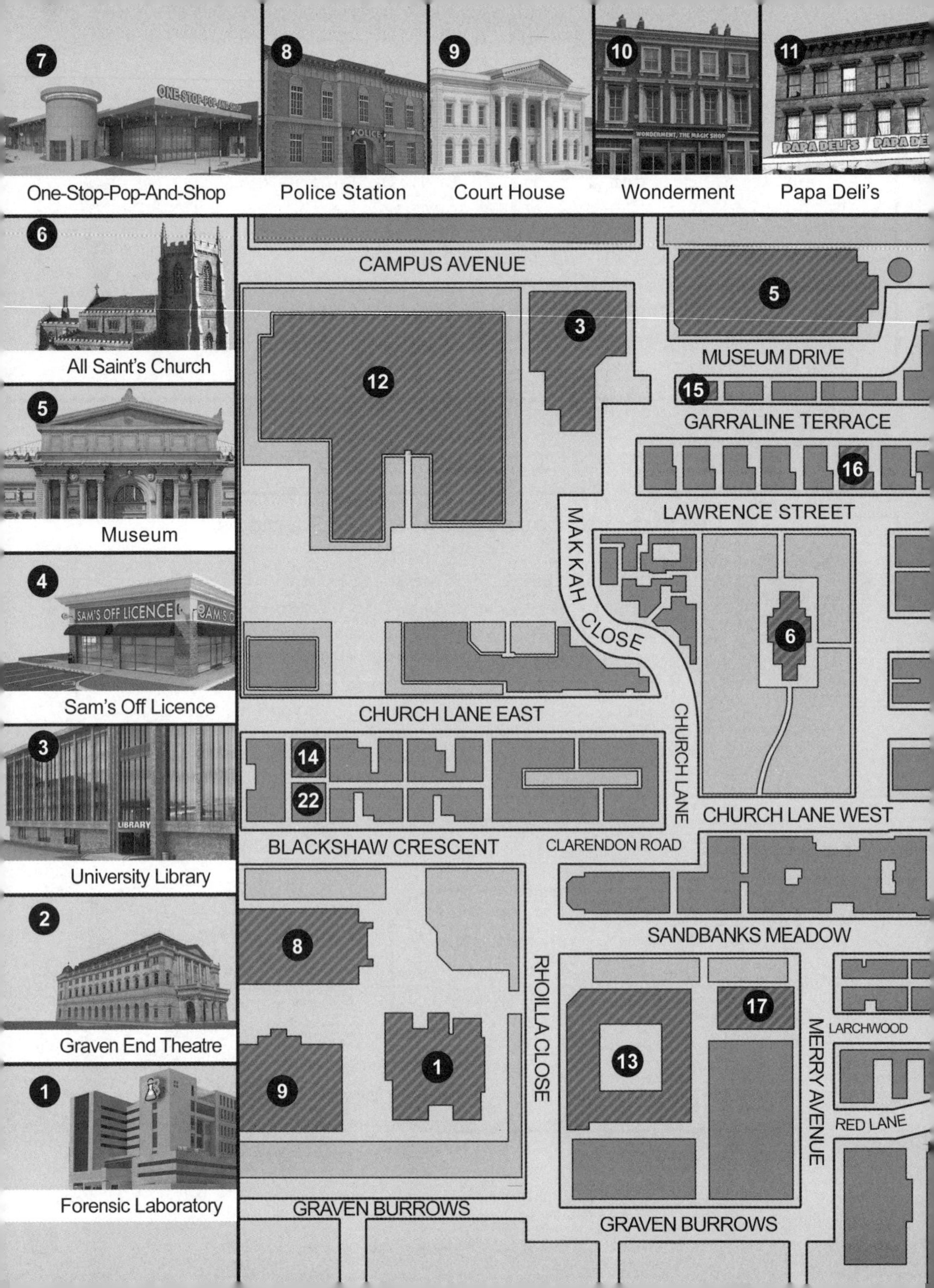

7
ONE-STOP-POP-AND-SHOP
One-Stop-Pop-And-Shop
8
POLICE
Police Station
9
Court House
10
WONDERMENT, THE MAGIC SHOP
Wonderment
11
PAPA DELI'S
Papa Deli's
6
All Saint's Church
5
Museum
4
SAM'S OFF LICENCE
Sam's Off Licence
3
LIBRARY
University Library
2
Graven End Theatre
1
Forensic Laboratory
CAMPUS AVENUE
MUSEUM DRIVE
GARRALINE TERRACE
LAWRENCE STREET
MAKKAH CLOSE
CHURCH LANE EAST
CHURCH LANE
CHURCH LANE WEST
BLACKSHAW CRESCENT
CLARENDON ROAD
SANDBANKS MEADOW
RHOILLA CLOSE
MERRY AVENUE
LARCHWOOD
RED LANE
GRAVEN BURROWS
GRAVEN BURROWS
12
3
5
15
16
6
14
22
8
1
9
13
17

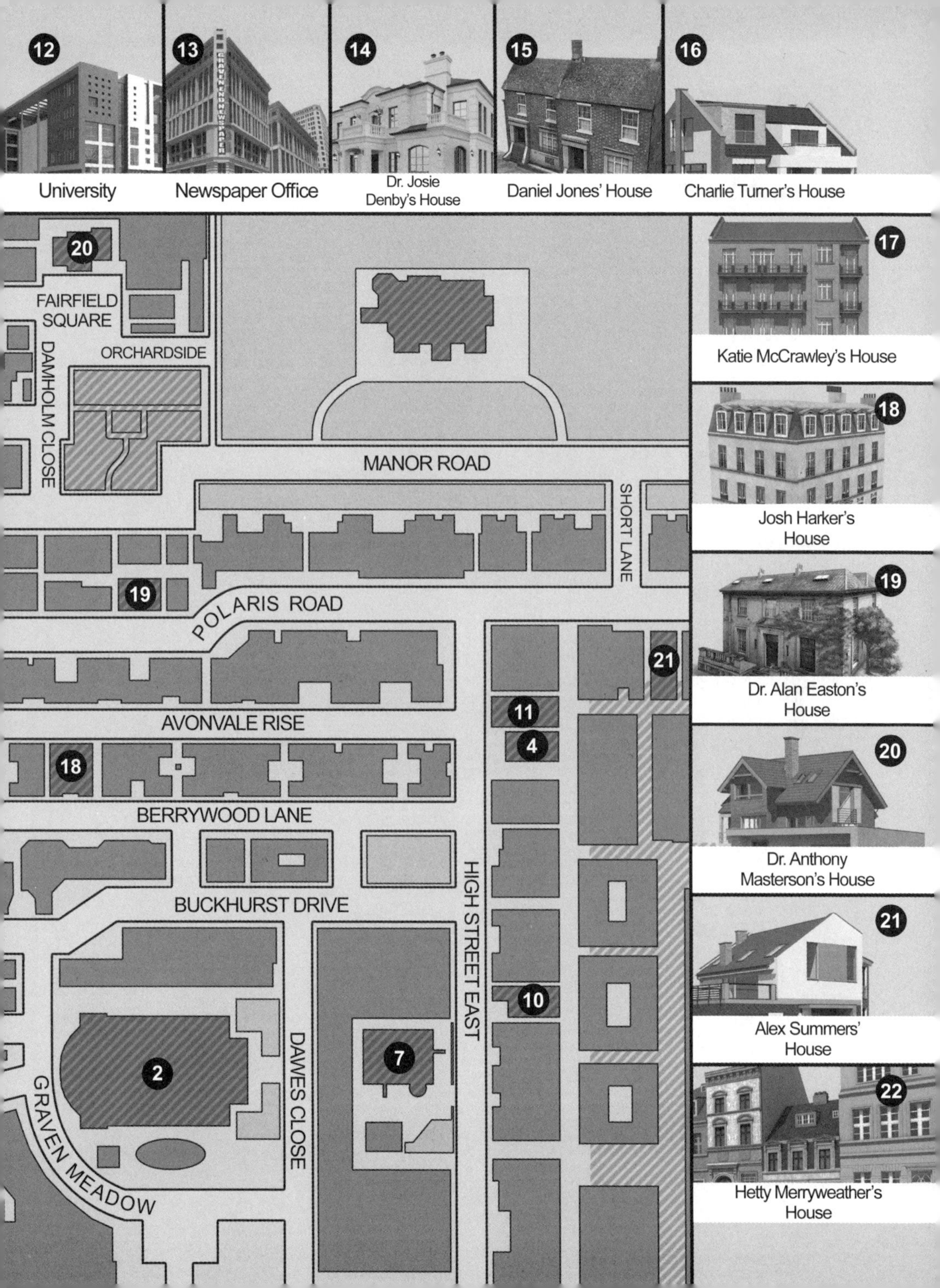
12
University
13
Newspaper Office
14
Dr. Josie Denby's House
15
Daniel Jones' House
16
Charlie Turner's House
17
Katie McCrawley's House
18
Josh Harker's House
19
Dr. Alan Easton's House
20
Dr. Anthony Masterson's House
21
Alex Summers' House
22
Hetty Merryweather's House
FAIRFIELD SQUARE
ORCHARDSIDE
DAMHOLM CLOSE
MANOR ROAD
SHORT LANE
POLARIS ROAD
AVONVALE RISE
BERRYWOOD LANE
BUCKHURST DRIVE
HIGH STREET EAST
DAWES CLOSE
GRAVEN MEADOW
20
19
21
11
4
18
10
7
2

How to Solve the Puzzles

The killer has an extensive knowledge of puzzle types. One of the officers has compiled a "how-to", for internal reference. Some will be familiar to you and others might not be.

A-Z
Each letter of the alphabet has been removed from the grid once, to leave 26 empty squares. Work out which letter fits in each of the blank squares.

ARROW WORDS
Answer the clues in the grid in the direction of each arrow.

BATTLESHIPS
Locate the position of each of the "ships" listed in the grid. Numbers around the edge show the number of segments in each row and column of the puzzle. "Ships" are surrounded on all sides by water, including diagonally.

JOURNEYS
Deduce a journey, visiting each square once, starting at 1 and ending at 100. Move one square in any direction at a time, including diagonally.

JIGSAW SUDOKU
Place the numbers 1-9 once in each row, column and bold-lined jigsaw region composed of nine cells.

KRISS KROSS
Each word must be placed in the grid once to solve the puzzle. Work out where each word goes in order to complete the grid.

PATHFINDER
Moving from letter to adjacent letter, find a path that visits every square and spells out words associated with the given theme. Start on the shaded square.

SUDOKU / LETTER-DOKU
Place each number from 1-9 once into each of the rows, columns and boxes in the grid. In Letter-Doku, the letters A-I replace the numbers 1-9.

CODEBREAKER
Work out which letter of the alphabet is represented by each number from 1-26, and place that letter in the grid wherever the number occurs.

KAKURO
Fill the white squares so that the total in each across or down run of cells matches the total at the start of that run. Use the numbers from 1-9 only and do not repeat a number in a run.

Investigation opened into death of teenager found in alleyway

Less than 48 hours after the discovery of Josh Harker's body in the alleyway behind his workplace, Papa Deli's Pizzeria in Graven End, the police have declared the death suspicious and announced that an investigation into the death has begun. While the statement named the officer in charge of the investigation (Detective Sergeant Katie McCrawley), no further details were given about the circumstances surrounding the death of the nineteen-year-old university student.

The Harker family told *The New Graven End News* they welcomed the news of the police investigation into the death of Josh. They would cooperate fully in any way that they could, but ask that "they please be left alone to grieve their beloved Josh".

Friends, family and local residents have been laying flowers and messages of sorrow in front of the cordoned-off alley where Josh was found by Sam Dreyfuss, owner of the off-licence on the high street next to Papa Deli's, in the early hours of yesterday morning. One friend who didn't want to be named, called Josh "the kindest, most lovely friend, anyone could ask for".

Mass expulsion at Graven End University after plagiarism-for-profit discovered

Nine students were officially expelled today after a three-month long investigation by the Academic Integrity Department at Graven End University uncovered an elaborate plagiarism ring, where three third-year medical students were offering essays for cash. Their downfall came when one of the professors recognised a recently submitted essay as a copy of one that was submitted by another student less than two years ago.

This isn't the first time the medical department at Graven End University has been rocked by a plagiarism scandal. More than forty years ago, medical student Leo Santana was one of two students found to have plagiarised more than half of their assignments during their four year attendance. The discovery was made by Dr Anthony Master-son, then Head of the Medical Department, and Daniel Jones, leader of the Academic Integrity Department. The widely publicised scandal rocked the local community. Santana was named and publicly expelled, but the other student's name was never released, and privately was allowed to quit.

At a time when medical students were considered to be upstanding members of society, the disgrace and public embarrassment heaped upon Leo led to his entire family moving away from Graven End under a cloud.

CRIME SCENE ONE

CONFIDENTIAL

LOCATION:
Inside a dumpster in the alley behind Papa Deli's Pizzeria, High Street.

MURDER WEAPON:
Metal dumpster

ELEMENTS OF THE FILE HAVE BEEN REDACTED DUE TO THE HIGHLY CONFIDENTIAL NATURE OF THE CASE. THE FILE AND CONTENTS ARE THE PROPERTY OF THE GRAVEN END POLICE DEPARTMENT. REMOVAL FROM THE BUILDING WILL RESULT IN IMMEDIATE ARREST.

VICTIM: Josh Harker

Harker is found inside the dumpster out the back of the pizza place where he worked as a delivery boy. The killer must have managed to get the victim's attention.

It is suggested that Harker stuck his head out—potentially in reaction to a noise—and that's when the killer slammed the lid down on his neck, breaking it instantly.

Detectives find a number of pieces of paper around the dumpster, but dismiss them all as trash. Still, takes them into evidence.

This pizza leaflet is found tucked into the victim's shirt pocket. Some of the letters have been blacked out. Can you work out the missing letters and find out if the killer left a message behind?

____

____

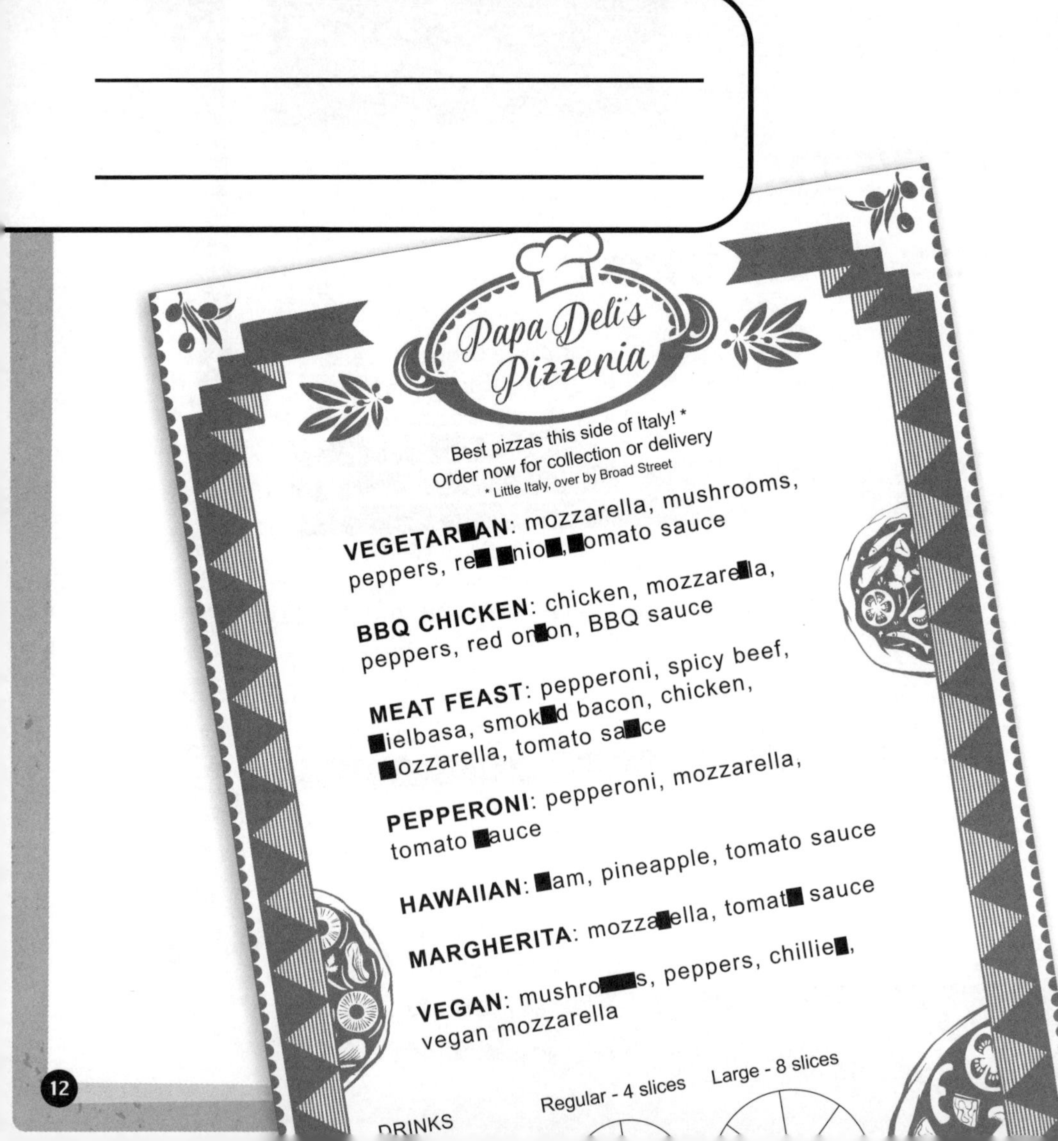

PUZZLE 2

H	P	X	X	I	R	S	W	E	E	T	C	O	R	N
H	L	I	S	E	I	V	O	H	C	N	A	E	S	M
N	O	I	N	O	C	A	B	T	U	N	A	U	S	U
S	A	S	Q	E	J	J	A	L	A	P	E	N	O	S
O	S	K	E	G	A	S	U	A	S	I	W	N	L	H
K	G	S	R	E	P	P	E	P	E	C	E	B	I	R
S	Q	C	B	M	R	W	P	S	U	K	J	Z	V	O
P	R	S	I	R	I	B	L	L	C	I	U	X	E	O
H	A	A	I	U	E	T	C	I	E	H	L	L	S	M
I	S	L	M	C	R	H	H	T	B	E	E	F	N	Z
E	V	A	S	Z	O	C	O	K	R	O	T	E	T	E
S	H	M	N	W	E	S	R	F	A	R	A	I	S	O
A	H	I	C	A	S	D	I	E	B	I	T	S	P	E
R	S	Q	Y	S	Q	T	Z	L	U	P	T	A	S	E
B	C	Q	O	T	A	M	O	T	A	N	R	B	T	R

ANCHOVIES
BACON
BARBECUE SAUCE
BEEF
CHEESE
CHICKEN
CHORIZO
HAM
HERBS
JALEPENOS
MUSHROOM
OLIVES
ONION
PEPPERONI
PEPPERS
PINEAPPLE
SALAMI
SAUSAGE
SWEETCORN
TOMATO
TUNA

Dr. Easton finds this word search in the victim's shoe prior to the autopsy. One of the words from the list does not appear in the word search. Can you work out which one?

Sara's PUZZLE PAGES

THE BEST-SELLING NEWSPAPER IN GRAVEN END

Crossword

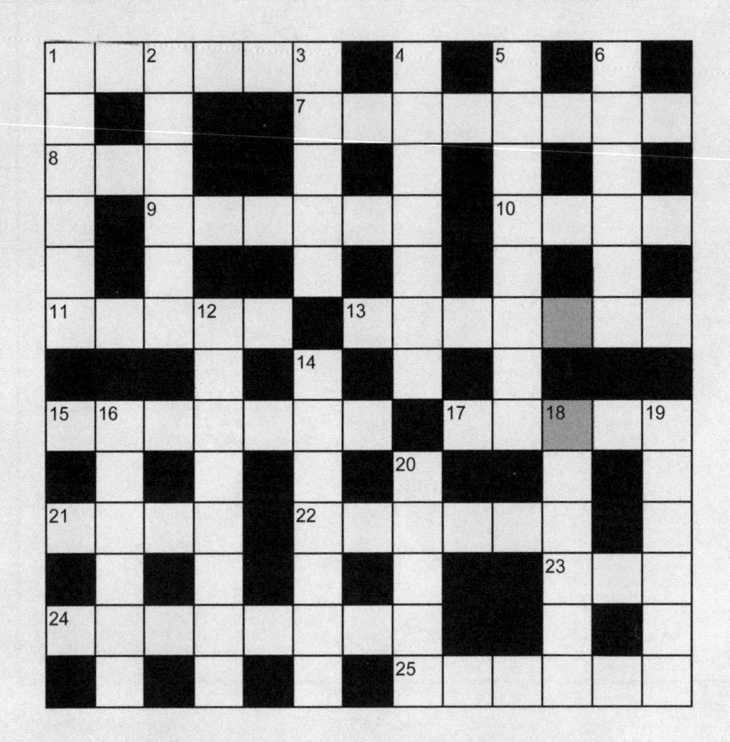

Across

1 Modern ballroom dance (3-3)
7 Speaks very quietly (8)
8 ___ Titmuss: TV personality (3)
9 Lure (6)
10 Chemical salt used in dyeing (4)
11 Long pointed elephant teeth (5)
13 Marked like a zebra (7)
15 Changed gradually over time (7)
17 Sum of money wagered (5)
21 Affirm solemnly (4)
22 Made fun of playfully (6)
23 ___ Tyler: actress (3)
24 Where one finds Glasgow (8)
25 E.g. summer (6)

Down

1 Item of neckwear (6)
2 Excuses of any kind (6)
3 Not asleep (5)
4 Composed or serious manner (7)
5 Beekeeper (8)
6 Game bird; grumble (6)
12 Unit of power (8)
14 In the middle (7)
16 In a lively manner (6)
18 Mixes up or confuses (6)
19 Ten plus one (6)
20 Attacks without warning (5)

Daily puzzles brought to you by Graven End's very own Enigmatologist

> Remember, it's always the small pieces that make up the big picture!

A - Z

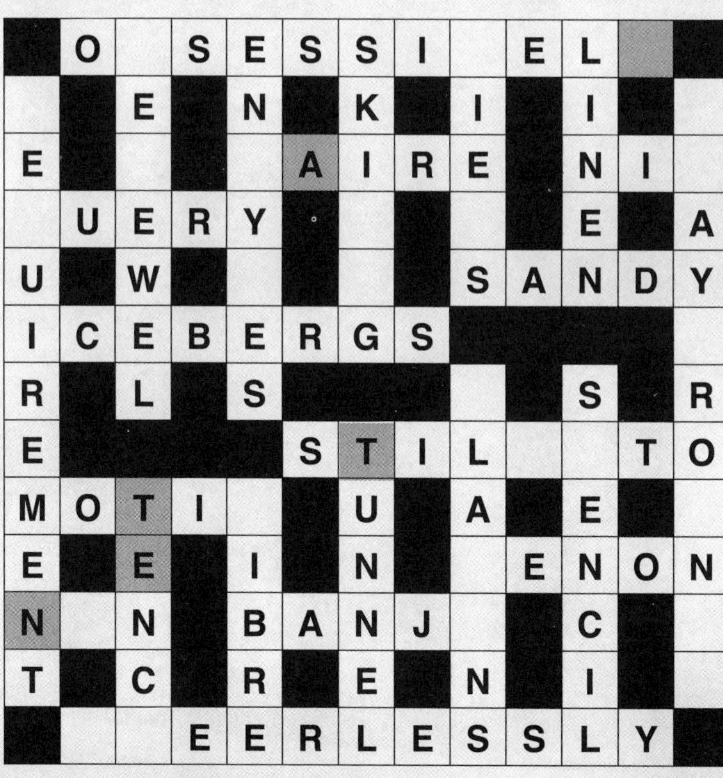

PUZZLE
5

After the victim's body is removed from the dumpster, McCrawley discovers a photo of the very same dumpster, left on top of the pile of trash underneath the body.

An additional photo is taken by the Crime Scene Techs. Can you determine **seven** differences between the two photographs?

Kriss Kross

3 letters
Ash
Eel
Eve
Foe
Lye
Nee
Nib
Not
Rev
Tor

5 letters
Ensue
Night
Poems
Thorn

6 letters
Butane
Eyelid
Ornate
Phylum
Sprang
Warden

7 letters
Placebo
Ravages

8 letters
Eleventh
Munchies

9 letters
Alleviate
Effectual
Statistic
Synthetic

10 letters
Betterment
Crescendos
Fatherland
Submarines

Jigsaw Sudoku

	2							
	4				2		1	
	7							
	9		5			2		3
			3					
5			8	3		7		
2		1	4					
		8						
		4	2					

PUZZLE 8

A scrap of paper is found in the victim's pocket. It looks like the victim listed his delivery locations in a type of shorthand. Can you use the Graven End map on pages 6-7 and the Papa Deli's leaflet on page 12 to determine which pizzas went where?

8.25 - Me - ShL
8.30 - Pep (+mush) - PR
8.40 - Me, Veg - AR
8.45 - BBQ x2 - GrM
8.50 - Veg x2, V, Marg, Me x2 - Rho
-
9.15 - Haw (+bacon), Marg, Me x2 - CLE
9.25 - Marg x2, BBQ x2 - Mak
9.35 - BBQ (no pep) - Or
9.40 - Me, Pep x2 - FSq
9.45 - Veg, Pep - FSq
-
10.05 - Pep x3, Veg x2, BBQ x4,
V x2 - Cam
10.15 - Marg x 2, Pep, Haw (ex. pine) - MR
10.25 - Pep (+bacon, +mush), Pep - AR
10.30 - Pep, Me - Da

8.25 - Me - **ShL** ....

8.30 - Pep (+mush) - **PR** ....

8.40 - Me, Veg - **AR** ....

8.45 - BBQ x2 - **GrM** ....

8.50 - Veg x2, V, Marg, Me x2 - **Rho** ....

9.15 - Haw (+bacon), Marg, Me x2 - **CLE** ....

9.25 - Marg x2, BBQ x2 - **Mak** ....

9.35 - BBQ (no pep) - **Or** ....

9.40 - Me, Pep x2 - **FSq** ....

9.45 - Veg, Pep - **FSq** ....

10.05 - Pep x3, Veg x2, BBQ x4, V x2 - **Cam** ....

10.15 - Marg x 2, Pep, Haw (ex. pine)- **MR** ....

10.25 - Pep (+bacon, +mush), Pep - **AR** ....

10.30 - Pep, Me - **Da** ....

The following pizzas are found beside the dumpster in the victim's delivery bag. Using the delivery route, can you work out a rough time frame for the murder? **3 Meat Feast, 1 Margherita, 3 Vegetarian, 2 BBQ Chicken, and 1 Vegan.**

________________ pm

Crossword

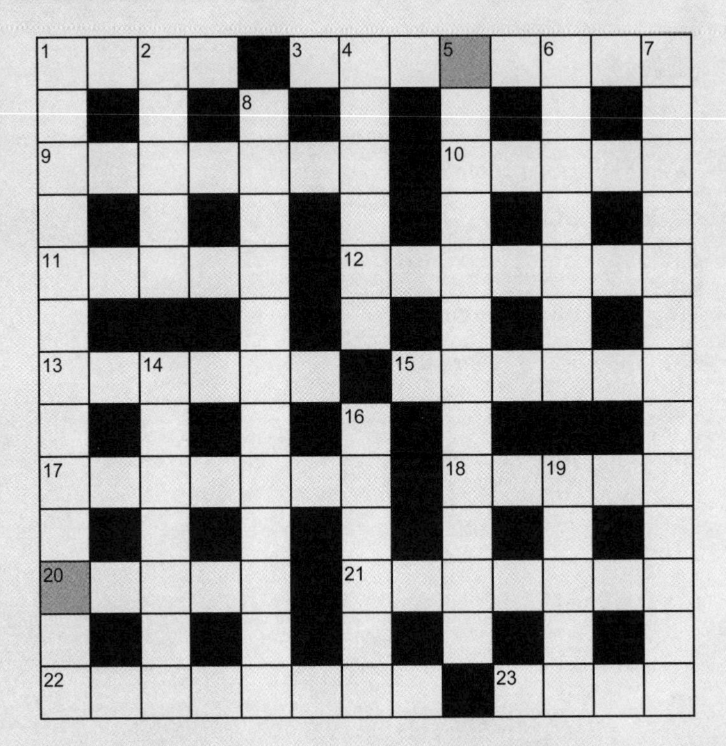

Across

1 Tall cereal grass (4)
3 Soft-bodied beetle (4-4)
9 A very long time ago (4,3)
10 Imposing poems (5)
11 Speed music is played at (5)
12 Concerned just with oneself (7)
13 Bad-tempered mythical creature (6)
15 Notable inconvenience (6)
17 One more (7)
18 Music with a recurrent theme (5)
20 Divide by two (5)
21 Freshness (7)
22 Act of moving around an axis (8)
23 Resist; refuse to obey (4)

Down

1 Codebreaker (13)
2 Furnish with new weapons (5)
4 Most recent (6)
5 Small garden carts (12)
6 Starting points (7)
7 Naughtily (13)
8 Firm rebuke (12)
14 Pamphlet (7)
16 Quickly (6)
19 Female relation (5)

Codebreaker

19	1	9	13	14	8			16		12	26	12
	16			9		26	25	9	11	6		11
8	21	6	13	9	8	21		7		11		5
	11			11		21		21	5	11	18	8
15	5	11	21	8	1	9	14			6		3
	14			24		11		9		10		5
11	9	2	26	1	16		8	16	9	9	20	9
6		1		16		8		15			26	
1		16			15	4	26	1	11	12	26	19
16	1	10	4	21		26		11			13	
12		13		11		11	5	15	21	1	26	16
26		9	23	1	15	21		13			10	
17	6	8		22			20	9	25	4	19	11

A B C D E F G H I J K L M N O P Q R S T U V W X Y Z

1	2	3	4	5	6	7	8	9	10	11	12	13
I	J											

14	15	16	17	18	19	20	21	22	23	24	25	26
D												

PUZZLE 11

Turn me on my side and I am everything, but cut me in half and I am nothing. What am I?

A bookcase is full of books. If on the top shelf a book is fourth from the left and sixth from the right, how many books are there on that shelf?

If 9 is 4 and 22 is 9, what is 18?

The victim's backpack is found next to the dumpster. A three-number combination lock has been slipped between the zippers of the main compartment, and the above piece of paper is found folded up in the front pocket. Can you work out the combination lock by answering the riddles?

After getting the lock off the backpack, Crime Scene Techs are disappointed to discover it is almost completely empty. It contains just one piece of paper, neatly folded, with the following crossword on it.

PUZZLE 12

Across

1 Finely chopped (8)
5 Blue dye (4)
8 Friend (Spanish) (5)
9 Reconstruct (7)
10 Engraving (7)
12 The North Star (7)
14 Scottish national emblem (7)
16 Table support (7)
18 Responded to (7)
19 Alphabetical list in a book (5)
20 Foolish (4)
21 Dreariness (8)

Down

1 Total spread of a bridge (4)
2 Nasal (6)
3 Reduces perspiration (9)
4 Eagles' nests (6)
6 Establish by law (6)
7 Emissary (8)
11 Inquisitiveness (9)
12 Ambled (8)
13 On ___ of: in the interests of (6)
14 Showing gentleness (6)
15 Walk laboriously (6)
17 Hatchets (4)

PUZZLE 13

Sam Dreyfuss, owner of the off-licence next door to the pizza shop, comes forward and mentions that he had heard a repeated banging sound last night. "As if someone was banging on metal", he said. The team pulls his CCTV tapes, but the camera is pointing in the wrong direction and they can't get a glimpse of the killer. However, the banging sound can still be heard.

```
.. /
.-- .. .-.. .-.. /
-... . /
-... .- -.-. -.- /
...- . .-. -.-- /
... --- --- -. /
-... ..- - /
.. /
.-- --- -. - /
-... ./
- .... ./
... .- -- ./
.--. . .-. ... --- -./
.- --. .- .. -.
```

A: .-
B: -...
C: -.-.
D: -..
E: .
F: ..-.
G: --.
H: ....
I: ..
J: .---
K: -.-
L: .-..

M: --
N: -.
O: ---
P: .--.
Q: --.-
R: .-.
S: ...
T: -
U: ..-
V: ...-
W: .--
X: -..-

Y: -.--
Z: --..
0: -----
1: .----
2: ..---
3: ...--
4: ....-
5: .....
6: -....
7: --...
8: ---..
9: ----.

One of the Crime Scene Techs points out that it sounds like Morse code. Can you work out the message the killer left behind for us to hear?

__ / __ __ __ __ / __ __ /

__ __ __ __ / __ __ __ __ /

__ __ __ __ /

__ __ __ / __ / __ __ __ __ /

__ __ / __ __ __ /

__ __ __ __ / __ __ __ __ __ __

Sara's PUZZLE PAGES

THE BEST-SELLING NEWSPAPER IN GRAVEN END

Word search: Everything starts with a G

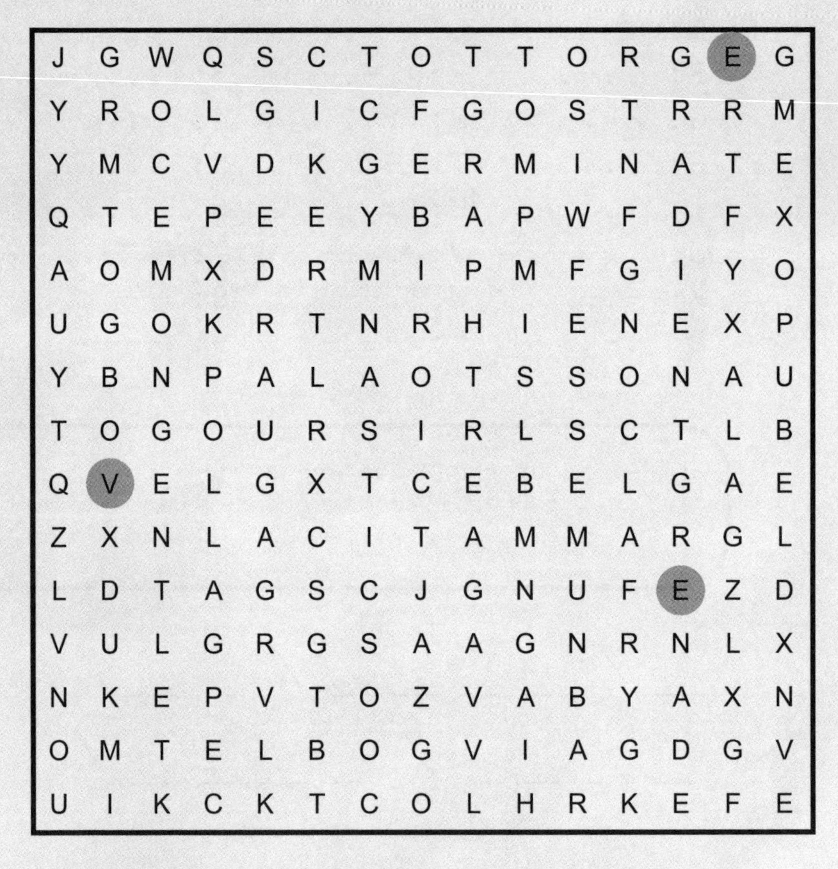

GALAXY
GALLOP
GENTLE
GERBIL
GERMINATE
GLASS
GLEBE
GLORY
GNOME
GOBLET
GOGGLE
GOVERNOR
GRADIENT
GRAFFITI
GRAMMATICAL
GRAPH
GRENADE
GROTTO
GUARDED
GYMNASTICS
GYRFALCON

Daily puzzles brought to you by Graven End's very own Enigmatologist

Arrow Words

Railway vehicle		Miserly		Jar lids		Unwell	Close at hand	Chatter
Sociable								
Ripped		Herb		Prayer				
				Stone block				
Foolish people (informal)					Liability	High spirits		People who rent property
				Detection technology				
Young kangaroo		Tends (anag)	Result		Strong alkaline solution			
Thought					Volcano in Sicily		Solicit custom	
Feud								
Feeling	Number of attendees							
Exploit unfairly				Social insects				

Transcript of telephone conversation between Detective Sergeant Katie McCrawley and Detective Constable Alex Summers.

McCrawley: Hello?

Summers: Hey, it's me.

McCrawley: I guessed. What's up?

Summers: We didn't find anything else in the bag apart from the crossword.

McCrawley: What was the crossword pointing us to?

Summers: Oh, polaris. Not sure why they wanted us to pay attention to the North Star, but there you are.

McCrawley: Then assume it's not about the North Star. Do we know any other polaris?

Summers: None that I can remember. I'll look back.

McCrawley: Okay, and the bag was a dead end?

Summers: Yup. Not like these alleyways. I've already gotten lost about four times.

McCrawley: Have you organised a sweep of the alleys?

Summers: No?

McCrawley: You're a pain. Okay, do that and then call me. [ends call]

[END OF TRANSCRIPT]

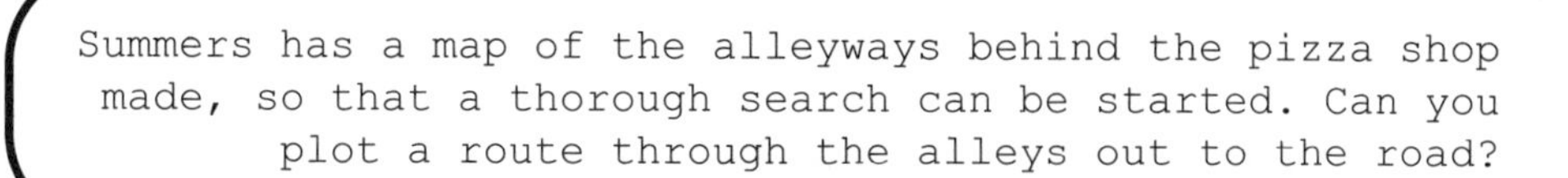

Summers has a map of the alleyways behind the pizza shop made, so that a thorough search can be started. Can you plot a route through the alleys out to the road?

Sara's PUZZLE PAGES

THE BEST-SELLING NEWSPAPER IN GRAVEN END

Kakuro

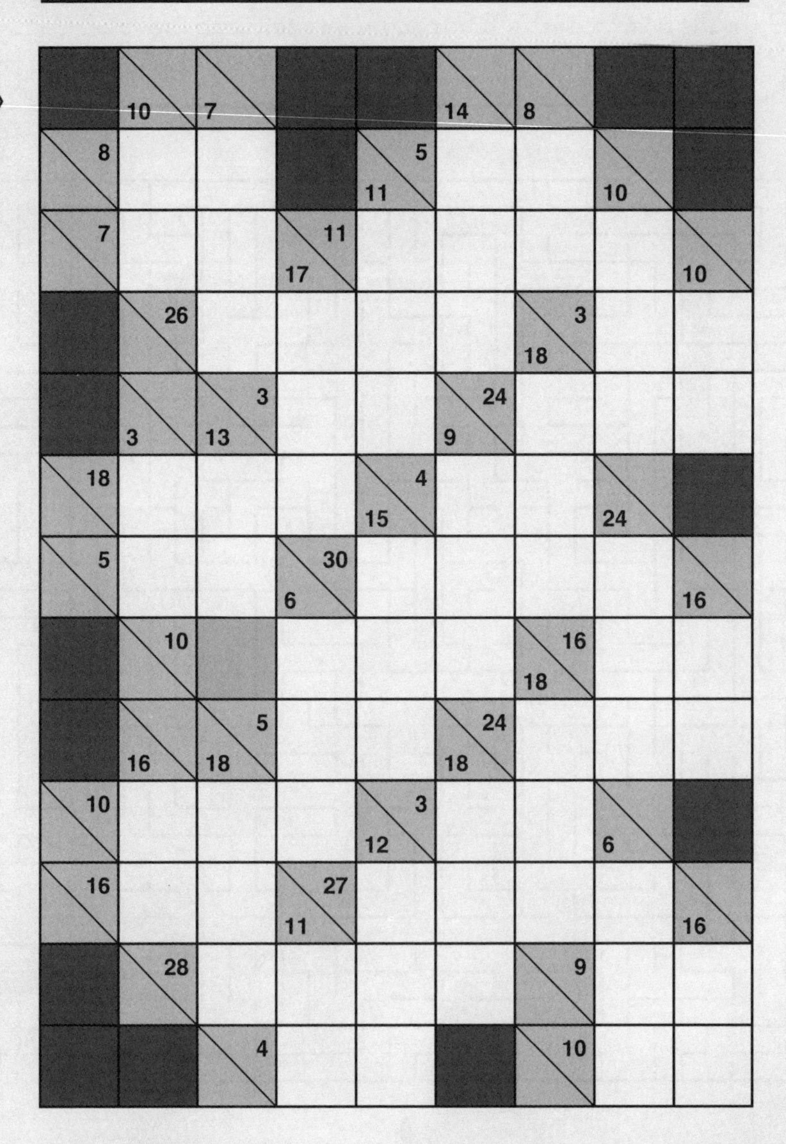

Pathfinder: Cities in Tennessee

PUZZLE 18

T	E	G	R	O	E	G	Y	D	N
O	U	R	N	K	N	B	G	S	A
W	B	G	A	L	I	I	I	B	R
N	S	F	R	P	M	R	C	V	E
L	R	E	I	H	E	M	H	I	R
A	V	Y	S	M	T	T	W	C	K
R	E	D	L	I	E	L	O	U	D
G	U	T	L	I	R	T	O	N	A
N	G	A	R	N	A	B	D	R	Y
E	F	A	R	G	T	O	N	S	M

BARTLETT
BIG SANDY
BIRCHWOOD
DUCK RIVER
DYERSBURG
FARRAGUT
FRANKLIN
GEORGETOWN
LA VERGNE
MEMPHIS
MILLINGTON
SMYRNA

We only regret the puzzles we didn't finish.

One of the officers involved in the alleyway search finds a Journeys puzzle printed on tracing paper. Summers notices that, when it is overlaid with the map, it forms a perfect grid. Can you work out down which alley the killer has left the next clue?

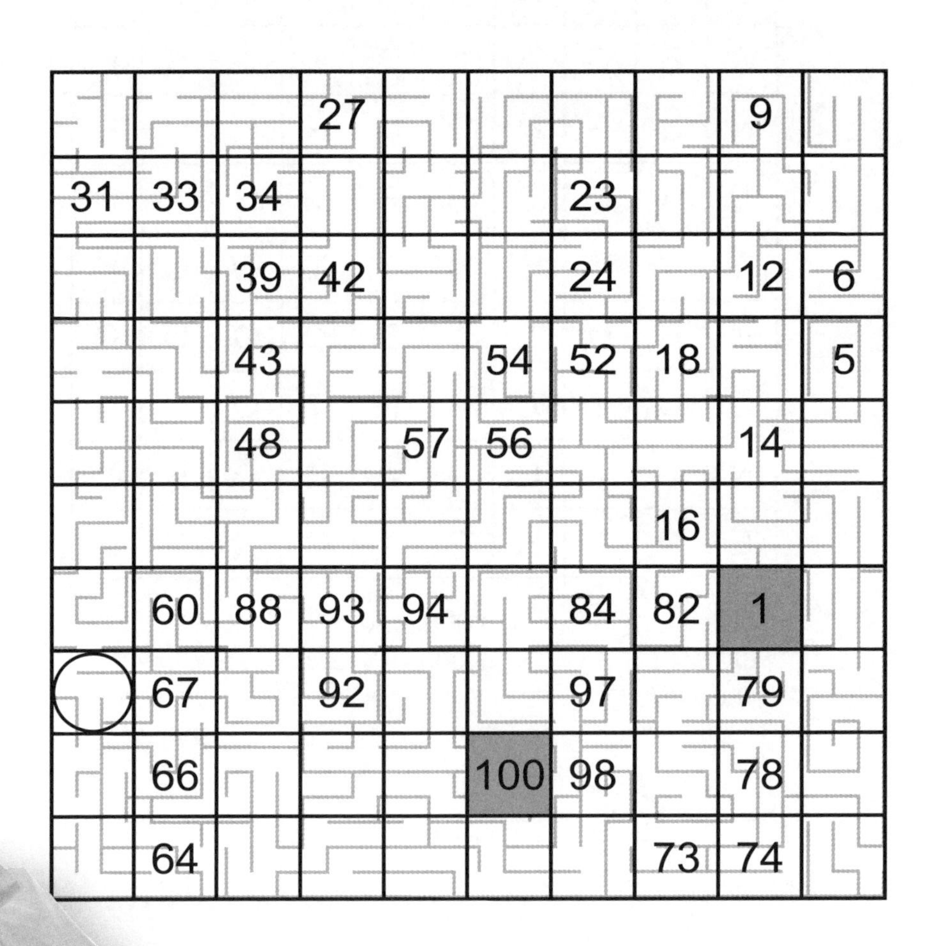

PUZZLE 20

At the end of the alleyway is a door, with five numbered keys dangling from the frame and a piece of paper taped underneath. Can you use the clues to find the correct key?

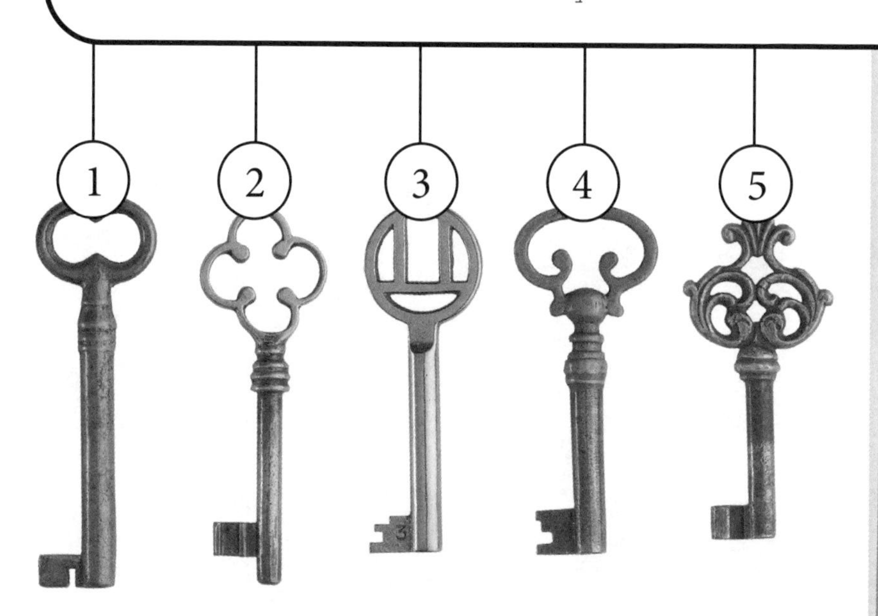

Using the clues, can you determine the order of the keys and which is the right key to open the door?

1: This key is somewhere to the left of the key to the door.

2: This key is not at one of the ends.

3: This key is three spaces away from the key to the door (2 between).

4: This key is next to the key to the door.

5: This key is directly in the middle.

One of these keys will open the door.

A - Z

PUZZLE 21

■	C	H	I		E	■	O		I	E	R	■
	■	Y	■	A	■		■		■	R	■	E
R	E	P		L	S	E	■	E	X	A	L	T
I	■	O	■	E	■	E	■	A	■	■	■	C
L		C		■	A		P	R	O	A	C	H
L	■	R	■	M	■	S	■	E	■	N	■	■
E		I			R	■		R	U	T	C	H
■	■	S	■	S	■		■	S	■	I	■	O
A	N			H		R	E	■	A		U	
D	■	■	■		■	I	■	D	■	U	■	
	E	B	R	A	■	E	M	E	R	A	L	
E	■	A	■	S	■		■		■	R	■	S
■	I		C	H	Y	■	S	T	A	Y	S	■

A B C D E F G H I J K L M N O P Q R S T U V W X Y Z

"There's power in words and in puzzles."

PUZZLE 22

Kriss Kross

3 letters
Chi
Elk
Gee
Hue
Pet
Sky
Use

4 letters
Beer
Isle
Knap
Nova
Ours
Putt
Rein
Rich
Taxi
Tows

5 letters
Camel
Enjoy

6 letters
Exotic
Yearns

7 letters
Chamber
Coxcomb
Degrees
Extinct
Offence
Padlock
Radiant
Retsina

8 letters
Athletic
Earnings
Kindling
Skeletal

9 letters
Judgement
Pseudonym

When the officers open the door a small combination safe is found inside. A piece of paper slipped underneath the safe has the words "Open with three but leave the four" written on it. Summers tries pressing just the 3 button, but it doesn't work. Can you work out how to open the safe?

PUZZLE 24

GI VK EE SF AH

IL DJ NL GO HM

UE SP HK RG RO

OS DM SL SV OD

MF KA HN YD TF

KI JM EF SS IE

TD KW HA SK BH

ID KS OB JW FN

FG AS UK JL TN

Opening the safe reveals yet another piece of paper. Try deleting one letter from each pair to discover the killer's final message.

Sara's PUZZLE PAGES

THE BEST-SELLING NEWSPAPER IN GRAVEN END

Codebreaker

10	■	10	■	13	■	■	■	9	■	25	■	10
13	14	12	26	15	12	■	3	25	7	11	12	4
23	■	13	■	10	■	21	■	25	■	5	■	13
3	13	4	14	12	21	23	■	11	12	12	20	21
12	■	6	■	4	■	13	■	25	■	4	■	19
4	25	25	20	■	8	4	25	10	21	■	■	■
21	■	17	■	2	■	23	■	1	■	6	■	21
■	■	■	22	15	13	11	24	■	16	12	26	23
21	■	19	■	26	■	18	■	14	■	26	■	15
20	3	13	20	18	■	26	12	13	4	12	21	23
18	■	21	■	19	■	10	■	16	■	8	■	23
24	25	23	11	12	1	■	11	15	19	18	26	12
19	■	1	■	4	■	■	■	13	■	23	■	4

A B C D E F G H I J K L M N O P Q R S T U V W X Y Z

1	2	3	4	5	6	7	8	9	10	11	12	13
						W						

14	15	16	17	18	19	20	21	22	23	24	25	26
V							S					

Daily puzzles brought to you by Graven End's very own Enigmatologist

Word search: Delicious Side Dishes

BREAD
BROCCOLI
CARROT SOUP
CHEESE
CHIPS
COLESLAW
GREEN BEANS
MASHED POTATO
MIXED SALAD
NACHOS
NEW POTATOES
ONION TART
PATATAS BRAVAS
POTATO SALAD
POTATO SKINS
POTATO WEDGES
RICE
SARDINES
SCALLOPS
SMOKED SALMON
SUMMER SALAD

N	K	I	L	O	C	C	O	R	B	R	E	A	D	P
E	P	S	C	A	L	L	O	P	S	W	O	Z	S	Y
W	C	P	S	U	M	M	E	R	S	A	L	A	D	N
P	P	C	O	M	R	M	T	A	J	L	P	H	A	O
O	O	T	A	T	O	P	D	E	H	S	A	M	L	C
T	T	T	R	R	A	K	S	D	E	E	G	L	A	G
A	A	I	A	A	R	T	E	O	D	L	A	P	S	R
T	T	E	L	T	T	O	O	D	H	O	A	S	D	E
O	O	O	C	A	O	N	T	W	S	C	T	S	E	E
E	S	E	E	H	C	S	O	S	E	A	A	Q	X	N
S	K	C	T	Z	I	D	A	I	O	D	L	N	I	B
G	I	I	U	Y	U	P	S	L	N	U	G	M	M	E
I	N	R	B	K	L	U	S	I	A	O	P	E	O	A
S	S	A	R	D	I	N	E	S	T	D	E	R	S	N
S	A	V	A	R	B	S	A	T	A	T	A	P	H	S

Great puzzles take time.

Use this page to record any notes or answers for this crime. This may help you to determine who you think the killer is at the very end.

PUZZLE	ANSWER
1	
2	
5	
8	
11	
12	
13	
16	
19	
20	
23	
24	

Did you notice anything strange about the puzzles in the Graven End newspaper?

____

____

From Katie McCrawley's personal notebook:

This was brutal – smashing the lid down on the kid's neck severed his spinal cord immediately. At least it was quick and painless, which is a small mercy. I liked Josh. He always made sure my pizzas were delivered first so they were as hot as possible.

I don't quite understand the motive behind this one. The killer didn't like mushrooms on his pizza? Is that it? They must be fairly unhinged if that's all it takes to set them off. Also, the puzzles make it seem like they're taunting us, but to what end?

Hopefully it's a one off, but I have a feeling it isn't. Turner doesn't agree, but my gut is telling me this isn't the last puzzle we see. Need to go to the newsagent and grab a puzzle book. Brush up on my crosswords, just in case.

CRIME SCENE TWO

CONFIDENTIAL

LOCATION:
Inside the academic library at Graven End University

MURDER WEAPON:
Monogrammed letter opener

ELEMENTS OF THE FILE HAVE BEEN REDACTED DUE TO THE HIGHLY CONFIDENTIAL NATURE OF THE CASE. THE FILE AND CONTENTS ARE THE PROPERTY OF THE GRAVEN END POLICE DEPARTMENT. REMOVAL FROM THE BUILDING WILL RESULT IN IMMEDIATE ARREST.

VICTIM: Daniel Jones

The victim was checking in and shelving a trolley full of new medical textbooks that had just come in from the printers.

Despite being deep in the stacks, it seems strange that he failed to hear the heavy wooden doors open or footsteps on the library's creaky wooden floor. It's been suggested by [redacted] that [redacted].

The working theory is that the killer crept up behind the victim and stabbed him in the back with the victim's own letter opener, taken from the library's front desk.

PUZZLE
27

As Detective McCrawley walks up the stairs to the university library, an officer waiting at the top hands her a piece of paper.

Hello, Detective McCrawley.

Can you work out where the body is?

I'll make it easy for you. It's in the only location listed in these library-themed anagrams.

casipnmurt

oilsfcstniacdi

lietts

slhscrod

aidilbrrn

vhriscae

oxetbtkos

gnenldi

Transcript of conversation between Detective Sergeant Katie McCrawley and Detective Constable Alex Summers, conducted via text message.

Summers: U here?

McCrawley: Just walking over. Easton?

Summers: No. Don't need him. Killer's givn time of death?

McCrawley: k. What is it?

Summers: Oh. Um. Not sure yet?

McCrawley: ...

[END OF TRANSCRIPT]

When McCrawley arrived at the crime scene, Summers hands her the following scrap of paper, with a shrug.

PUZZLE 28

Can you solve the following puzzle and work out the time of death?

Two hours ago it was as long after 1 p.m. as it was before 1 a.m.

What time is it now?

Arrow Words

Not outside		Part of the eye		Eternal	Entice to do something	Small storage rooms or cupboards	Birthplace of St Francis	Domestic animal
Drink consumed before bed								
Dr ___: US record producer				Otherwise				
Viscous liquid				Opposite of least				
				23rd Greek letter				Secret agent
Garden watering device		Meaning; purpose		___ Daly: TV presenter				
				Large	Turn upside down			
Egyptian goddess	Female sheep (pl)		Conceal		Jackie ___: famous actor		Public houses	
Principle of morality						Frozen water		Acquire
Measuring heaviness								
Finish				Spots				
Sent rest (anag)								

Daily puzzles brought to you by Graven End's very own Enigmatologist

> Behind every puzzle is a new mystery waiting to be uncovered.

A- Z

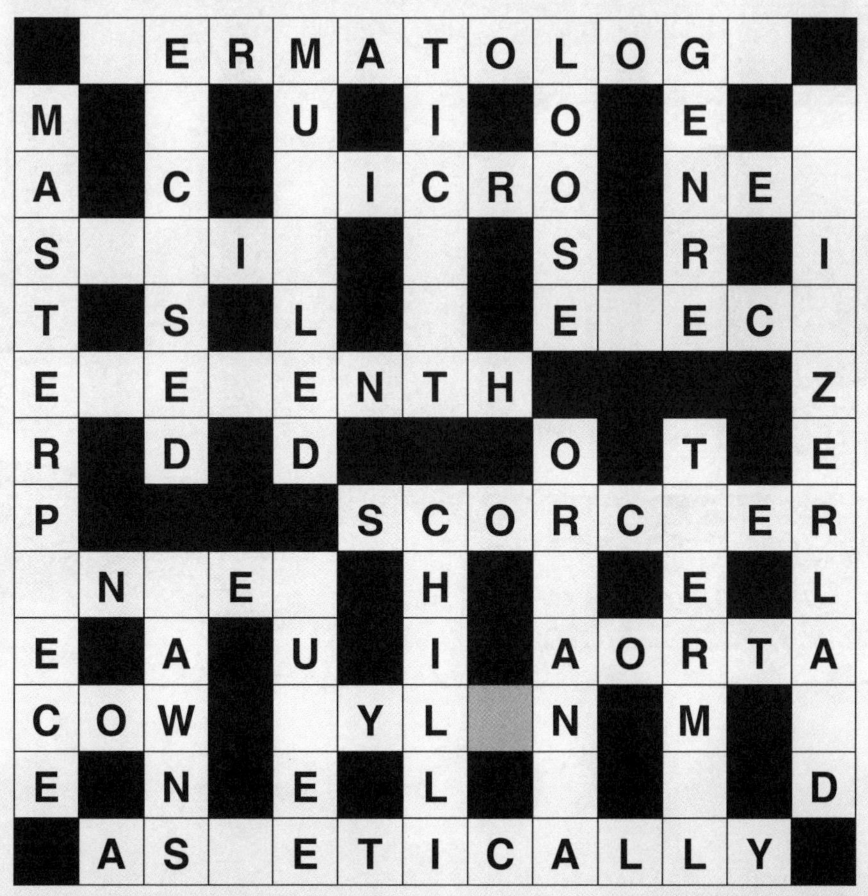

A B C D E F G H I J K L M N O P Q R S T U V W X Y Z

Once the body has been removed, McCrawley and Summers stood in the stacks, studying the location of the murder. It takes less than five minutes for them to spot that the books on the shelves behind where the victim's body had rested are not all medical texts. Noticeable, as they are standing in the medical section of the library.

Can you spot anything special about these particular titles?

Crossword

Across

1 Person who looks identical to another (6,5)
9 Assembly of witches (5)
10 Trouble in body or mind (3)
11 Ethical (5)
12 Hermann ___ : author of Steppenwolf (5)
13 Unmarried woman (8)
16 Distance marker in a race (8)
18 ___ on: urged; encouraged (5)
21 Momentary oversight (5)
22 Not well (3)
23 Egg-shaped (5)
24 Pretentious display (11)

Down

2 Resistance to change (7)
3 Hermit (7)
4 Idolise (6)
5 Period of time lasting of 28-31 days (5)
6 Incites (5)
7 Creating an evocative mood (11)
8 Byword for the British Press (5,6)
14 Cause to deviate (7)
15 Underwater projectile (7)
17 Deposit knowledge (6)
19 Very strong winds (5)
20 Semiconductor (5)

Pathfinder: Famous Books

S	I	R	A	L	C	R	I	A	F
S	I	X	O	T	O	B	Y	D	Y
A	U	O	D	E	M	Y	S	I	T
T	Q	N	S	L	I	B	K	C	I
H	E	S	E	O	N	T	H	A	N
I	G	S	Y	L	V	O	E	V	D
N	R	M	A	U	A	B	R	O	A
G	E	S	N	Y	R	E	M	A	D
O	O	C	Z	O	H	E	I	A	A
P	H	E	R	G	T	T	R	L	M

CLARISSA
DON QUIXOTE
HERZOG
MADAME BOVARY
MOBY-DICK
ON THE ROAD
SCOOP
SYBIL
THE GINGER MAN
THE TRIAL
ULYSSES
VANITY FAIR

You are capable of doing amazing puzzles.

PUZZLE
34

During a search of the library's archives, a torn up piece of paper is found underneath one of the bookshelves. Can you piece it back together?

orm

PMI
s from

GRAVEN END
UNIVERSITY

lds little value when applied
" (Sutherland, et al., 2003),
versial and widely accepted,
st-mortem reveals new ways of
better assist law enforcement.

, cadaveric spasm, PMI

e can be caused by the cadaver
thed in a shirt or a well-
cket), and the condition of
pre-mortem (an emaciated
lated than an obese one).
ot account for the pre-
of the cadaver, as
out in the elements
nowy December
rnal temperature

Vol. 46 (4), 201
International Journal of Evi

The key is in the stomach
estimations and methods
ca

Leo
Department of Biolo
leo.san

Abstract: Currently, "PM
to human remains

14, pp. 465-472
dence-Based Justice Ref
n - rethinking current
of taking temperature
davers
o Santana
gy, Graven End University
tana@geu.edu

to ... in re
but a review of the curr
of determining cadaveric t
calculating PMI estimation

Keywords: thermoregula

1. INTRODUCTION

The body maintains a co
temperature of approx
(98.6°F), the optimum
the thousands of che
needed for life. As bra
so does the cessatio
body functions. Th
which controls th
feature of thermoreg
function and the t

estimation approach ho
l criminal investigation,
ent methods, both contro
emperature immediately pos
is, allowing forensic teams to

tion, soup, tissue dehydration

onstant internal
ximately 37°C
temperature for
mical reactions
in-death occurs,
n of autonomic
hypothalamus,
e homoeostatic
ulation, ceases to

difference
being clo
insulated ja
the cadaver p
body less is insu
It also does no
mortem temperature
someone who has been o
for hours during a sn
would have a lower inte

cadaver in question b
syncing with the an
of the area in whi
This cooling is kno
Research
Al-Alousi, et al.
that there can be
three hours post-
temperature of
to drop, which
widely accepted
decrease per hou
measurement d
account externa
of the cadaver
position?), the
subzero tempe
environmental
rate than thos
the presence c

begins to warm up,
nbient temperature
ch death occurred.
wn as algor mortis.
carried out by
in 2002, shows
a delay of up to
mortem before the
the cadaver begins
contrasts with the
rate of a 1°C (33.8°F)
r. Also, this accepted
oes not take into
factors: the position
(is it in the foetal
location (bodies in
ratures will reach an
equilibrium at a faster
e in humid climates),
f clothing (temperature

the same period. Nev
Cooling is inefficient,
can not be imputed int
The accuracy with whic
temperature can currentl
remains less than is p
reliable forensic patholo
This article will lo
methods that can be appli
in order to obtain a much
temperature at the time
gaining more knowledge
we will be able to offer
COD recommendations an
assistance to law enforcem

2. THE SOUP METHOD

One controversial, but wide
of obtaining cadaveric tempe
soup method. The pathologist
(9 in) glass needle and careful

indoors during
wton's Law of
as these factors
o the equation.
ch post-mortem
y be calculated
referred for a
ogical opinion.
ok at various
ed to cadavers
more accurate
of death. By
in this area,
more precise
d give better
nent officials.

ly used way
rature is the
uses a 23 cm
lly inserts it

Sara's PUZZLE PAGES

THE BEST-SELLING NEWSPAPER IN GRAVEN END

Codebreaker

16	11	18	13	8	9	2	21		26	21	11	9
3		3		11		16		2		22		2
26	13	3	15	4		22		3	12	1	10	15
10		1		4		1		1		5		22
			7	10	4	4	22	26	3	1	10	5
1		10		15		20		10		10		22
10	6	13	3	26	10		13	15	10	26	10	4
12		22		2		15		17		26		23
2	3	14	14	3	25	11	22	9	14			
3		3		4		26		4		18		24
18	9	19	22	2		26		3	15	22	8	22
10		11		16		22		15		1		1
15	10	10	21		14	9	5	23	14	22	21	10

A B C D E F G H I J K L M N O P Q R S T U V W X Y Z

1	2	3	4	5	6	7	8	9	10	11	12	13
									E			P

14	15	16	17	18	19	20	21	22	23	24	25	26
							K					

Word search: Countries of Europe

Y	D	L	Z	I	A	R	Y	L	X	Z	D	L	C	L
X	I	R	E	L	A	N	D	N	A	L	O	P	S	T
W	L	F	B	U	L	G	A	R	I	A	L	S	P	P
Y	R	C	N	X	C	A	Y	D	F	T	L	K	A	A
C	A	C	Z	E	C	H	R	E	P	U	B	L	I	C
O	Y	W	L	M	T	E	R	N	K	P	C	A	N	C
H	X	P	R	B	E	H	I	M	M	R	E	G	A	E
V	M	V	R	O	A	I	E	A	E	A	U	U	I	B
S	L	U	A	U	N	P	L	R	V	I	S	T	K	T
F	C	A	I	R	S	T	K	K	L	T	E	R	A	I
R	H	U	N	G	A	R	Y	L	R	A	C	O	V	X
S	X	M	N	I	L	D	R	I	B	O	N	P	O	P
S	G	R	E	E	C	E	A	I	L	R	A	D	L	E
T	M	R	P	S	T	A	B	M	L	C	R	T	S	T
U	D	E	S	G	N	E	D	E	W	S	F	K	M	Y

AUSTRIA
BELGIUM
BULGARIA
CROATIA
CYPRUS
CZECH REPUBLIC
DENMARK
FRANCE
GREECE
HUNGARY
IRELAND
LUXEMBOURG
MALTA
NETHERLANDS
NORWAY
POLAND
PORTUGAL
SLOVAKIA
SPAIN
SWEDEN
TURKEY

PUZZLE 37

Stack #42

One among these seven holds the answer you crave.
And there's a clue in the answer, and a life you could save.
The tome you're after is neither short, nor tall.
Its title has just letters and no numbers at all.
You won't find it at the start, the middle, or end.
And when looking for answers, food isn't your friend.
The category is fiction, because fantasy is best,
So books about real people won't help in this quest.
Finally, the story's about magic, knights and of mages.
Understand, there are no feathers betwixt these pages.

One of the Crime Scene Techs hands McCrawley a piece of paper that has been found in the bin beside the library's front desk, where the victim had been working.

Can you use the riddle on the left and the photo below to work out which of the books the killer is directing us to?

Sara's PUZZLE PAGES

THE BEST-SELLING NEWSPAPER IN GRAVEN END

PUZZLE 38

Letter-Doku!

	B			A				
			D		G	B	A	
F	D				E		G	
H	F	D	G		A	C		
		I	F		D	G	B	H
	E		H				C	G
	G	B	E		F			
				G			F	

A new one for you today, fellow puzzlers. This is just like regular sudoku, but I've replaced the numbers 1–9 with the letters A–I. Easy-peasy.

Sara x

Daily puzzles brought to you by Graven End's very own Enigmatologist

Crossword

PUZZLE 39

Across

1 Makes a garment from wool (5)
4 Skilled job (5)
10 Dignified conduct (7)
11 Tycoon (5)
12 Destroy (4)
13 Taking to be true (8)
16 Detects; feels (6)
17 Put on a production (6)
20 False impression (8)
21 Cut (4)
23 Single seed of a cereal (5)
25 Flight hub (7)
26 Unwanted plants (5)
27 Amplify a signal (5)

Down

2 Active at night (9)
3 Period of imprisonment (4)
5 Gets back on a horse (8)
6 Mist (3)
7 Loves dearly (6)
8 Entertain (5)
9 Stop up a hole (4)
14 Unsuspecting; innocent (9)
15 Diminished (8)
18 Repositories (6)
19 Pertaining to the sun (5)
20 Canines (4)
22 Bond movie (2,2)
24 Affirmative vote (3)

■	1	2		3		■	4	5		6		■
7	■		■		■	8	■		■		■	9
10							■	11				
	■		■		■		■		■	■	■	
12				■	13					14		
	■		■	15	■		■		■		■	■
16						■	17					18
■	■		■		■	19	■		■		■	
20								■	21			
	■	■	■		■		■	22	■		■	
23		24			■	25						
	■		■		■		■		■		■	
■	26					■	27					■

PUZZLE 40

Written in pencil inside the front cover of The Elephant's Castle is a note to turn to "page 394". A codeword puzzle has been pasted onto the page.

The Elephant turned to the girl and laughed. "There's

26		6		20				5		8		16
8	6	13	13	15	21		25	1	18	22	6	1
15		22		22		12		17		6		6
20	6	3	6	9	22	6		22	3	7	4	19
20		23		22		22		25		19		21
22	10	6	12		6	11	4	4	24			
18		21		24		21		10		9		26
			25	4	6	2	21		18	8	22	6
21		11		13		18		20		22		11
26	18	6	2	8		4	7	22	18	6	9	2
22		2		4		12		6		2		14
6	21	8	4	18	22		6	9	9	22	23	22
18		22		3				8		23		21

A B C D E F G H I J K L M N O P Q R S T U V W X Y Z

1	2	3	4	5	6	7	8	9	10	11	12	13
1	1	N	1				2	3	1			

14	15	16	17	18	19	20	21	22	23	24	25	26
	2		K	1		P	2	2	1			

book

"No!" cried the girl. "That's not true. ... and bathes and your family. He feeds you and brings you treats, and bathes ... if you can carry people around or

McCrawley thinks that the killer is leading them towards the title of a book they've probably come across before. Do you agree?

Anagram

Numbers - how many times a letter is used?

Arrow Words

Piece of code to automate a task	Area of land	Make less miserable	Kingdom	Sphere or globe	Lacking knowledge		Type of bus (6-6)	
					Sticky substance			
US pop star					Marine flatfish		Wireless	
Assimilate again								
Slippery fish				By word of mouth				
Jellylike citrus preserve		Large deer	Smell	___ Blyton: writer				
				Makes a mistake	Foot extremity			
Short note	Lyric poems					Pay (anag)	Shola ___: singer	
Barrier between rooms					Wild ox			
Ales	Eg Jones or Smith							
					Level golf score			

Kriss Kross

PUZZLE 43

3 letters
Sec
Yet

4 letters
Help
Tack

5 letters
Carve
Nanny
Pilot
Stray

6 letters
Entrap
Greens
Ironic
Prises
Sample
Slalom

7 letters
Annexes
Compute
Concept
Lasagne
Skidded
Smelled
Studied
Wattage

8 letters
Ailments
Anaconda
Ballpark
Clarinet
Littoral
Predator

9 letters
Authentic
Developed

A library assistant explains that the library holds over 300 different copies of *The Codex Chrisicus*, and there are around 298 in stock, which is too many to search efficiently. When McCrawley types the title into the system, a blank screen with the following puzzle appears.

6	2	9	7	8	3	5	6	7	3	9	1	6	9	9
6	7	3	9	4	6	8	9	2	7	2	9	1	7	0
9	3	9	7	8	0	9	0	8	8	2	7	4	8	3
7	7	7	8	1	2	7	9	7	5	5	8	8	6	7
8	8	8	3	5	8	8	1	6	6	3	3	7	7	4
0	9	1	5	6	4	2	8	5	9	2	3	9	9	2
9	7	8	9	8	8	6	5	3	8	2	1	2	0	1
8	0	2	6	9	7	6	2	4	7	3	0	7	6	6
6	9	7	8	1	5	7	7	3	5	3	0	2	5	7
5	2	3	0	3	5	7	7	3	4	9	6	3	3	9
3	5	4	0	8	9	4	3	2	3	9	3	4	5	0
5	6	9	7	8	2	3	1	8	2	4	4	9	8	0
6	7	7	3	1	4	2	6	1	3	0	2	6	8	6
9	7	8	9	8	5	0	5	6	4	3	6	7	9	7
9	1	9	7	8	1	1	6	7	5	8	8	2	1	1

9780908827483
9781827349789
9782318244980
9782667743201
9783310063426
9781577355025
9783596800739
9781167588211
9784677834221
9783567931369
9785698754323
9786790653588
9789850564367
9789886538212

Can you find the ISBN of a particular copy of the Codex Chrisicus that the killer is pointing you towards?

PUZZLE 45

II

The Codex Chrisicus

Page number?

6	5		8					
9					6		5	
	4			5				
		4	5		7		6	
7				4				9
	1		3		9	8		
				3			1	
	2		1					3
					2		9	5

Summers locates the book first and brings it to McCrawley. When asked why he had failed to complete the puzzle pasted on the cover, his response is: "I can't do sudokus. Too many numbers."

Sara's PUZZLE PAGES

THE BEST-SELLING NEWSPAPER IN GRAVEN END

A -Z

A B C D E F G H I J K L M N O P Q R S T U V W X Y Z

Even the hardest puzzle has a solution.

Pathfinder: The Good Ol' USA

H	O	H	I	T	E	U	S	E	L
N	L	W	E	R	H	O	U	O	A
O	L	Y	W	O	S	U	N	M	S
T	G	O	O	M	H	R	T	I	V
I	N	D	E	S	S	A	R	M	E
H	S	F	M	I	Q	U	E	A	G
W	A	L	A	T	O	F	M	I	A
S	E	O	D	N	R	I	L	H	S
E	L	R	I	I	A	C	A	O	U
G	N	A	S	O	L	N	O	T	S

CALIFORNIA
FLORIDA
HOLLYWOOD
HOUSTON
LAS VEGAS
LOS ANGELES
MIAMI
MOUNT RUSHMORE
TIMES SQUARE
WASHINGTON
WHITE HOUSE

Hello amateur enigmatologists! Hope you've enjoyed this week's puzzles. Just reminding you that there will be no puzzles for the rest of the week. I'm off to Puzzleby for a murder mystery weekend. See you next week!

Sara x

PUZZLE 48

On page 194, there is another puzzle glued onto the page.

You didn't think it would be that easy, did you? Perhaps it's on this page?

37				33			3		
		41	76				1		6
			96		88	79			8
43		○	97					29	
			100	98	91				11
		72	93		85			27	
46		70	71		83				
				65	64	60		20	
48	52								15
			55	56	23				

Partial email conversation between Detective Sergeant McCrawley and Doctor Alan Easton

TUES 18/04/2020 10:24

FROM: Dr. Alan Easton <a.easton@gravenlaboratory.com>
TO: Det. Katie McCrawley <kmcrawley@ge-police.com>

Re: Quick question!

Katie,

I did go to Graven End's own illustrious university, but that was many moons ago and I was a completely different person back then.

I guess I must have run into Daniel Jones somewhere around the campus but, like I said, it was so long ago now.

Sorry I couldn't be more helpful. Do let me know if there's anything else I help with (or not help with, as the case may be).

Best,
Alan

TUES 18/04/2020 09:58

FROM: Det. Katie McCrawley <kmcrawley@ge-police.com>
TO: Dr. Alan Easton <a.easton@gravenlaboratory.com>

Quick question!

Alan,

You went to GE Uni back in the day, right? Is there any chance you knew the victim? We were just following up on a few leads when I remembered you went there possibly around the same time as the victim.

Sara's PUZZLE PAGES

THE BEST-SELLING NEWSPAPER IN GRAVEN END

Hello again, amateur enigmatologists! Thanks to everyone who asked about my murder mystery weekend. It was a blast! I had a great time but I am back and raring to go with some new, tricky puzzles.

Sara x

PUZZLE 49

Word search: Book Characters

ANNA KARENINA
ATTICUS FINCH
CHARLIE BUCKET
CINDERELLA
ELINOR DASHWOOD
FRODO BAGGINS
GANDALF
HARRY POTTER
JANE BENNET
JAY GATSBY
JULIET
MAD HATTER
MARY CRAWFORD
MATILDA
MISS TRUNCHBULL
PETER PAN
QUEEN OF HEARTS
ROMEO
SLEEPING BEAUTY
SNOW WHITE
WILLY WONKA

E	G	S	T	T	A	K	N	O	W	Y	L	L	I	W
Q	B	L	M	E	G	A	N	D	A	L	F	L	Q	T
P	F	E	A	K	H	Y	Q	R	A	A	Z	U	O	E
A	R	E	R	C	C	X	H	E	N	T	E	B	E	I
Y	O	P	Y	U	I	L	C	T	I	E	T	H	M	L
B	D	I	C	B	N	M	N	T	N	N	I	C	O	U
S	O	N	R	E	D	A	I	O	E	N	H	N	R	J
T	B	G	A	I	E	D	F	P	R	E	W	U	A	N
A	A	B	W	L	R	H	S	Y	A	B	W	R	D	A
G	G	E	F	R	E	A	U	R	K	E	O	T	L	P
Y	G	A	O	A	L	T	C	R	A	N	N	S	I	R
A	I	U	R	H	L	T	I	A	N	A	S	S	T	E
J	N	T	D	C	A	E	T	H	N	J	A	I	A	T
S	S	Y	Z	I	R	R	T	X	A	D	N	M	M	E
E	L	I	N	O	R	D	A	S	H	W	O	O	D	P

Daily puzzles brought to you by Graven End's very own Enigmatologist

Codebreaker

	20		10		5		15		5		4	
6	10	26	3	23	18		22	21	17	15	22	7
	22		26		15		19		15		26	
1	7	3	2		13	22	10	11	8	26	15	17
			23		25		26		25		11	
5	21	11	26	21	3	26		8	1	21	8	5
	13		4		19		9		25		1	
16	21	1	17	5		20	21	10	5	17	26	22
	11		25		11		22		15			
11	26	5	21	12	21	25	23		17	25	23	14
	17		3		21		26		25		22	
22	26	17	15	25	3		4	18	21	17	21	3
	22		1		5		5		3		24	

A B C D E F G H I J K L M N O P Q R S T U V W X Y Z

1	2	3	4	5	6	7	8	9	10	11	12	13
								F				

14	15	16	17	18	19	20	21	22	23	24	25	26
	A									W		

A search is conducted for the specific copy of the Codex Chrisicus with the ISBN 9784677834221. Upon removing the book from the shelf, a piece of paper flutters out.

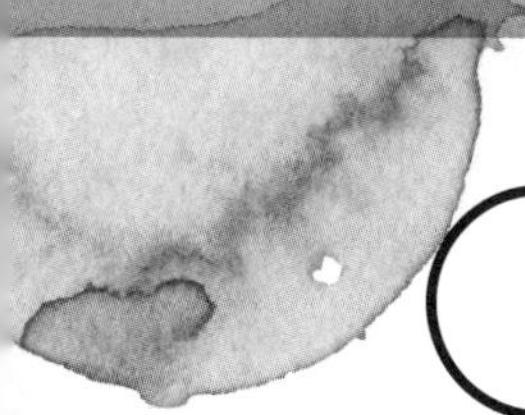

Officer Gibson finds a translation of the Codex.
Can you decode the message left by the killer?

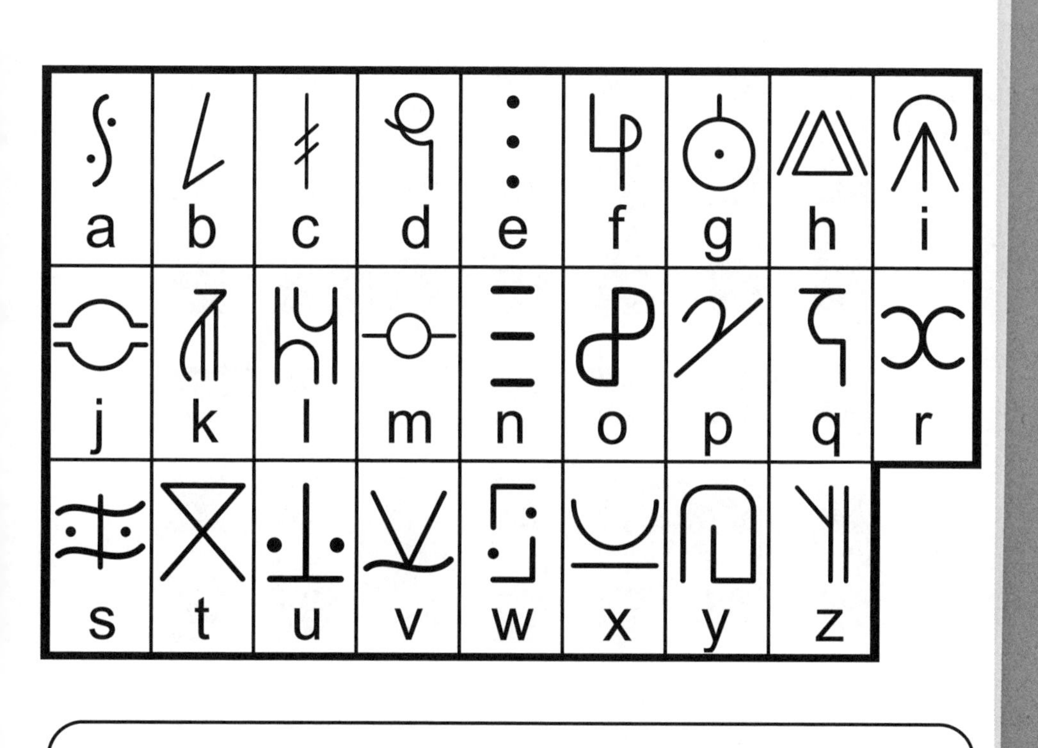

Crossword

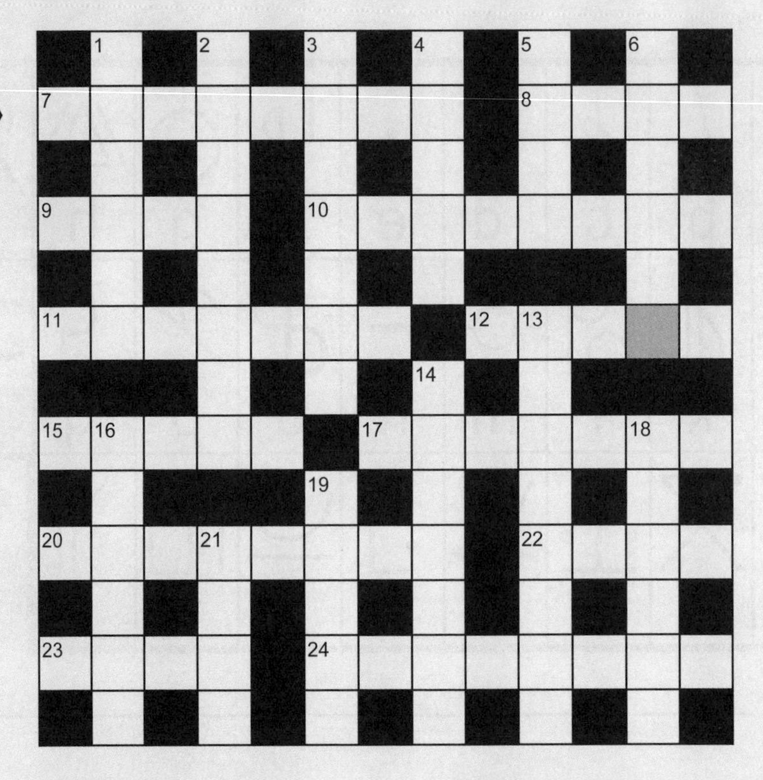

Across

7 Peacemaker (8)
8 Cereal grains (4)
9 Passionate desire for something (4)
10 Lacking knowledge (8)
11 Safe places (7)
12 Inferior to (5)
15 Religious groups (5)
17 Go backwards (7)
20 Muttered (8)
22 River in central England (4)
23 Not as much (4)
24 State of being the same (8)

Down

1 Coniferous tree (6)
2 Cause deliberate damage to (8)
3 Hopes to achieve (7)
4 Main stem of a tree (5)
5 Not sweet (4)
6 Causes a sharp pain (6)
13 Capable of being used (8)
14 Necessary (7)
16 Displayed freely (6)
18 Fires a bullet (6)
19 Small container (5)
21 Sentimentality (4)

"Everything you need is right in front of you. You need only pay attention."

A-Z

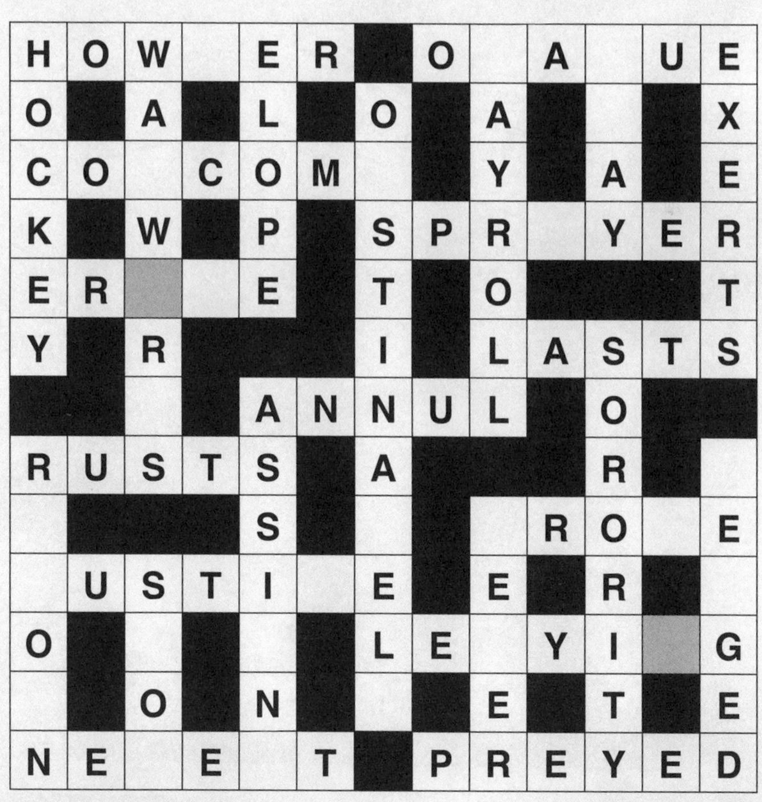

A B C D E F G H I J K L M N O P Q R S T U V W X Y Z

PUZZLE 54

McCrawley knows that the murder weapon - a monogrammed letter opener - was taken from the victim's desk near the entrance to the archives. She obtains CCTV stills from the camera that overlooks the entrance.

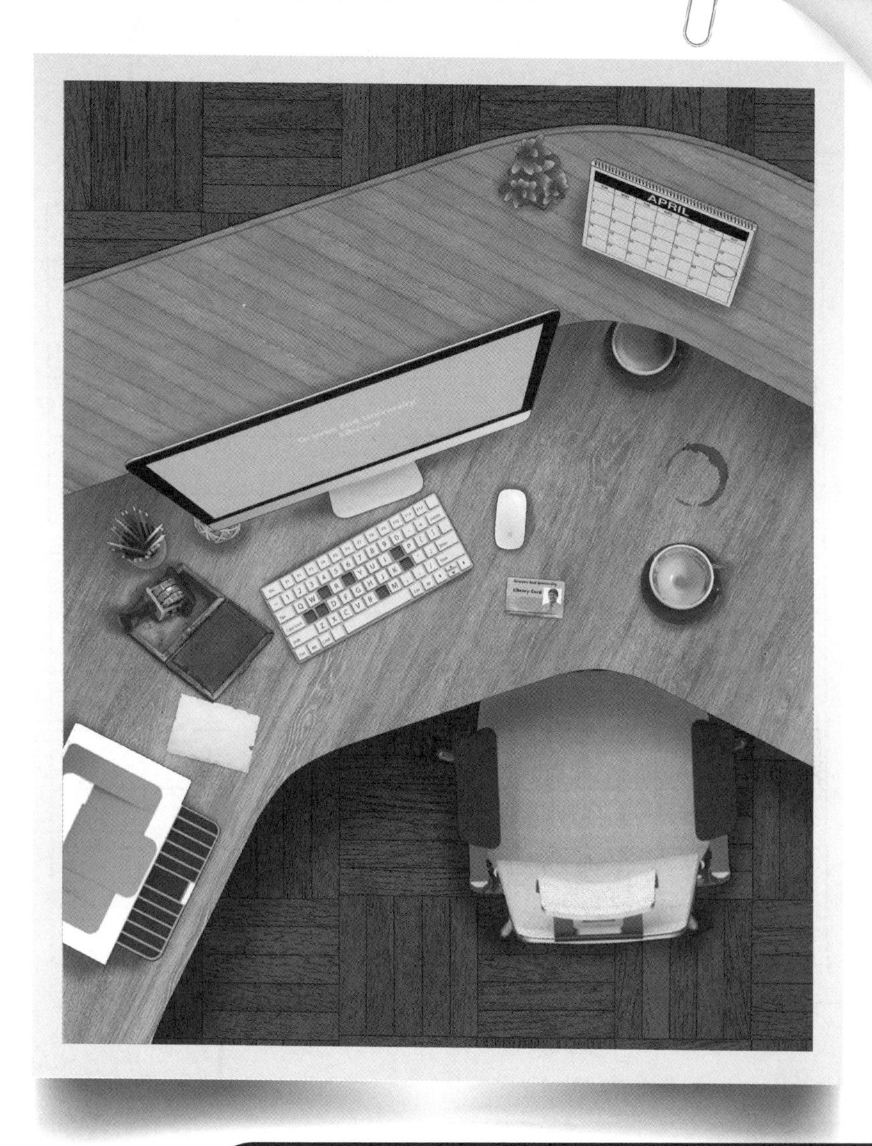

An additional photo is taken by the Crime Scene Techs. Did the killer change or alter the desk? Can you determine all **ten** differences between the two photographs?

Use this page to record any notes or answers for this crime. This may help you to determine who you think the killer is at the very end.

PUZZLE	ANSWER
27	
28	
31	
34	
37	
40	
41	
44	
45	
48	
51	
54	

Did you notice anything strange about the puzzles in the Graven End newspaper?

From Katie McCrawley's personal notebook:

I tempted fate! I should've known not to write about this being a "one off". However, good to know I can trust my gut, still.

Stabbed in the back with his own letter opener. Is that suggestive of the killer's mindset? Payback for being metaphorically stabbed in the back? This murder definitely seemed like the killer was getting revenge. Did Jones and the killer have a history?

The killer seems to be having fun with the puzzles this time, getting in their stride. I wish I knew what their endgame was. It's like they're showing us how smart they are.

But why???

CRIME SCENE THREE

LOCATION:
The One-Stop-Pop-And-Shop car park, Dawes Close

MURDER WEAPON:
The victim's own walking stick

CONFIDENTIAL

ELEMENTS OF THE FILE HAVE BEEN REDACTED DUE TO THE HIGHLY CONFIDENTIAL NATURE OF THE CASE. THE FILE AND CONTENTS ARE THE PROPERTY OF THE GRAVEN END POLICE DEPARTMENT. REMOVAL FROM THE BUILDING WILL RESULT IN IMMEDIATE ARREST.

VICTIM:
Hetty Merryweather

Sixteen days before the victim is found in the supermarket car park, beaten to death with her own walking stick, she had been part of an altercation in the same car park.

The victim had pulled out of a parking space without looking and driven into the side of an in-motion car. It was a low-speed collision, but she refused to take any blame for the incident, or hand over insurance details, leaving the other driver to pay for repairs out of pocket.

Further investigation uncovered that the victim was eighty-nine years old and had been banned from driving for the past seven months. Neighbours also described her as an ██████████████ who was not very ██████████████████.

Word search: Bowling Fun

A	M	T	T	N	D	I	R	I	A	A	Q	T	V	G
E	R	I	A	Q	W	O	S	U	Q	T	F	M	C	I
R	C	L	B	T	V	W	U	U	T	O	I	O	S	N
I	N	P	O	C	K	E	T	B	M	T	T	F	J	S
F	L	S	B	H	O	O	K	F	L	U	S	H	D	X
B	I	E	R	U	O	F	G	I	B	E	B	T	G	V
R	A	O	O	C	K	T	O	A	R	T	A	F	A	M
P	R	C	O	E	U	X	H	I	K	T	S	I	S	Q
J	H	H	K	O	L	S	E	C	O	P	S	N	I	P
A	S	Q	L	E	E	S	G	Z	A	F	L	A	E	T
P	U	L	Y	Q	N	F	D	R	S	O	P	O	X	I
I	O	L	N	R	N	D	E	B	F	U	R	T	U	X
R	O	H	C	N	A	A	H	T	F	L	A	P	A	E
S	W	O	C	V	H	T	U	D	M	A	T	A	P	B
R	S	W	U	C	C	S	S	T	Z	A	U	R	P	A

ANCHOR	DOUBLE	POCKET
APPROACH	FLUSH	RAIL
BACK END	FOUL	ROLL-OUT
BIG FOUR	HEDGEHOG	SERIES
BROOKLYN	HOOK	SPARE
CHANNEL	LOFT	SPLIT
CHOP	PINS	STRIKE

Crossword

Across

1 Slender freshwater fish (4)
3 Opera texts (8)
9 Devoted time to learning (7)
10 Small farm (5)
11 Moved quickly on foot (3)
12 A written document (5)
13 Upright (5)
15 Loutish person (5)
17 Solemn promises (5)
18 23rd Greek letter (3)
19 Declare invalid (5)
20 Giving the ball to another team member (7)
21 Boating (8)
22 Large group of people (4)

Down

1 Available for use as needed; optional (13)
2 Stir milk (5)
4 One of the halogens (6)
5 Person who receives office visitors (12)
6 Groups of actors (7)
7 Fascinatingly (13)
8 As quickly as possible (7-5)
14 Of great size (7)
16 Occur (6)
18 Cost (5)

PUZZLE 57

A word search is found carefully placed on the victim's forehead, and the Crime Scene Techs find a receipt in her car. The detectives need to know if the types of food the victim purchased on the day of her murder match those found in the word search.

A	P	P	L	E	S	Y	V	H	G	R	A	P	E	S
T	U	L	M	P	S	T	N	P	F	A	W	Z	N	Q
Q	B	A	T	T	U	X	O	E	S	E	A	I	Z	A
H	H	M	B	U	T	T	E	R	T	T	S	T	U	N
K	L	B	L	U	E	B	E	R	R	I	E	S	D	O
Z	L	F	Z	F	Z	P	R	I	A	A	T	E	Y	M
Z	N	E	K	C	I	H	C	R	W	A	C	I	G	U
T	O	L	X	G	Z	E	H	D	B	L	H	R	L	T
E	A	T	O	S	C	B	O	X	E	L	E	R	L	R
L	S	T	S	A	L	A	C	H	R	R	E	E	T	J
U	A	A	K	Q	F	C	O	S	R	Y	S	B	K	A
D	A	E	R	B	T	O	L	P	I	T	E	P	M	S
A	S	S	A	N	A	N	A	B	E	N	G	S	Z	L
L	C	K	S	X	L	P	T	O	S	J	G	A	A	S
I	R	U	I	S	S	E	E	B	H	G	S	R	O	S

ONE-STOP-POP-AND-SHOP
Dawes Close, Graven End

CASHIER: MARINA

APPLES	£0.49
BACON	£1.89
BANANAS	£0.98
BEEF	£11.29
BLUEBERRIES	£2.09
BREAD	£0.89
BUTTER	£1.25
CARROTS	£0.99
CHEESE	£3.26
CHICKEN	£4.19
CHOCOLATE	£1.49
EGGS	£1.89
GRAPES	£2.79
HAM	£1.69
LAMB	£15.63
LEEKS	£2.09
NUTS	£1.99
RAISINS	£1.63
RASPBERRIES	£2.19
RICE CAKES	£2.55
STRAWBERRIES	£1.79

TOTAL: £63.05

PAYMENT METHOD: CARD
TRANSACTION #153326577

DATE: 12/6/2020 2:06:14 PM
THANK YOU

The Crime Scene Techs discover some bunting between the trees in the car park. There are multiple routes in this puzzle but only one is correct. If you can find the correct path, you will reveal a message left behind by the killer. The first word in the killer's message is YOU.

Kriss Kross

PUZZLE 59

3 letters
Ask
Cub
Ear
Met
Sag
Sup
Tau

4 letters
Auks
Case
Gape
Ibis
Ohms
Sash
Scud
Tans
Uses
Yoga

5 letters
Cowed
Emery

6 letters
Drives
Thence

7 letters
Cantata
Infuses
Muddied
Roofing
Skidded
Stimuli
Towpath
Yttrium

8 letters
Currents
Minstrel
Obduracy
Platform

9 letters
Oscillate
Woodchuck

Daily puzzles brought to you by Graven End's very own Enigmatologist

Letter-Doku!

			B			A	E	
				F		G		
			A				F	H
E				B				
F	D	B				I	H	C
				C				A
D	E				A			
		F		I				
	B	I			H			

PUZZLE
61

There are a lot of footprints on the ground at the crime scene, but McCrawley notices that one set doesn't match the samples they've collected from witnesses and staff. Can you find the set that doesn't match?

1.

Chris Parris
Crime Scene Technician

2.

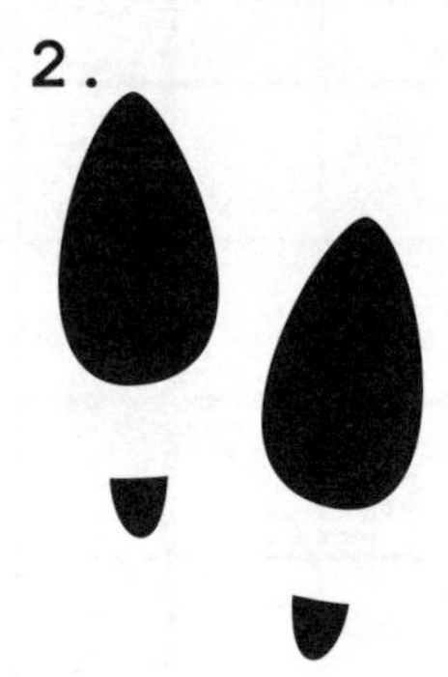

Marina May
Owner of the One-Stop-Pop-and-Stop

3.

PC Sam Wick
First officer on the scene

4.

Sergeant Amy Bryant
Officer on scene

5.

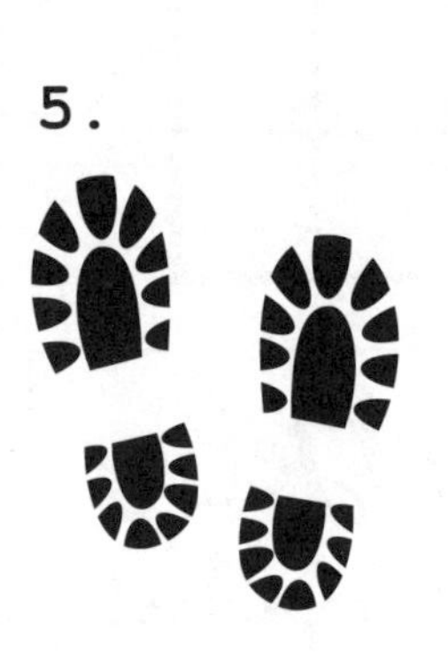

Rich Mills
Bystander

6.

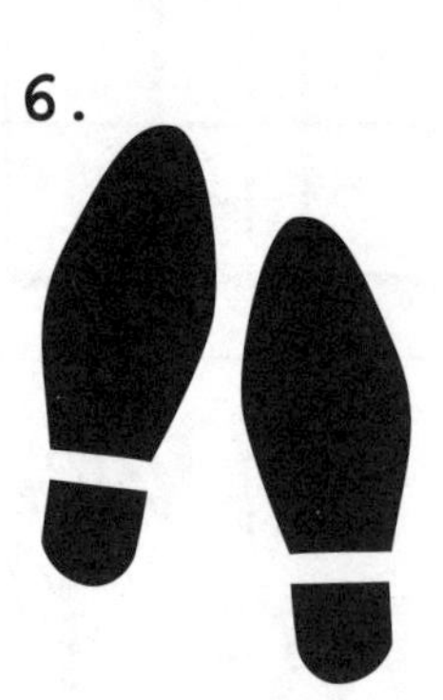

Detective Sergeant Kate McCrawley

7.

Jason Gacey
The teen who found the body

8.

Hetty Merryweather
Victim

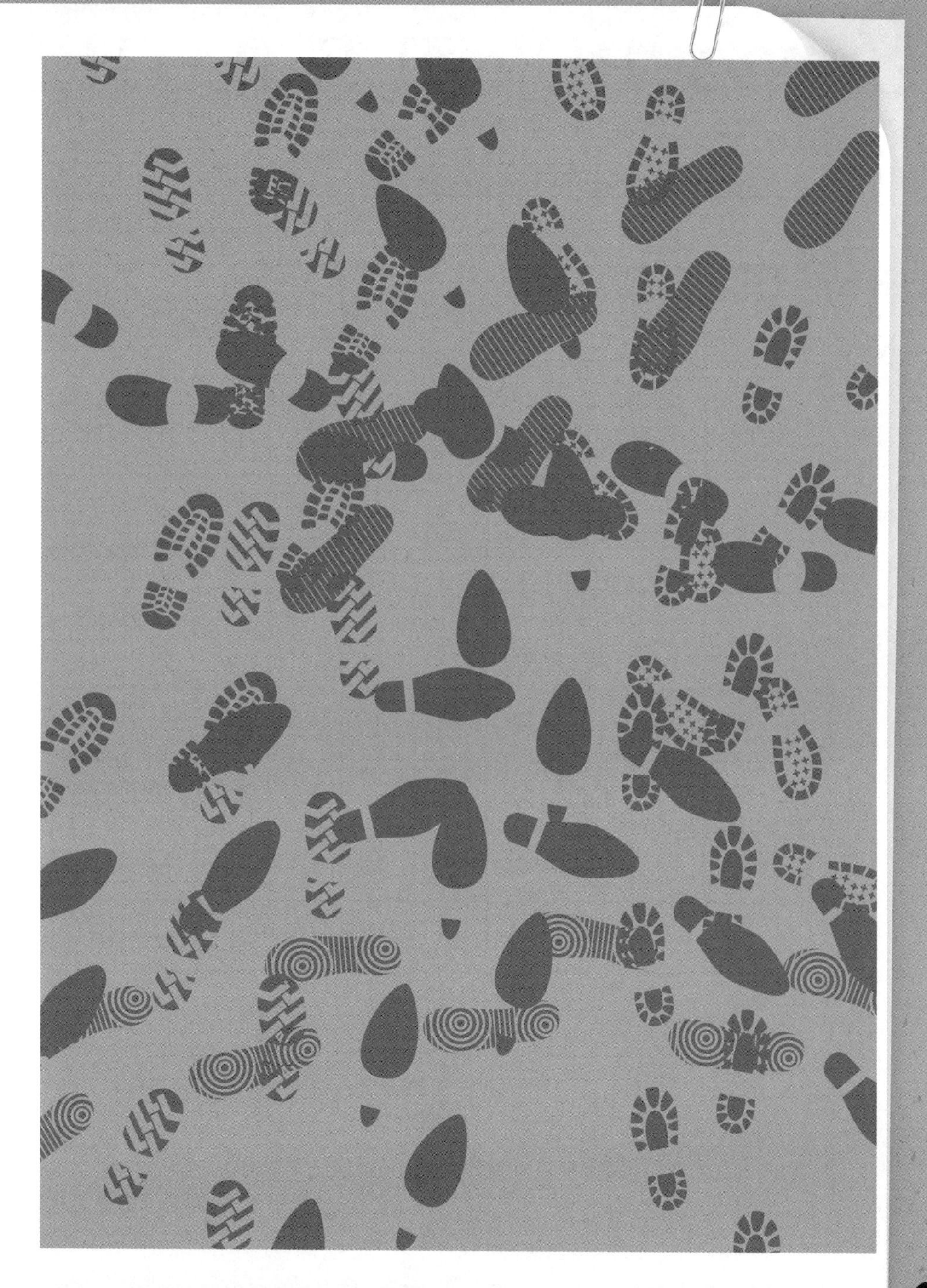

Pathfinder: Mammal Madness!

T	A	C	E	L	O	P	R	E	G
W	R	C	T	E	G	O	A	T	I
O	A	C	I	L	P	O	E	O	T
L	F	F	V	O	A	R	L	X	E
F	X	O	T	N	C	D	N	E	E
E	E	L	H	A	H	I	A	N	Z
R	O	E	P	H	I	M	P	K	B
R	O	G	N	C	P	M	U	N	E
E	R	A	A	K	N	O	B	R	A
T	C	A	M	E	L	S	I	E	V

ARCTIC FOX
BEAVER
BISON
CAMEL
CHIMPANZEE
CHIPMUNK
ELEPHANT
FERRET
GOAT
KANGAROO
LEOPARD
OXEN
POLECAT
TIGER
VOLE
WOLF

Daily puzzles brought to you by Graven End's very own Enigmatologist

"Like people, some puzzles aren't what they seem. You have to look deeper."

A - Z

A B C D E F G H I J K L M N O P Q R S T U V W X Y Z

PUZZLE
64

				1				28	
		9			97	100	33	32	
7			23		99				
13	15			95					
	17				89	90			
	20		62	87		85	81	72	
	59		77		79				
				76					39
		57	65		68		46	44	
53		51							41

When the footprints are identified, Detective McCrawley notices that there is a trail of them around the car park. Can you use the Journeys puzzle an officer finds in the bin to work out the killer's route in and out of the car park?

After Dr Easton and his team have taken the victim's body back to the Graven End laboratory for further tests, a search of the immediate area finds no trace of the victim's car. The officers on the scene discover a piece of paper slipped under the windscreen wiper of a car on the far side of the car park.

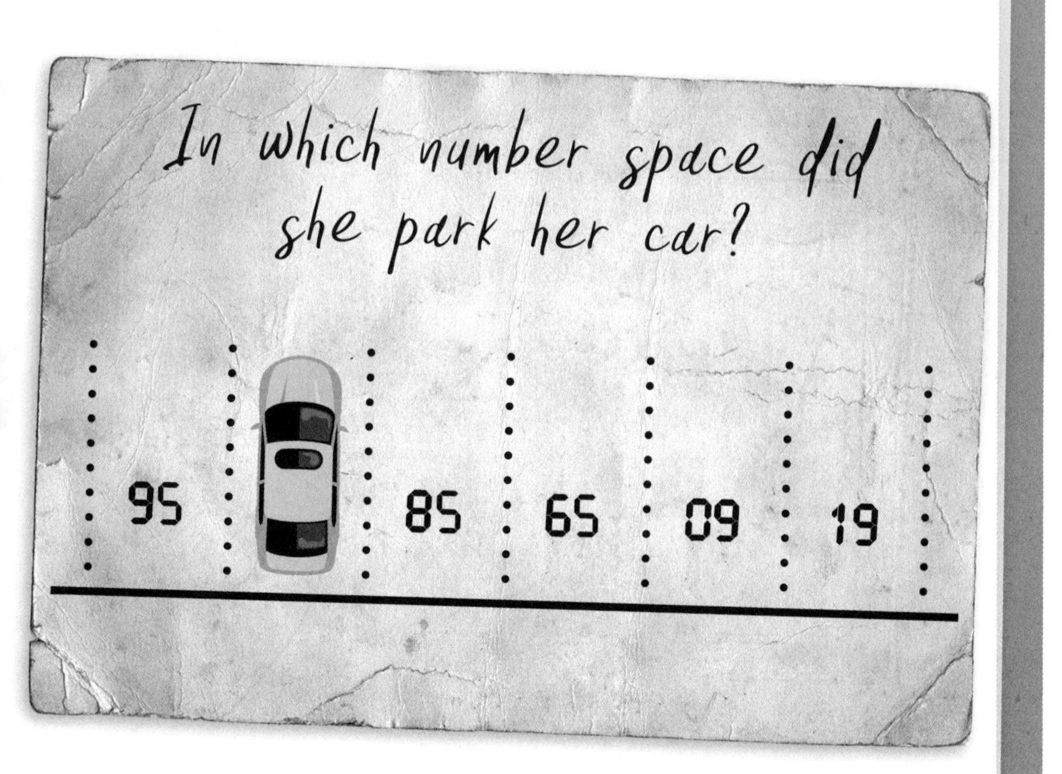

Can you work out in what number space the victim's car is parked?

Sara's PUZZLE PAGES

THE BEST-SELLING NEWSPAPER IN GRAVEN END

Codebreaker

8	■	13	■	14	■	■	■	15	■	2	■	5
24	19	12	13	9	4	■	14	24	25	10	11	1
13	■	6	■	17	■	10	■	8	■	7	■	9
22	10	5	1	13	5	26	■	3	5	7	24	24
10	■	13	■	20	■	15	■	12	■	4	■	6
5	10	22	12	■	16	17	10	20	18	■	■	■
9	■	18	■	15	■	22	■	18	■	8	■	9
■	■	■	18	21	12	12	20	■	23	17	22	24
18	■	18	■	5	■	11	■	2	■	20	■	17
26	24	20	24	13	■	8	5	23	24	9	12	22
10	■	5	■	5	■	12	■	24	■	5	■	12
9	12	18	18	24	11	■	12	13	5	18	12	18
12	■	21	■	21	■	■	■	22	■	18	■	20

A B C D E F G H I J K L M N O P Q R S T U V W X Y Z

1	2	3	4	5	6	7	8	9	10	11	12	13
			Y				C	L				

14	15	16	17	18	19	20	21	22	23	24	25	26

Daily puzzles brought to you by Graven End's very own Enigmatologist

Arrow Words

Possess	Sticky yellowish substance		Small arm of the sea	Young men	Type of word puzzle	Garment maker	Liberties	
			Coming after					
Mammal related to the llama							Document allowing entry to a country	
			Propel forwards					
Sharp chopping implement	Series of subject lessons		Of definite shape					
Desert in northern China		Study of the past		Mediocre (2-2)				
				Public transport vehicle				
Etiquette		___ Sharif: Egyptian actor		Look at amorously		E.g. Shrek	Princess ___: Star Wars character	
								Auction item
Type of air pollution					Come together			
					___ Ferdinand: England footballer			
Jewel from an oyster shell	Cereal plant				Consume food			

PUZZLE 68

There are multiple tyre tracks around the area the body was found. Using the tyre print taken of the victim's car, can you determine if any of the tyre tracks match the victim's, so that the officers can work out if the killer moved her car after she was killed?

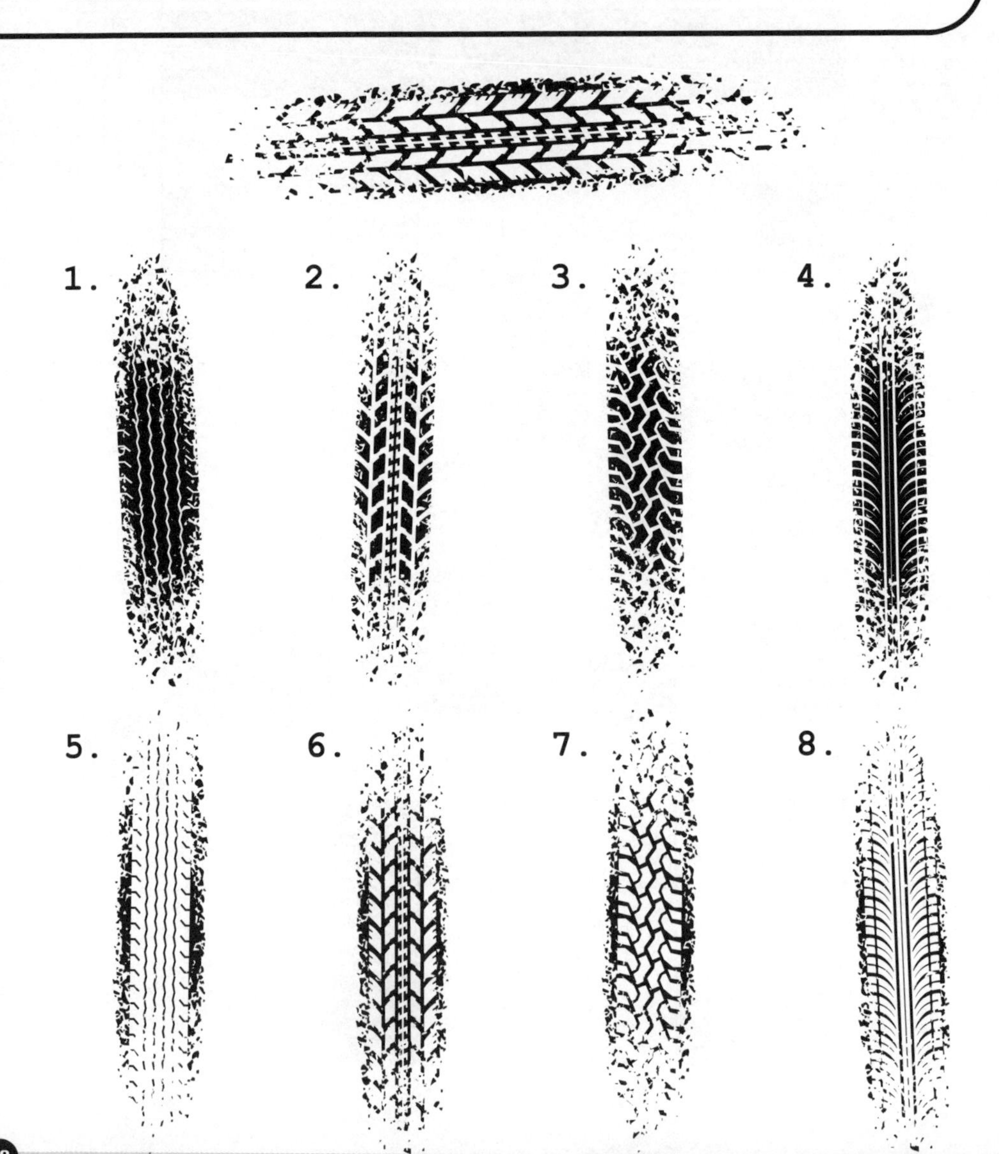

PUZZLE
69

The New Gra

Friday, 18th June 2021

Murder in the Car Park

Ex-school teacher and town elder, Hetty Merryweather, was found dead n the car prk of the Graven End One-Stop Pop-and-Shop late onday night

Whilst investigations are still on-going, detetives beieve that Merryweather, 89, was struck ver the head repeatedly with her own walk-ing stick, which was found a hort distanc away fom he body.

Police are appealing to anyone who may have been in the sop or in the cr park at the time of the murder to come forward. Marina May, owner of the One-Stop-Pop-and-Shop, cofirmed that the CCTV cameras that cover the car park were vandalised last month and had not been repaired b the time f the mrder.

I is not known if te beloved ex-headmstress kew her attacer, or if it was a crime of opportunity.

The evening after the murder, Sara Dougherty, the enigmatologist from *The New Graven End News*, catches up with McCrawley and hands her an article torn out of the paper. "I noticed this was printed in today's issue. There's something strange about it."

Kriss Kross

PUZZLE 70

4 letters
Anon
Aura
Garb
Gods
Hire
Inns
Puma
Rump
Sari
Seer

5 letters
Adieu
Anger
Hopes
Inane
Noses
Stash

6 letters
Divest
Easter
Eclair
Outwit

7 letters
Bigness
Custard
Omnibus
Pebbles
Retsina

8 letters
Arpeggio
Irritant

9 letters
Standards
Tradesman

12 letters
Inadequately
Triumphantly
Unacceptable
Unhesitating

Crossword

Across

7 Backward-looking (13)
8 Not extreme (8)
9 Scarce (4)
10 Framework (7)
12 Obscure road (5)
14 Later (5)
16 Foot pedal (7)
19 Pile (4)
20 Thing used for tying (8)
22 Easy to deal with (13)

Down

1 Short note or reminder (4)
2 Silver (literary) (6)
3 With an attitude of suspicion (7)
4 Number of deadly sins (5)
5 Tempestuous (6)
6 Take to pieces to examine (8)
11 In the open air (8)
13 Army unit (7)
15 Give a job to (6)
17 Sagacious (6)
18 Purple fruits (5)
21 Payment to a landlord (4)

Transcript of conversation between Detective Sergeant Katie McCrawley and Detective Constable Alex Summers, conducted via text message.

McCrawley: Before u come to the scene can u bring the metal detector, plz

Summers: where is it??

McCrawley: Charlton was playing with it last. ask him.

Summers: will do. why?

McCrawley: found the car but no key. Easton's office said there was no key in vic's belongings

Summers: cant u just bust the door?

McCrawley: No, the Crime Scene Techs dont want to in case they damage "vital evidence".

Summers: oh

McCrawley: yes. exactly. so we go key-hunting with the detector. Found it?

Summers: Charlton said he gave it to Nielson last Tuesday. Don't know where she is

McCrawley: ur a detective. Go detect her. and some coffee. black, 2 sugars, plz. Dont take too long. its cold and I want to go home sometime tonight

[END OF TRANSCRIPT]

PUZZLE 72

A search with the metal detector finds a bunch of identical looking keys underneath a nearby car. Can you match the correct key to the lock and save any potential evidence?

Letter-Doku!

PUZZLE 73

C								G
	I	F				B		
	E			D		F		
			B	F			D	
		B	H		I	C		
	H			A	D			
		C		E			B	
		D				E	C	
A								F

"In life, each puzzle we tackle fulfils a larger goal. It's up to you to discover that goal."

Word search: Oscar-winning Films

O U T O F A F R I C A O O R I
D Y N Q A H S H T I C E N O G
L S R A W R A T S S K V T R O
C V U M Y Y K H I U J E H E I
U F H A D G X E L M P T E P N
C O N D A I R S S F I U W M G
O R E E L J C T R O H O A E M
R R B U R H A I E D D B T T Y
P E G S I T T N L N N A E S W
A S R C A E O G D U A L R A A
T T A I F R O A N O G L F L Y
T G V I Y A K M I S I A R E S
O U I O M B S D H E G V O H K
N M T I T A N I C H I R N T K
S P Y O P C S W S T X N T K Z

ALL ABOUT EVE
AMADEUS
BEN-HUR
CABARET
CHICAGO
FORREST GUMP
GANDHI
GIGI
GOING MY WAY
GRAVITY
MY FAIR LADY
ON THE WATERFRONT
OUT OF AFRICA
PATTON
SCHINDLER'S LIST
STAR WARS
THE LAST EMPEROR
THE SOUND OF MUSIC
THE STING
TITANIC

PUZZLE 75

Using the key, officers finally manage to open the boot of the victim's car. A photo of the victim's boot is sitting on top of her things.

Can you compare it to a photo taken by the Crime Scene Techs and see if anything has changed? There are **six** differences between the two photographs.

A - Z

PUZZLE 76

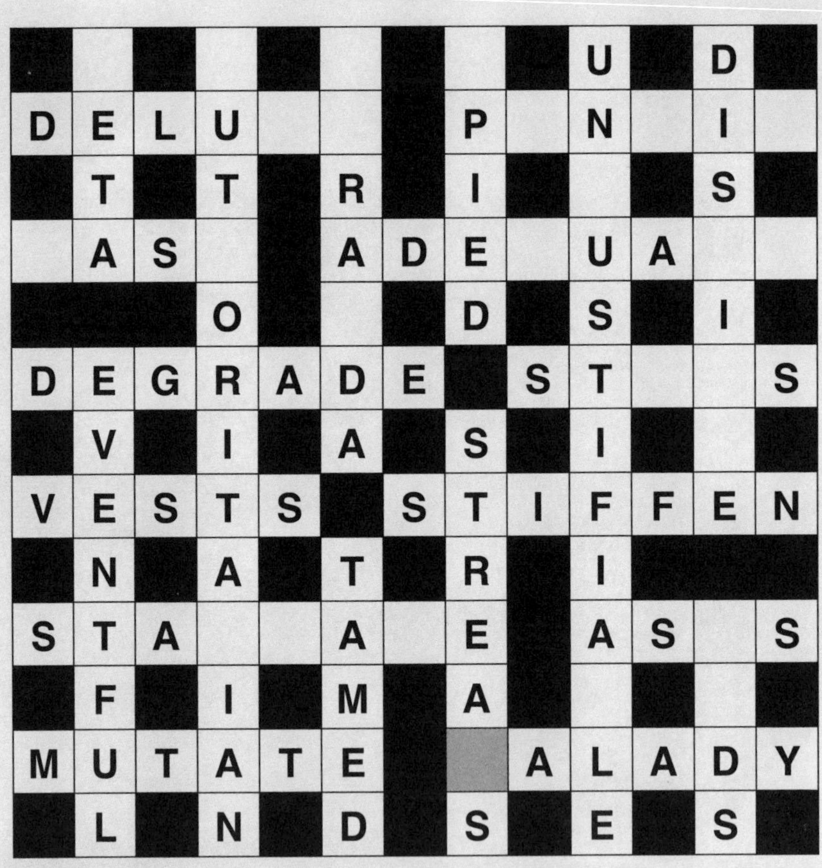

Arrow Words

Stage play	Tearing	Keep away from	___ Simpson: cartoon character	Small social insect	The day after today		Untimely	
					Possess			
___ Lendl: former tennis star					Pull		Foreign language (informal)	
Small window on a ship								
Hog				Song for a solo voice				
Patches of facial hair		Particle that holds quarks together	Charming and elegant	Company symbol				
				Was aware of; understood	Came first			
Hens lay these	Third Gospel					Fall behind	Beer	
Chinese monetary unit					Scientific workplace (abbrev)			
Rejuvenate	Generally; in summary							
					Command to a horse			

PUZZLE 78

After an extensive search, the victim's phone is finally found taped inside the front passenger's side wheel arch. Somehow, the killer has managed to change the phone's lock to a puzzle.

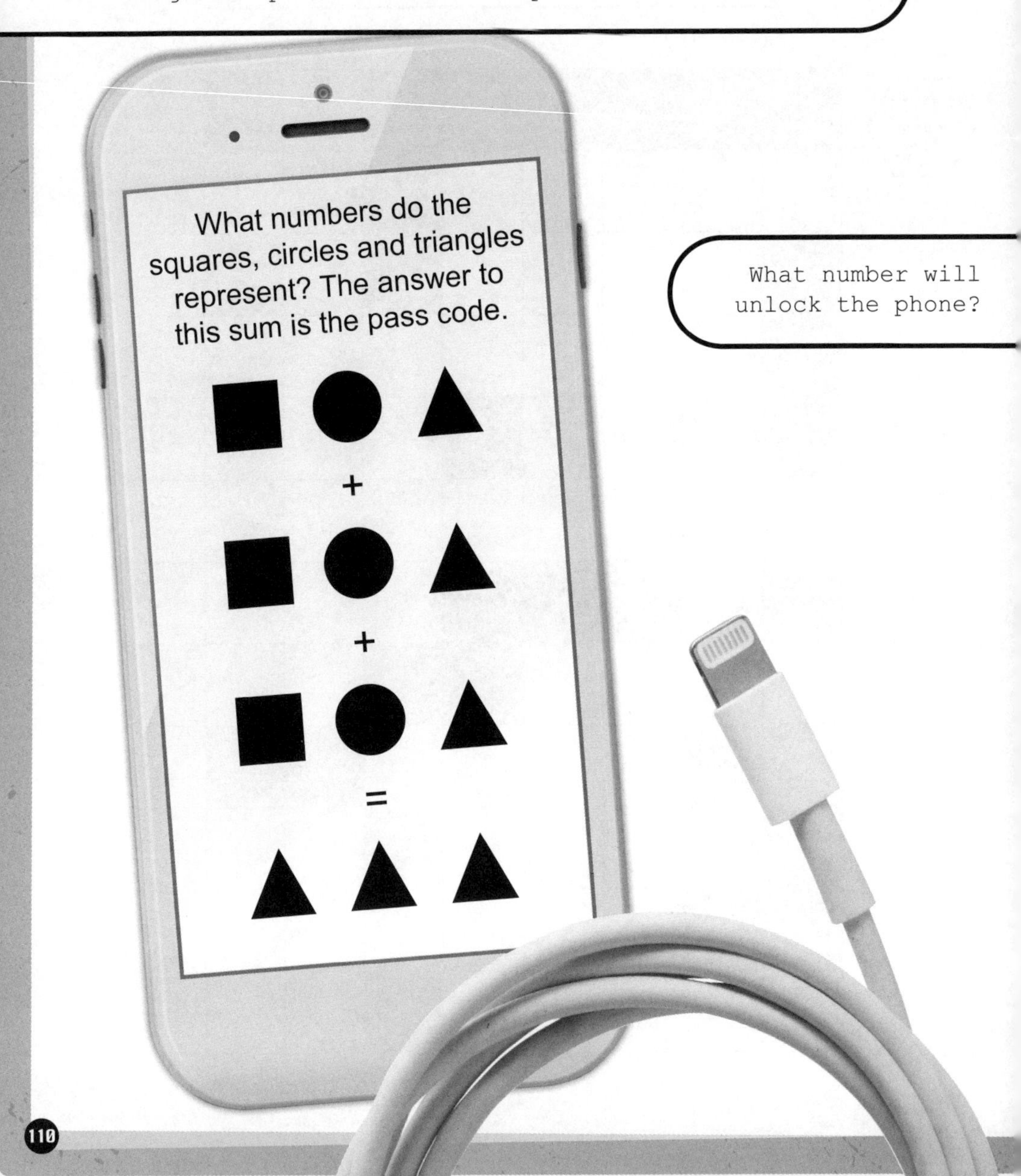

What number will unlock the phone?

When the team unlocks the phone, Summers notices that the text message icon is flashing. What does the message say?

Sender: Unknown

**19 8 5 23 1 19 1 18 21 4 5,
2 9 20 20 5 18 15 12 4 23 15 13 1 14
23 8 15 4 5 19 5 18 22 5 4
5 22 5 18 25 20 8 9 14 7
19 8 5 7 15 20. 9’4 4 15 9 20
1 7 1 9 14 9 6 9 3 15 21 12 4.**

Received: 04:36

Pathfinder: Car Parts

A	D	L	S	C	B	U	R	E	T
E	H	I	T	A	R	K	C	A	T
O	T	G	H	N	I	W	F	R	O
O	B	C	S	D	T	S	O	T	R
R	D	R	A	T	L	R	O	Y	R
A	E	E	E	B	E	A	T	S	E
O	N	H	S	G	A	I	S	B	O
B	N	A	A	K	B	R	U	N	N
H	D	B	R	E	B	R	A	E	T
S	A	D	S	E	K	A	H	X	E

AIRBAG
BONNET
BOOT
BRAKES
CARBURETTOR

DASHBOARD
EXHAUST
HANDBRAKE
HEADLIGHTS

ROOF
RACK
SEAT BELTS
TYRES
WINDSCREEN

Daily puzzles brought to you by Graven End's very own Enigmatologist

Codebreaker

■	9	■	1	■	4	■	24	■	20	■	17	■
1	26	9	4	10	17	19	26	21	26	1	19	13
■	9	■	12	■	17	■	4	■	12	■	4	■
9	12	10	15	3	4	10	1	■	3	4	14	15
■	■	■	4	■	18	■	1	■	15	■	8	■
18	10	4	11	8	15	1	■	22	12	13	25	4
■	4	■	■	■	1	■	18	■	■	■	19	■
21	11	8	26	22	■	23	12	10	25	19	4	11
■	16	■	9	■	1	■	10	■	19	■	■	■
6	4	10	5	■	9	10	21	15	21	7	21	12
■	12	■	4	■	12	■	26	■	21	■	8	■
12	11	2	4	10	15	8	1	4	22	4	3	15
■	1	■	9	■	4	■	4	■	1	■	5	■

A B C D E F G H I J K L M N O P Q R S T U V W X Y Z

1	2	3	4	5	6	7	8	9	10	11	12	13
S									R			

14	15	16	17	18	19	20	21	22	23	24	25	26
					L							

Use this page to record any notes or answers for this crime. This may help you to determine who you think the killer is at the very end.

PUZZLE	ANSWER
57	
58	
61	
64	
65	
68	
69	
72	
75	
78	
79	

Did you notice anything strange about the puzzles in the Graven End newspaper?

From Katie McCrawley's personal notebook:

Beaten with her own walking stick? Ouch.

Strange killing, though. Merryweather may have been a grumpy old woman, but what harm could she have done to the killer?

Revenge for something? Just for fun?

So far there's not been any DNA evidence from the killer at any of the crime scenes. They're either really good at cleaning up after themselves, or they know what we're looking for. Inside job?

This killing doesn't seem to match that of Jones. Seems to me to be more of a rage killing, more in line with the first crime than the second.

CRIME SCENE FOUR

LOCATION:
WONDERMENT
(a magic shop owned by The Mysterious Sydney Blackstone, aka Joe Fraiser), High Street

MURDER WEAPON:
Formaldehyde poisoning

CONFIDENTIAL

ELEMENTS OF THE FILE HAVE BEEN REDACTED DUE TO THE HIGHLY CONFIDENTIAL NATURE OF THE CASE. THE FILE AND CONTENTS ARE THE PROPERTY OF THE GRAVEN END POLICE DEPARTMENT. REMOVAL FROM THE BUILDING WILL RESULT IN IMMEDIATE ARREST.

VICTIM:
Joe Fraiser

The victim had lived in Graven End all of his life. He had a previous conviction for ████████████████ . As a teenager, the ██████ victim studied chemistry at Graven End University, but was expelled after being caught breaking into the administration building in an attempt to change his grades.

Less than an hour before the victim was found face down behind the counter of WONDERMENT by his girlfriend, Sarah Burnham, neighbours had heard the sounds of an argument on the premises. None had reported it to the police, stating that it wasn't uncommon to hear shouting coming from the shop.

Officers find him unconscious at the scene and he later dies in hospital after medics are unable to revive him. A comprehensive toxicology screening completed by the laboratory finds high levels of formaldehyde in his stomach and bloodstream.

"You are never too old to do another puzzle."

Pathfinder: Herbs and Spices

PUZZLE 82

L	A	L	L	I	D	M	A	D	R
L	I	C	E	G	M	O	V	E	A
S	P	L	R	A	C	H	I	S	C
J	C	I	A	D	H	A	M	O	R
A	O	R	R	I	S	R	E	S	E
S	H	S	E	E	L	Y	F	Y	M
M	S	S	A	M	L	N	E	H	T
I	E	G	R	O	E	N	M	A	R
N	R	A	G	N	T	M	M	A	O
E	O	N	O	N	U	E	G	R	J

ALLSPICE
CARDAMOM
CHIVES
DILL
FENNEL
GARLIC
HORSERADISH
JASMINE
LEMONGRASS
MARJORAM
NUTMEG
OREGANO
ROSEMARY
THYME

Crossword

Across

1 Device that chops up documents (8)
5 Coalition of countries (4)
8 Move to music (5)
9 Taken as a whole (7)
10 Chats (7)
12 Gloss (7)
14 Most favourable (7)
16 Signs up (7)
18 Suitor (7)
19 Mexican plant fibre (5)
20 Not difficult (4)
21 Breed of dairy cattle (8)

Down

1 Soft drink (US) (4)
2 Pierre-Auguste ___ : French artist (6)
3 Bandages (9)
4 Sufficient (6)
6 Introduction (4-2)
7 Gigantic (8)
11 Luggage items (9)
12 Revere (8)
13 Fastening devices (6)
14 Fish-eating bird of prey (6)
15 Breakfast food (6)
17 Sheet of floating ice (4)

PUZZLE 84

The first thing that Detective McCrawley notices about WONDERMENT is the maze that has been pasted onto the shop window. It looks like there's a message *within* the maze, which is strange. What does it say?

In between showing off his ridiculous card tricks and doing his actual work, Dr. Easton knocks over the shop's phone and this sticky note is found underneath.

99966688
6633333
8666
55566666655
44466
84433
7777233333

Can you work out what it means?

Arrow Words

PUZZLE 86

Currents of air

Close by

Wedding

Person granted a permit

At the present time

Departs

Making law

For each

Queen ___: fairy in Romeo and Juliet

Dove sound

Injure

Female sheep

Military unit

Cut of pork

Country in Western Asia

Embarrass

Gaming tile

Droop

Peruse

Make a choice

Fill a suitcase

Link a town with another

Short note

Greek letter

Tree liquid

Deep hole in the ground

In what way

Inspires fear and wonder

Hip (anag)

Quotation

Summit of a small hill

One and one

PUZZLE 87

"Winners are not people who never fail, but people who never quit."

Letter-Doku!

		B			E			A
I			C					
	H		A	D		E		
	I	G					C	
			D		F			
	F					G	E	
		I		C	H		F	
					B			E
B			E			H		

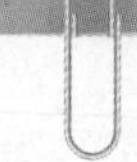

The Crime Scene Techs notice that a piece of paper has been taped to the front of the safe, and that the symbols look like the four card suits. A pack of cards was discovered nearby, but no immediate connection is found.

Code: ______________________________

McCrawley spreads the pack of cards out over the shop's sales counter to see if she can find a connection. Can you spot one between the cards, the symbols, and the safe?

Crossword

Across

1 Glassy (8)
5 ___ Khan: British boxer (4)
8 Flexible insulated cables (5)
9 Colloquial speech (7)
10 Imparts knowledge (7)
12 Unit of sound intensity (7)
14 Restrain (7)
16 Pass across or through (7)
18 Far-reaching; thorough (7)
19 Let (5)
20 Fall slowly downwards (4)
21 Sheath for a sword (8)

Down

1 Bad habit (4)
2 Material used for surfacing roads (6)
3 Groups of performers (9)
4 Uncover (6)
6 Scanty (6)
7 Type of resistor (8)
11 Boxing film with Brad Pitt (5,4)
12 Upsets; agitates (8)
13 Make unhappy (6)
14 Sloping (of a typeface) (6)
15 Yellow fruit (6)
17 Peruse (4)

Daily puzzles brought to you by Graven End's very own Enigmatologist

> You've got this. Never doubt yourself.

PUZZLE 90

Kriss Kross

3 letters
Boa
Coy
Ell
Ski
Ton
Tub

4 letters
Bran
Club
Ebbs
Else
Pier
Pint
Posh
Rued

6 letters
Anoint
Earths
Tiling
Tutors

7 letters
Anodyne
Nibbled

8 letters
Assesses
Bagpiper
Confetti
Elevator
Escapist
Initiate
Malaysia
Subtract
Thanking
Wretched

9 letters
Egotistic
Embattled

PUZZLE 91

Inside the safe is a ledger detailing WONDERMENT'S transactions. Dusting reveals a number of different partial fingerprints. Can you match them to the fingerprints that are on file, or that we've seen so far throughout the case?

Stock #	Cost £
31235	47.02
56464	16.12
56588	5.46
315568	11.09
64544	0.49
56276	7.99
62752	9.50
76727	6.40
76272	4.46
36842	9.16
75756	33.66
121135	5.69
35158	7.44
41252	4.45
78966	8.64
31535	4.45
12152	7.37
22256	57.53
45345	7.30
35158	10.40
76727	4.04
31556	4.54
45756	.6.35
64544	3.85
36842	1.25
75275	

Date		Name
3rd	*	Herbert Nelson
4th		Ida McDonald
		Dilbert Warner
		Chris Penn
		Stanley Connely
		Ezra Catt
		Michael Harker
5th	*	Delia King
		Leo Santana
		Daniel Penner
		~~Jeremiah Bull~~ *
6th		Steven Mantle
		Sarah Jones
7th	*	Tommy O'Shea
		Barbara Craton
		Chad McDuckett
		Jack Cather
8th		Henry Weeks
		Walt Whitty

07.2020 1711

Stock #	Cost £
31235	3.73
35158	14.72
64544	7.43
75275	17.29
74535	7.38
63875	6.66
89393	45.52
10455	6.37
73753	19.50
12347	0.49
~~76272~~	~~33.66~~ R
48651	9.66
76375	13.56
45354	6.78
52572	4.35
45757	6.87
64544	10.59
33387	19.21
91351	0.49

PRINTS ON FILE

Joe Fraiser
Victim

Artie Fraiser
Victim's nephew
Sometimes helps out at the shop

Darren Miller
Accountant
Looks over the books on a monthly basis

Sarah Burnham
Victim's girlfriend
Was in the shop the evening of the murder

Toby Underwood
Customer (Child)
A frequent visitor, often visiting to watch the victim perform tricks

Jeremiah Bull
Customer
Witnessed having an argument with the victim less than half an hour before the murder.

Sara's PUZZLE PAGES

THE BEST-SELLING NEWSPAPER IN GRAVEN END

A - Z

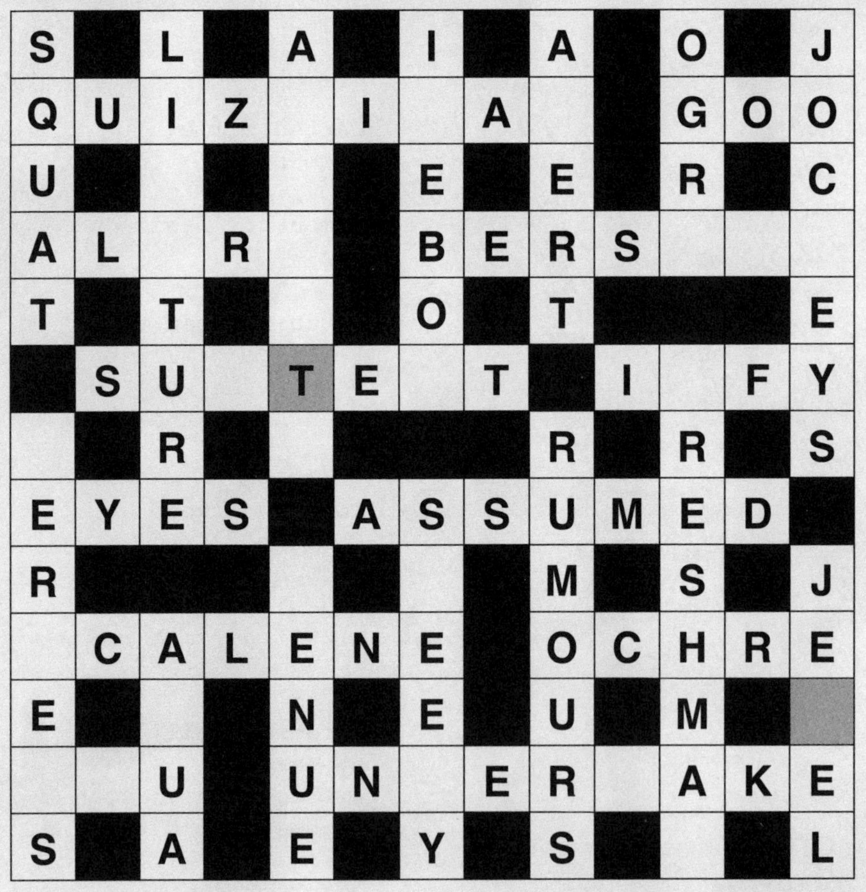

A B C D E F G H I J K L M N O P Q R S T U V W X Y Z

Daily puzzles brought to you by Graven End's very own Enigmatologist

Pathfinder: Family

PUZZLE 93

AUNT
BROTHER
CLAN
COUSIN
DESCENDANTS
FAMILY TREE
GRANDMOTHER
HERITAGE
HUSBAND
IN-LAW
NIECE
PARTNER
SPOUSE
UNCLE
WIFE

O	U	A	N	P	A	R	T	N	E
P	S	L	H	T	O	R	B	C	R
S	E	C	E	G	R	A	T	O	U
E	E	N	R	D	N	N	N	U	S
T	R	I	S	B	A	D	M	A	I
Y	C	E	U	H	E	T	O	W	N
L	E	C	L	E	G	H	E	A	I
I	U	N	E	H	A	W	R	L	N
M	S	T	R	I	T	I	F	E	D
A	F	N	A	D	N	E	C	S	E

"All will make sense soon enough. Just keep going."

Inside the back of the ledger is an old receipt for the installation of a second safe – a floor safe in the basement. Upon conducting a search of the basement, an officer finds the following note taped to a shelf.

Oh dear. All these paving stones look the same and you can't dig up the whole basement...

	51		58			62			
49					80				66
	54	56			93	99		96	68
40	47		77			100	98		
	41			○		91			
35					84		87		
						73	72	26	
			31		29				
		16	17	18		20	21	1	3
12					7				

Solve the Journeys puzzle to find the correct paving stone to reveal the safe.

Careful removal of the paving stone reveals a digital combination safe sunk into the floor, and a piece of paper with familiar writing.

3	5	4	8	One digit is right but it is in the wrong place
4	6	7	1	Two digits are correct but only one is in the correct place
3	7	8	1	Two digits are correct but both are in the wrong place
8	3	9	7	One digit is wrong. The others are correct but in the wrong places
5	2	1	4	All digits are wrong
2	9	3	4	One digit is right but it is in the wrong place
5	1	3	6	One digit is both right and in the correct place

Code: ____________________

Codebreaker

19	8	4	2	10		17	25	5	24	4	2	10
5		25		2		5			5		15	
2		13		3		25		21	25	1	13	26
23	25	12	11	13	16	18	9		6		4	
16		10		12		18		20	2	18	26	18
18	26	5	16	14	22	2	12		12			2
16		7		26				25		18		19
8			14		8	19	2	5	2	26	26	25
12	16	21	9	26		8		26		8		5
	5		25		2	26	9	16	8	19	16	25
1	8	5	19	9		2		14		19		26
	12		2			12		4		2		2
14	7	14	4	16	18	26		2	5	5	2	10

A B C D E F G H I J K L M N O P Q R S T U V W X Y Z

1	2	3	4	5	6	7	8	9	10	11	12	13
		F							D			

14	15	16	17	18	19	20	21	22	23	24	25	26
	X											

Word search: Pop Groups

O	M	Q	I	O	M	S	E	L	G	N	A	B	S	D
A	X	K	U	V	Z	A	I	P	U	Q	L	N	U	B
S	Z	J	G	E	E	R	B	X	X	S	L	B	S	R
I	Y	W	M	Y	E	N	O	B	J	L	S	P	L	R
S	V	A	T	A	S	N	I	Y	A	T	A	E	R	F
D	R	O	L	I	D	U	U	J	A	N	I	T	I	Y
F	K	A	J	P	E	N	T	R	D	F	N	S	G	A
S	R	S	U	N	D	E	E	A	R	L	T	H	E	S
I	H	O	A	T	O	L	U	S	X	A	S	O	C	S
S	B	E	A	C	H	B	O	Y	S	O	S	P	I	C
E	Z	T	E	X	A	S	X	C	O	M	C	B	P	L
N	G	I	R	L	S	A	L	O	U	D	F	O	S	U
E	F	I	L	T	S	E	W	E	N	O	Z	Y	O	B
G	S	E	U	R	Y	T	H	M	I	C	S	S	Y	X
P	T	Y	G	Y	O	L	J	E	A	O	O	Y	U	S

ABBA
ALL SAINTS
BANGLES
BEACH BOYS
BON JOVI
BONEY M
BOYZONE

COLDPLAY
DUBSTAR
EURYTHMICS
GENESIS
GIRLS ALOUD
MADNESS
OASIS

PET SHOP BOYS
QUEEN
S CLUB
SPANDAU BALLET
SPICE GIRLS
TEXAS
WESTLIFE

Transcript of conversation between Detective Sergeant Katie McCrawley and Detective Constable Alex Summers, conducted via text message.

Summers: its full of champagne

McCrawley: What?

Summers: the safe. Theres 20 bottles of champagne in it

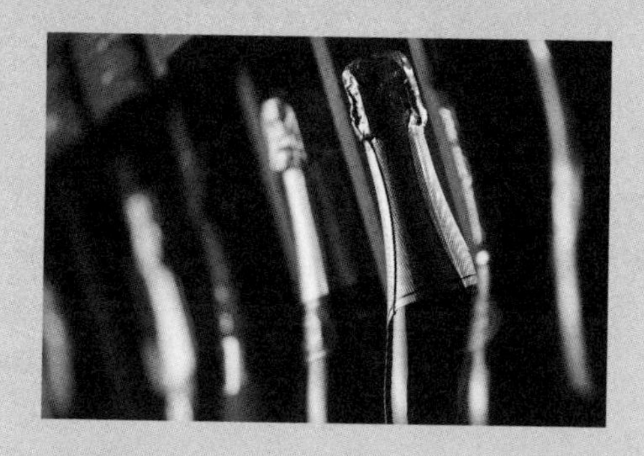

McCrawley: is it cheap, One-Stop-Pop-And-Shop stuff?

Summers: Dont think so. never heard of some of it

McCrawley: right. anything else?

Summers: yep. word search. 21 different champagne names on it.

McCrawley: do they match the bottles in the safe?

Summers: Yep, looks like it.

McCrawley: but there r only 20 bottles in the safe?

Summers: oh, so 1 is missing. clever!

McCrawley: 1 of us has to be...

[END OF TRANSCRIPT]

PUZZLE 98

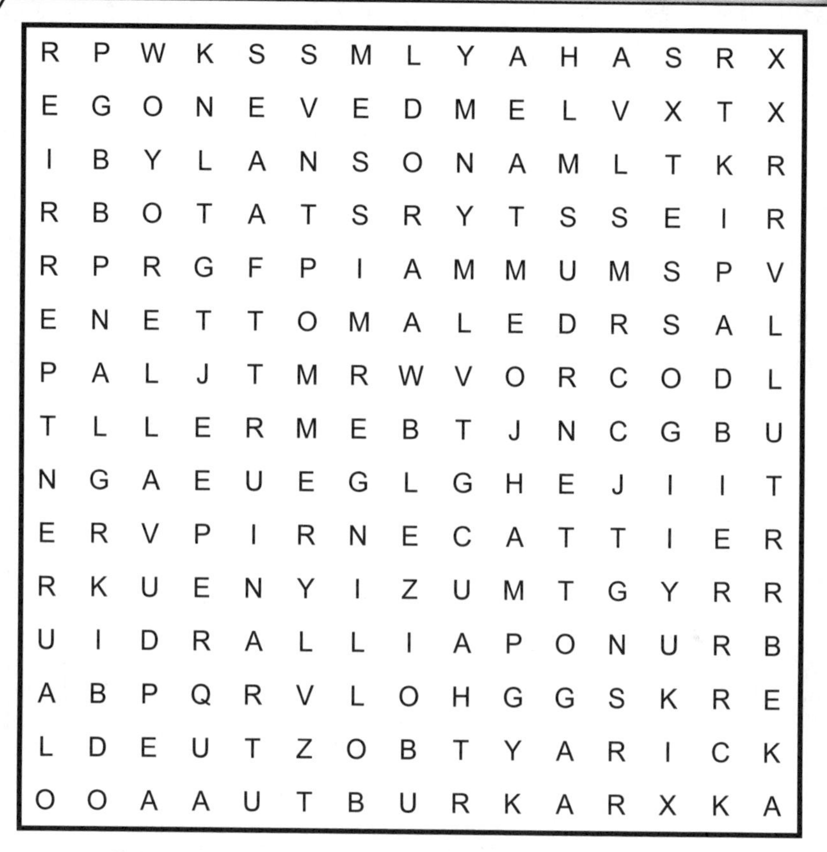

AYALA	DEUTZ	LAURENT-PERRIER
BOIZEL	DUVAL-LEROY	MERCIER
BOLLINGER	GOSSET	MUMM
BRUNO PAILLARD	HENRIOT	POL ROGER
CATTIER	JEEPER	POMMERY
DE VENOGE	KRUG	RUINART
DELAMOTTE	LANSON	SALON

Use the word search to work out which of the champagne bottles is missing.

Kriss Kross

PUZZLE 99

3 letters
Coo
Gas
Ivy
Pop
Tic
Tor

5 letters
Audio
Croft
Dwell
Emery
Flirt
Least
Needy
Occur
Sedan
Tubes

7 letters
Abyssal
Diorama
Elegant
Flotsam
Gorilla
Oxidise
Pimples
Satisfy

8 letters
Glorious
Luscious
Militant
Plethora
Rightful
Tricycle

9 letters
Flowerpot
Yachtsman

13 letters
Abbreviations
Inexperienced

Crossword

Across

1 One image within another (5)
4 Getting bigger (7)
7 Body of burning gas (5)
8 Create an account deficit (8)
9 Leashes (5)
11 ___ hour: the latest possible moment (8)
15 Higher in rank (8)
17 Make law (5)
19 Harmful (8)
20 Garment worn in the kitchen (5)
21 James Joyce novel (7)
22 The Norwegian language (5)

Down

1 Impertinence (9)
2 Plotter (7)
3 Walks laboriously (7)
4 Racing vehicle (2-4)
5 Drooped (6)
6 Titled (5)
10 One deputising for another (9)
12 Edible jelly (7)
13 Separator (7)
14 ___ the board: applying to all (6)
16 Seventh planet (6)
18 Country in the Himalayas (5)

Underneath the bottles in the safe is a tiny little notebook, filled with code. It looks like it's a list of who bought which bottles, but it needs decoding.

April

6th 4 23 12 1 14 19 15 13

May

1st 13 18 12 1 21 18 5 14 20-16 5 18 18 9 5 18

9th 19 3 2 15 12 12 9 14 7 5 18

10th 3 13 11 18 21 7

June

1st 5 3 3 1 20 20 9 5 18

3rd 8 14 2 15 12 12 9 14 7 5 18

5th 12 19 16 15 12 18 15 7 5 18 19

7th 2 3 13 21 14 14

Once you've decoded it, look at the initials. Do any of them look familiar to you?

PUZZLE
102

D	K	K	L	R	E	E	N	A	C	C	U	B	Q	T
D	R	E	K	A	E	R	B	E	S	U	O	H	P	N
D	E	I	R	I	R	S	D	F	J	N	U	R	T	I
E	K	X	N	B	D	C	S	G	U	B	S	E	R	S
W	C	W	T	K	C	N	E	A	V	T	X	L	E	S
P	A	A	S	O	D	R	A	N	P	P	L	G	G	A
I	R	R	T	H	R	R	A	P	I	S	T	N	G	S
C	C	E	C	B	O	T	I	W	P	S	E	A	E	S
K	E	G	D	R	U	P	I	V	L	E	T	R	L	A
P	F	G	O	I	I	R	L	O	E	E	R	T	T	E
O	A	U	I	G	R	M	G	I	N	R	R	S	O	P
C	S	M	T	A	D	Y	I	L	F	I	R	M	O	Y
K	A	Z	V	N	T	G	O	N	A	T	S	H	B	O
E	S	L	K	D	A	F	V	J	A	R	E	T	G	O
T	S	B	L	A	C	K	M	A	I	L	E	R	X	R

ASSASSIN
BLACKMAILER
BOOTLEGGER
BRIGAND
BUCCANEER
CAT-BURGLAR
DRINK-DRIVER
EXTORTIONIST
FORGER
HOUSEBREAKER
JOYRIDER
KERB-CRAWLER
KIDNAPPER
LARCENIST
MUGGER
PICKPOCKET
SAFE-CRACKER
SHOPLIFTER
STRANGLER
TRESPASSER
WAR CRIMINAL

The Lab finds this word search pasted onto one of the bottles. Can you work out if it's a clue left behind by the killer?

If you think about it, everything is a puzzle.

Word search: 'Ace' Words

A	W	T	P	A	A	E	C	A	R	B	M	E	P	M
T	L	Y	S	A	P	A	X	O	Q	O	D	C	Z	I
C	A	P	T	E	C	A	T	B	P	I	O	A	B	S
P	R	E	F	A	C	E	P	E	S	M	E	F	P	L
B	E	F	R	O	A	A	D	G	M	E	X	L	S	E
E	B	A	L	O	M	L	R	O	C	D	A	A	T	C
M	I	C	C	A	S	A	N	A	E	E	C	O	T	A
I	R	E	P	E	C	P	R	F	O	C	E	C	A	L
S	T	R	U	E	L	B	A	E	C	A	R	T	N	U
P	H	E	F	A	N	C	L	C	U	F	B	T	N	P
L	P	U	C	I	E	O	S	U	E	R	A	S	L	O
A	L	E	A	K	S	O	L	A	C	E	T	L	A	P
C	A	M	U	Y	U	I	W	R	E	T	E	Y	L	T
E	C	A	F	R	U	S	E	R	O	N	U	D	V	Q
R	E	C	A	L	E	O	H	S	G	I	R	I	U	G

AEROSPACE
BIRTHPLACE
COALFACE
COMMONPLACE
DEFACE
DISGRACEFUL
EMBRACE
EXACERBATE
INTERFACE
MAINBRACE
MISPLACE
PACED
PEACE
POPULACE
PREFACE
RESURFACE
SHOELACE
SOLACE
TACET
TYPEFACE
UNTRACEABLE

Codebreaker

23	21	26	3	10	4	15	6		26	4	15	14
2		19		12		10		8		24		19
1	4	20	5	2		11		10	26	3	4	11
1		15		8		7		15		19		10
			5	4	26	4	26	20	4	5	4	8
6		5		18		5		4		6		2
16	19	4	17	21	11		15	11	4	4	3	22
10		6		2		4		10		8		15
15	6	5	21	13	6	21	5	4	8			
6		4		10		5		7		10		6
10	26	2	25	4		4		10	12	17	4	5
12		6		15		9		12		17		21
25	21	15	6		25	2	5	25	19	22	11	4

A B C D E F G H I J K L M N O P Q R S T U V W X Y Z

1	2	3	4	5	6	7	8	9	10	11	12	13
						V						C

14	15	16	17	18	19	20	21	22	23	24	25	26
												M

fermentations – one ... fermentation ...
... it is drunk. The second fermentation ... product.
... dioxide and ethanol that are vital for the finished product.

PUZZLE 105

Chemical Analysis of Champagne

The average 0.75 litre bottle of champagne contains 7.5 grams of dissolved carbon dioxide. When the bottle is opened, it releases approximately 5 litres of carbon dioxide gas before becoming completely flat. A single champagne flute, assuming a volume of 0.1 litres, contains approximately 20 million bubbles.

The Graven End Lab runs a carbon dioxide analysis on the 20 bottles of champagne. Do any of them match the control sample?

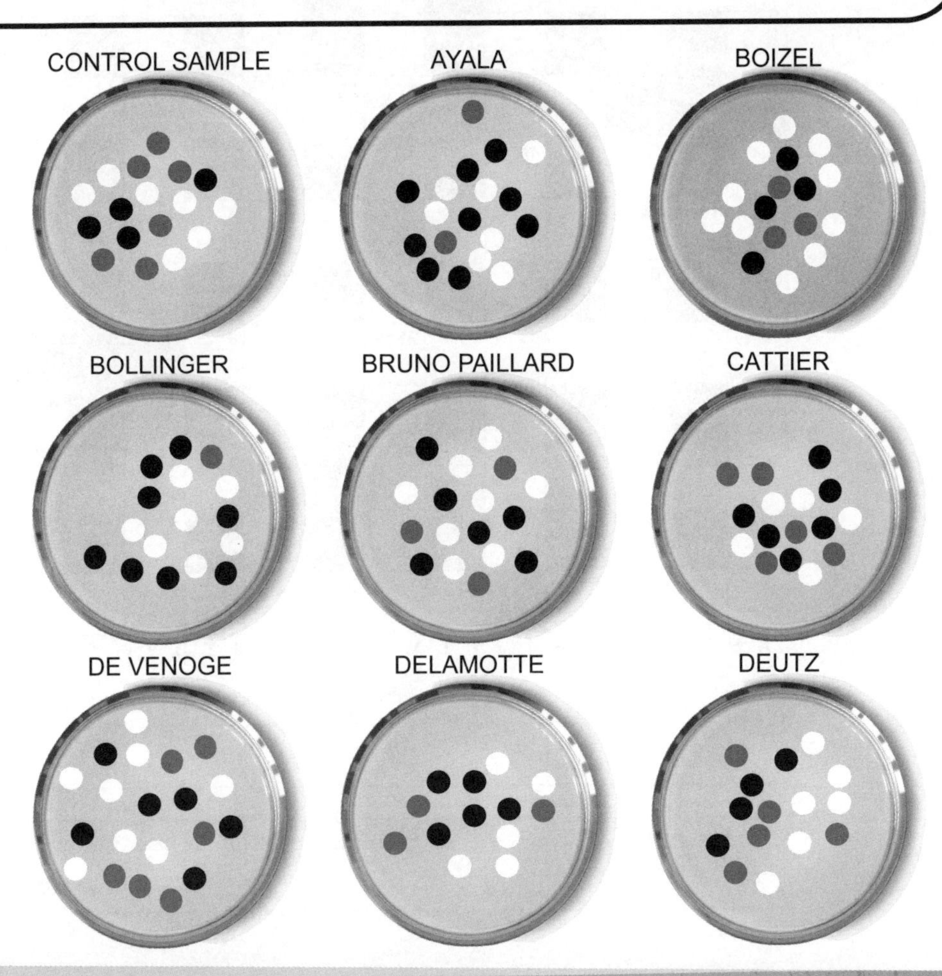

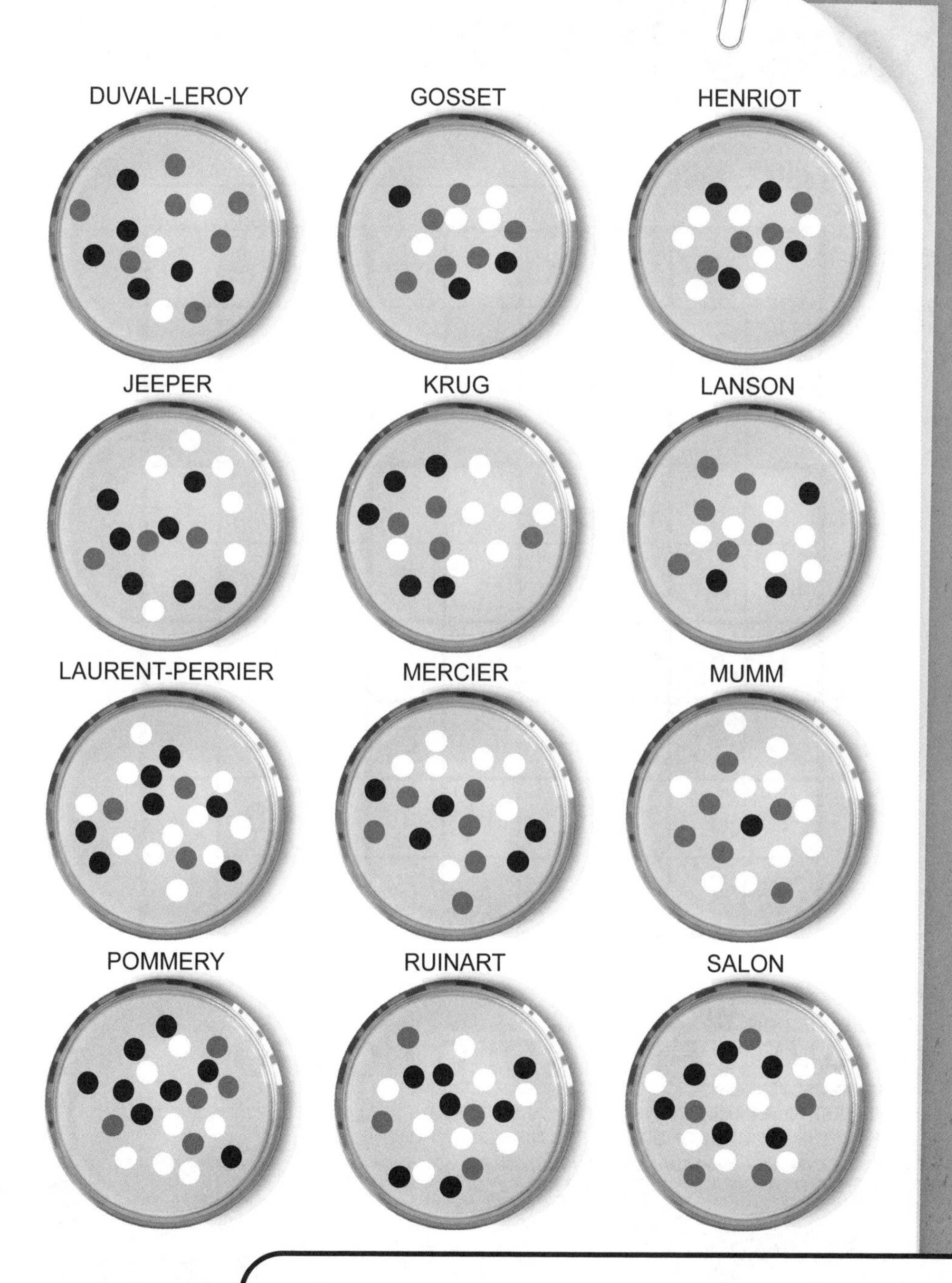

What can you conclude from this experiment?

Sara's PUZZLE PAGES

THE BEST-SELLING NEWSPAPER IN GRAVEN END

Letter-Doku!

PUZZLE 106

	C		A			I		
	G		H	I			A	
F			C					
		D						F
A			I		F			H
I						E		
					B			D
	F			H	I		B	
		G			C		F	

Crossword

Across

1 Walks up and down (5)
4 E.g. from Ethiopia (7)
7 Appeal (5)
8 Suspenseful adventure story (8)
9 Craftily (5)
11 Official list of names (8)
15 Popular lunch food (8)
17 Particle that holds quarks together (5)
19 Wheeled supermarket vehicles (8)
20 Embed; type of filling (5)
21 Segmented worm (7)
22 MacArthur: sailor (5)

Down

1 Vain posing (9)
2 Bravery (7)
3 Smart and fashionable (7)
4 Assent or agree to (6)
5 Breathe in (6)
6 Pertaining to the ear (5)
10 Sailor of a light vessel (9)
12 Flatter (7)
13 Given generously (7)
14 Place where something is set (6)
16 Overseas (6)
18 Cloth woven from flax (5)

PUZZLE 108

In their haste to solve the case, one of the officers takes the champagne bottles out of the safe before the Crime Scene Techs could photograph them. He only remembers the location of 3 bottles. Can you recreate the positions of all the bottles? Some could go in more than one location, which is fine as the Techs just need an approximate layout.

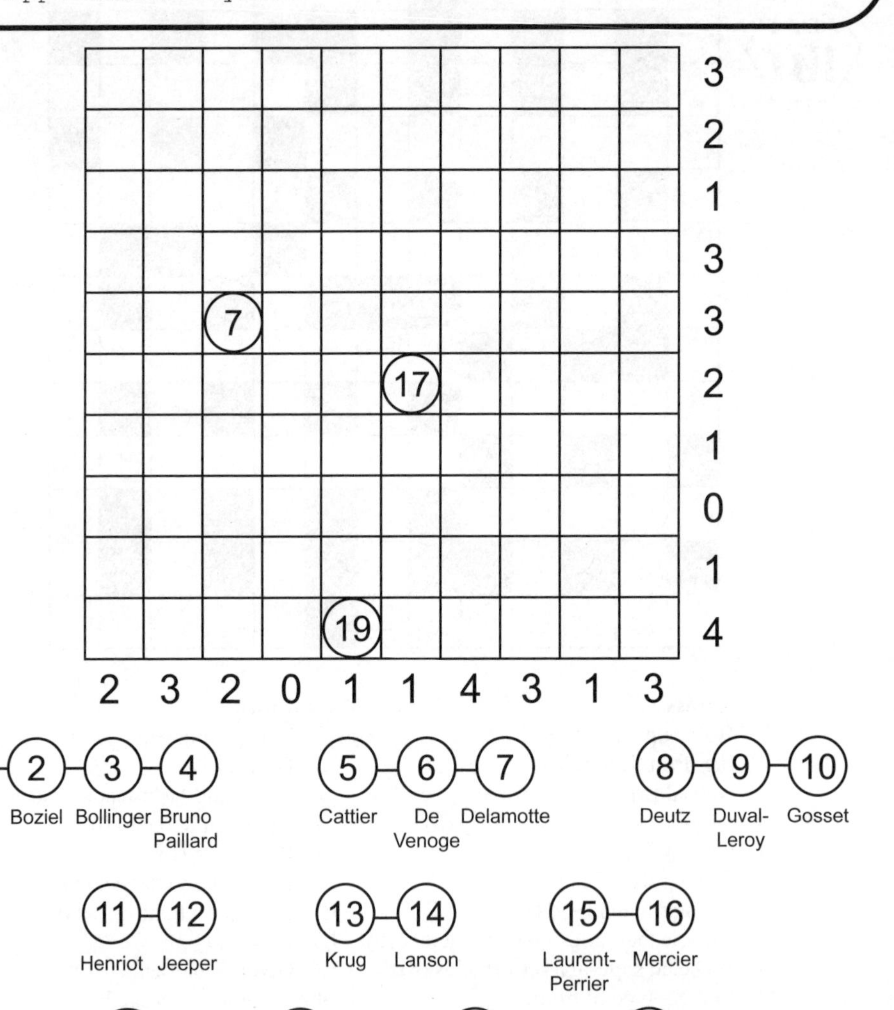

The following riddle is found in a box of corks on a workbench in the basement.

A person was locked in a room. In it were two doors, a table and chair, and a hole in the ceiling 15cm wide. Behind the first door was a hungry lion. Behind the second door was a glass tunnel that magnified the sun, creating a temperature so high that it would scorch you if you opened the door. The person escaped.

How?

PUZZLE

110

After solving the riddle, McCrawley looks up. Sure enough, she can see a small hole in the ceiling, next to the light fixture. A tiny camera is found, looking directly down at the work table. While initially the team are excited to find out the identity of the killer, they soon realise that the cheap, rubbish camera takes cheap, rubbish video. Only two stills are decent enough to see anything.

It looks like the items on the desk have changed. Can you find the **six** differences between the two photos?

Use this page to record all your answers for this crime. This may help you to determine who you think the killer is at the very end.

PUZZLE	ANSWER
84	
85	
88	
91	
94	
95	
98	
101	
102	
105	
108	
109	
110	

Did you notice anything strange about the puzzles in the Graven End newspaper?

From Katie McCrawley's personal notebook:

So, Frasier was a forger. Admittedly, I never saw that one coming, but there was always something... off about him. Incredibly intelligent, but just not sure how to use it? However, from what Easton says, formaldehyde poisoning is a horrible way to go. To slip it in the champagne is a little bit of genius.

I notice that the name Leo Santana keeps popping up, first in Jones' murder and then in Frasier's.
I don't know of anyone by that name. The university has records, but they're sealed, and Turner doesn't think "my gut feeling" warrants a judge ordering them unsealed. All the records I can find — bank, driving licence, etc — just end after the 70's. Like he died?

Probably just coincidence. You're over thinking this, McCrawley.

CRIME SCENE FIVE

LOCATION:
The Egyptian wing of the Graven End Historical Society Museum

MURDER WEAPON:
Asphyxiation, caused by a bronze amulet lodged in his oesophagus

ELEMENTS OF THE FILE HAVE BEEN REDACTED DUE TO THE HIGHLY CONFIDENTIAL NATURE OF THE CASE. THE FILE AND CONTENTS ARE THE PROPERTY OF THE GRAVEN END POLICE DEPARTMENT. REMOVAL FROM THE BUILDING WILL RESULT IN IMMEDIATE ARREST.

VICTIM: Dr. Anthony Masterson

Before the museum, the victim worked in the medical department at Graven End University, where he taught the history of medicine. His appointment as Head Curator at the museum twenty years ago was welcomed by most, but opposed by some who felt he was too critical of the authenticity of some of the museum's artefacts.

He was often seen arguing with the museum's owner, Matthew Jessup, over large sums paid for unauthenticated items, and how neither the victim nor Jessup were able to ████████ ████████████████████ ████████████████.

The morning before a special press event is due to be held, unveiling a new treasure, the victim is found dead inside the museum. A small, precious amulet, taken from the museum's bronze display, is found lodged in his throat.

Sara's PUZZLE PAGES

THE BEST-SELLING NEWSPAPER IN GRAVEN END

Crossword

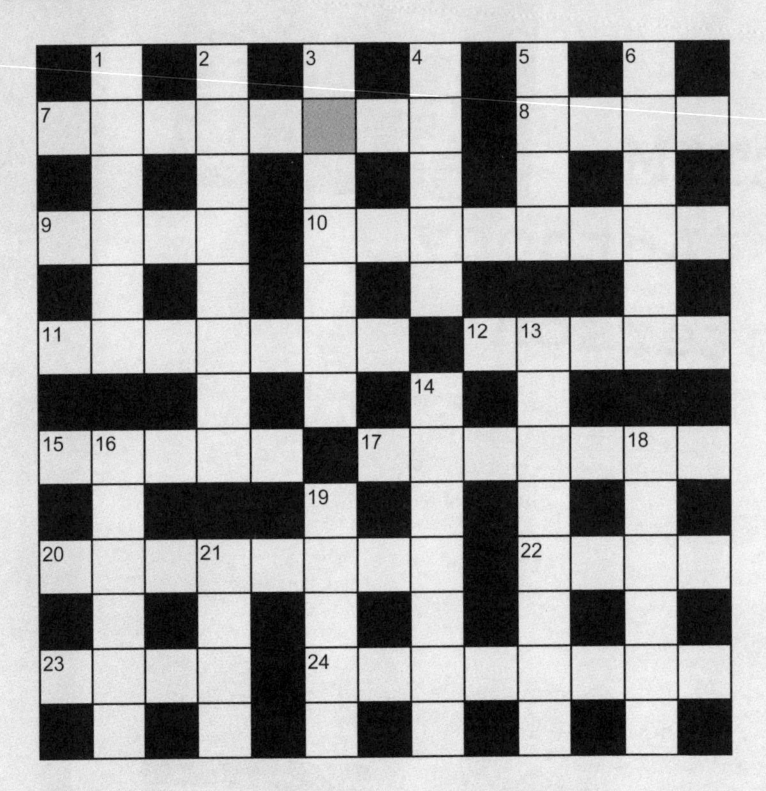

Across

7 Unstrap (8)
8 Use these to row a boat (4)
9 Burkina ___ : African country (4)
10 Pleasantness (8)
11 Sticks to (7)
12 Smash into another vehicle (5)
15 Crunch; wear down (5)
17 Narrow fissure (7)
20 Cocktail (8)
22 Central (4)
23 Flaring star (4)
24 Prodigal (8)

Down

1 Ahead (6)
2 E.g. from Italy or Spain (8)
3 Thick-___ : insensitive to criticism (7)
4 Barrier (5)
5 Sprinkled with seed (4)
6 Comes up (6)
13 Renovated (8)
14 Walk aimlessly (7)
16 Explanation (6)
18 Exclusive circle of people (6)
19 Opinions (5)
21 Wharf (4)

Arrow Words

Tree		Manages		Animal carapaces	Entrance		Machine; automaton	Uttered
Learned people								
				Far away from home	First on the list			
Protective foot covering	Inactive pill							
Squander	Creature with pointed ears				Frying pan			
Gems	Fencing sword	Equipped	Recycle		Grain storage chambers		Express; complete	
						Headland		Dispatched
Foretells								
Flightless bird				Tardy				
				Unwrap a gift				
Pollinating insects	Sweet course							

This word search has been left on the steps of the police station. The officer on duty puts it on Detective McCrawley's desk, but doesn't try to solve it. Can you?

Q	O	T	R	O	U	K	U	Z	S	H	E	O	A	A
V	Y	K	S	W	Q	U	A	S	C	I	L	E	R	P
I	T	S	S	T	E	N	I	B	A	C	M	R	R	U
S	I	T	T	S	T	L	L	E	C	H	U	S	C	M
I	R	A	R	I	E	E	Y	R	O	T	S	I	H	O
T	U	T	Q	N	B	W	D	L	S	P	E	E	W	H
O	C	U	C	K	A	I	H	C	T	H	U	I	L	C
R	E	E	R	G	S	S	H	C	U	X	M	P	U	D
S	S	S	P	P	U	L	G	X	M	K	I	R	A	Q
S	L	T	L	O	P	I	O	F	E	R	B	B	T	A
Y	K	A	H	T	H	S	D	U	S	O	E	N	A	Q
T	Y	C	B	T	Y	S	A	E	R	W	J	A	Y	J
S	X	T	P	E	N	O	A	S	S	T	E	Z	L	Y
U	S	J	Z	R	L	F	D	E	R	R	A	P	K	I
D	S	T	I	Y	S	S	R	E	T	A	S	Q	Z	N

ANTIQUES	EXHIBITS	QUIET
ARTWORK	FOSSILS	RELICS
CABINETS	GUIDES	SECURITY
COSTUMES	HISTORY	SILENCE
CURATOR	LABELS	STATUES
DISPLAYS	MUSEUM	TEASHOP
DUSTY	POTTERY	VISITORS

Transcript of conversation between Detective Sergeant Katie McCrawley and Detective Constable Alex Summers, conducted via text message.

McCrawley: Theres another 1

Summers: seriously?

McCrawley: Yea. Looks like the curator @ GE museum

Summers: What r they playing @? I havent even eaten breakfast yet

McCrawley: No idea

McCrawley: Dont think he cares about ur brkfast, tho

McCrawley: heading over in 10

Summers: right. Meet u there in 30?

McCrawley: oh by all means take ur time with brkfast. its only a murder. nothing special

Summers: bUT theyre pancakes

McCrawley: ...

[END OF TRANSCRIPT]

Codebreaker

22	24	10	4	6	■	22	17	7	13	7	13	18
16	■	13	■	16	■	16	■	■	16	■	4	■
15	■	14	■	12	■	6	■	24	21	16	3	4
4	6	5	24	12	7	6	22	■	21	■	1	■
6	■	10	■	14	■	20	■	8	20	14	4	6
5	11	4	3	3	7	4	6	■	4	■	■	26
4	■	2	■	22	■	■	■	6	■	25	■	16
13	■	■	7	■	24	20	20	4	20	16	7	24
22	11	7	13	18	■	14	■	24	■	25	■	17
■	24	■	2	■	25	14	19	6	22	7	5	10
12	7	23	7	4	■	6	■	14	■	22	■	7
■	3	■	18	■	■	4	■	13	■	6	■	13
9	19	18	14	13	4	6	■	6	17	16	13	18

A B C D E F G H I J K L M N O P Q R S T U V W X Y Z

1	2	3	4	5	6	7	8	9	10	11	12	13
	D						F					

14	15	16	17	18	19	20	21	22	23	24	25	26
								T				

Crossword

1		2		■	3	4		5		6		7
	■		■	8	■		■		■		■	
9							■	10				
	■		■		■		■		■		■	
11					■	12						
	■	■	■		■		■		■		■	
13		14				■	15					
	■		■		■	16	■		■	■	■	
17							■	18		19		
	■		■		■		■		■		■	
20					■	21						
	■		■		■		■		■		■	
22								■	23			

Across

1 Small restaurant (4)
3 Unusual (8)
9 In a nimble manner (7)
10 Religious doctrine (5)
11 Trite (anag) (5)
12 Seven-a-side game (7)
13 Strong (6)
15 Restore honour (6)
17 Tidies (7)
18 Alcoholic beverage (5)
20 Dwelling (5)
21 Break between words (in verse) (7)
22 Buffed (8)
23 Nuisance plant (4)

Down

1 Artisanship (13)
2 Force upon (5)
4 Purchasing (6)
5 Fully extended (12)
6 Artificial (3-4)
7 The ___ / ___ : Fairy tale by Hans Christian Andersen (6,7)
8 Notwithstanding (12)
14 Not sudden (7)
16 Soul; spirit (6)
19 Extinguish (a fire) (5)

Less than ten minutes after the puzzle has been solved, officers arrive at the museum. This note is found taped above the electronic keypad on the locked door of the staff entrance.

Officers, I have hidden three puzzles in this alleyway. Complete all three to receive the code to this door. Don't take too long, though...

2	○				7	3	4	
8	4					9		2
	1		4	8				7
				3			8	6
			8		5			
3	8			6		○		
4				2	6		7	
1		2					5	4
	3	8	5					1

The second puzzle is found tucked underneath a bucket in the corner of the alley.

Number Two

		7		4			○	8
	1	4	3					
6	2		1					9
		6	8					
4		○		1				5
					4	2		
1					7		5	6
					3	9	7	
7			5	9		3		

Hurry up....

PUZZLE
118

The final sudoku is found by Summers, tucked into the street sign.

Last one. Have you worked it out, yet?

		3						5
8				5	2		6	
						2	7	
4				1	7	5		2
5		2	8	6				3
	4	8						
	2		4	7				8
1						6		

Full Code: ____________________

As McCrawley enters the staff room, she notices an officer staring at the letterboard on the wall. When asked, the officer replies that "there are missing letters. I just can't work out which ones".

CAN WE REMEMBER O R ATES, PLE SE? DONT
LET YOU SELF B CAUGH   UT. HILDREN
ALW YS OVE TO SEE US FUMB E.
RE EMB R AARON?

STONE GE	2.5 MI LION-3000 BCE
BRONZE AGE	3000-1300 BCE
RON GE	1300-600 BCE
PERSIAN EMPI E	550 BCE-330 BCE
NCIENT REECE	600 BCE-600 D
ANC ENT ROME	753 BCE-476 AD
MIDDLE AGES	476 AD-1450 AD
BYZANTINE EMPIRE	285 AD-1453 AD
EUROPEAN RE AISSANCE	1450 AD-1600 AD

A - Z

■	A	D	A	G	E	■	S	C	R		P	■
E	■	E	■	R	■	S	■	O	■	R	■	S
C	A		T	I	O	N	■		A	C	A	
H	■	O	■	D	■	I	■		■	■	■	A
O	U	S	T	■	A	F	F	I	N	I	T	
E	■	I	■	E	■		■	N	■	N	■	■
S	E	T	T		E	■	C	E		T	R	E
■	■		■	I	■	E	■	S	■		■	
A		D	I	T	I		E	■	R	I		E
	■	■	■	I	■	(shaded)	■	E	■		■	C
O	O		E		■			M		U	A	T
N	■	E	■	T	■	E	■		■	E	■	S
■	A	N	I	S	E	■	S		A	S		■

A B C D E F G H I J K L M N O P Q R S T U V W X Y Z

Kriss Kross

PUZZLE 121

3 letters
Arc
Elm
Icy
Nod

4 letters
Ajar
Eels
Epic
Muck
Ogre
Race

5 letters
Gecko
Olden
Stern
Stomp

6 letters
Bounce
Casing
Except
Gallic
Pigsty
Tidied

7 letters
Ecuador
Elastin
Erratum
Octagon
Polemic
Topiary

8 letters
Anecdote
Employed
Leapfrog
Nickname

9 letters
Contralto
Margarine
Misdirect
Objecting

13 letters
Communication

The Crime Scene Techs find nothing in the staff room, but they do report that all the lockers are empty, except one. They are unable to look inside the locker, as it is locked with a combination padlock. There is no code nearby, but there is another puzzle taped to the back of the staff room door.

If you want to look in the locker, you're going to have work out the combination first...

There are 10 lockers and 10 members of staff. All lockers are closed. As the staff enter, the first employee (E1), opens every locker. Then the second employee (E2) begins with the second locker, L2, and closes every other locker. Employee E3 begins with the third locker and changes every third locker (closes it if it was open and opens it if it was closed). Employee (E4) starts at locker L4 and changes every fourth locker. Employee E5 starts with locker L5 and changes every fifth locker, and so on, until employee 10 changes locker 10.

After all the employees have passed through the locker room and changed the lockers, which lockers are open?

Open = ✓

Closed = ✕

LOCKERS

EMPLOYEES

	1	2	3	4	5	6	7	8	9	10
1										
2										
3										
4										
5										
6										
7										
8										
9										
10										

Code: ____________________

Pathfinder: Capital Cities

ADDIS ABABA
AMSTERDAM
BAGHDAD
BANGKOK
BRIDGETOWN
DUBLIN
HAMILTON
KUALA LUMPUR
LA PAZ
LAGOS
LONDON
NAIROBI
ULAN BATOR

H	G	I	D	D	A	R	B	R	O
D	A	S	A	B	N	I	D	A	T
A	B	L	B	A	W	E	G	B	N
D	N	I	U	B	O	T	U	L	A
L	N	G	D	A	R	O	N	O	T
A	A	K	N	A	I	B	I	L	L
G	B	O	K	M	A	A	P	A	I
O	N	N	O	L	D	Z	H	A	M
S	O	D	A	L	R	E	T	S	M
K	U	A	L	U	M	P	U	R	A

"The world is a puzzle.
One we'll never make sense of.

Letter-Doku!

B								D
	G	E				I		
	A			E		G		
			D	C			A	
		D	E		A	B		
	B			I	F			
		G		B			D	
		C				E	G	
E								H

The locker contains three bars of melted chocolate (whole nut), four pens (ink dried up), and a maze. Can you work your way through it and find out which area it's leading us to?

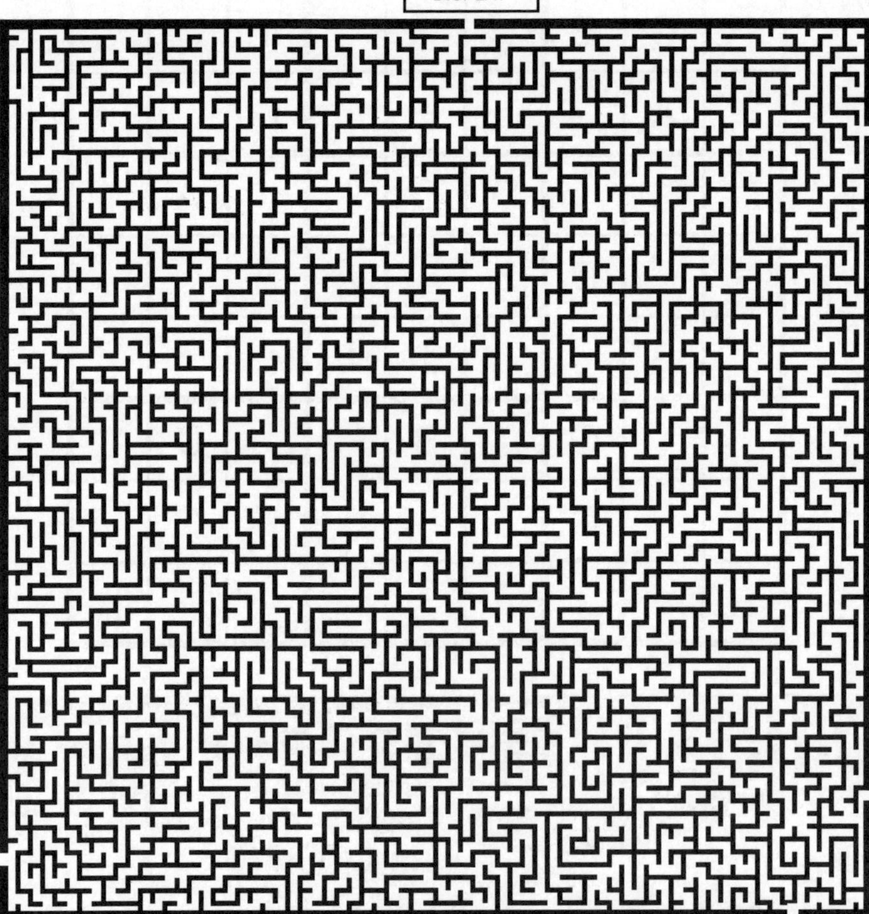

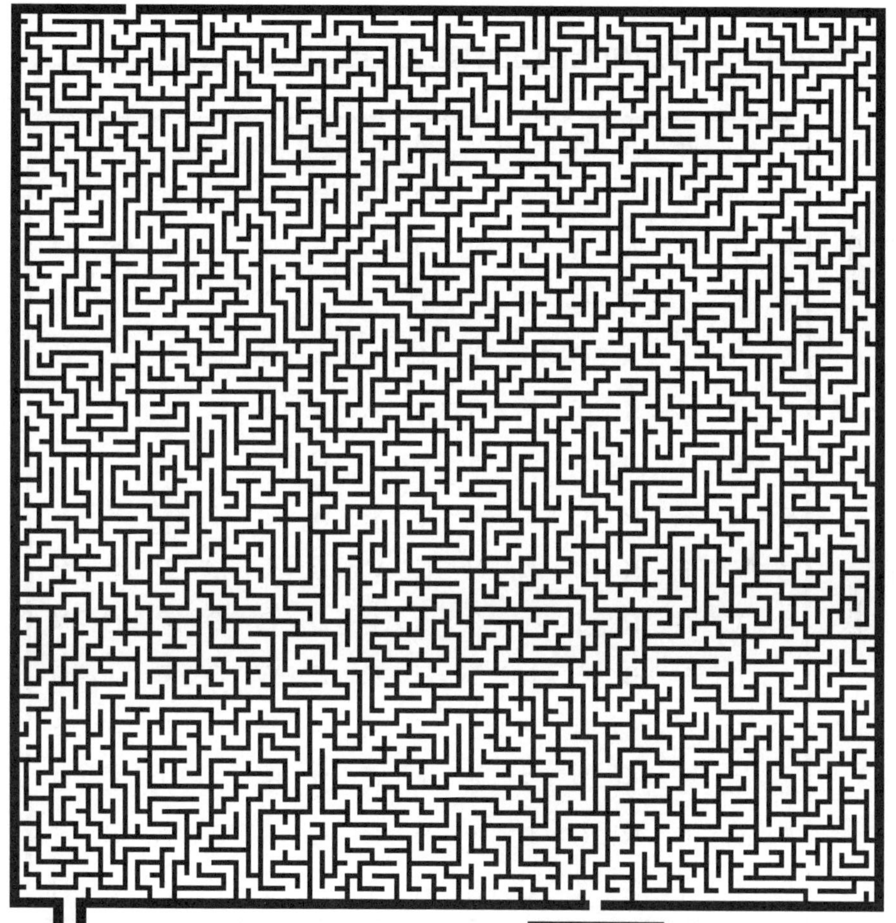
EGYPTIAN
EXHIBIT
CHINESE
CORNER

Word search: Roller-Coaster Types

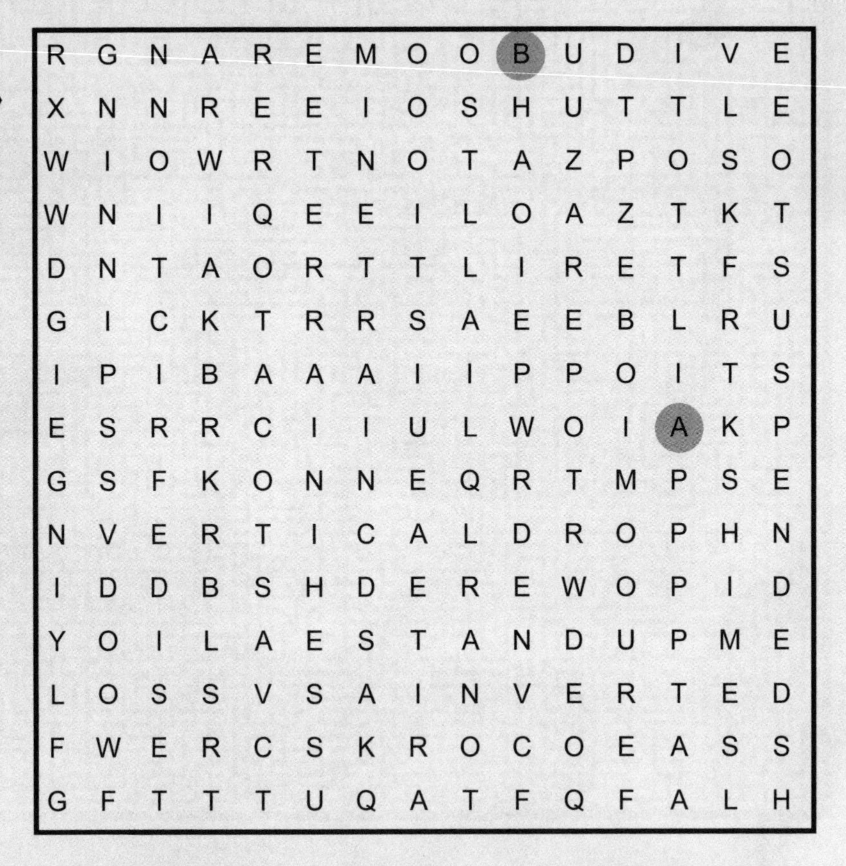

BOOMERANG
CORKSCREW
DIVE
DUAL-TRACKED
FLOORLESS
FLYING
INVERTED
MINE TRAIN
MOTORBIKE
PIPELINE
POWERED
SHUTTLE
SIDE FRICTION
SPINNING
STAND-UP
STEEPLECHASE
SUSPENDED
TERRAIN
TWISTER
VERTICAL DROP
WING

Letter-Doku!

G							E	C
		B	I				D	
	F		D		C			
			E				G	H
F								A
C	G				A			
			B		G		C	
	H				D	G		
A	I							D

"Amazing puzzles are coming your way.
Just keep going."

When McCrawley and Summers arrive at the Egyptian area of the museum, they notice that a piece of paper has been laid on the information desk.

Where oh where is your next clue?

	22			19			11		9
		27	54			16	14		
				59	58				
		61	63	64			1	6	5
	51								4
			99	100			72	68	
32				98	92	89	76		
						88	85		
	37		44	47					○
35		38	39				82	80	

PUZZLE

129

When the police officers find the correct location, they come face-to-face with a row of six ancient mummies. The lead curator of the Egyptian exhibits is horrified to find out that one of the mummies has a note stapled to its delicate wrappings.

Oh dear. These mummies are out of order. What terrible person could commit such a crime? Can you work out which one actually goes where? If you do, I promise you there's a clue in it for you...

Front Row	1	2	3
Back Row	4	5	6

Mummy A: This one is not next to, in front of, or behind Mummy C

Mummy B: This one is not in the front row

Mummy C: Don't put this one on the left or the right

Mummy D: This one shouldn't be put in the back row, or on the left

Mummy E: This mummy is on the right

Mummy F: This one is not on the front, or on the left

So, which mummy goes where? Tick tock, Detective...

Crossword

Across

7 ___ Q: musical (6)
8 Fast (6)
10 Light fabric often made of silk (7)
11 Henrik ___ : Norwegian dramatist (5)
12 Flat and smooth (4)
13 Growing thickly (of a beard) (5)
17 ___ Bellamy: Welsh footballer (5)
18 Adult male singing voice (4)
22 Female fox (5)
23 Not tidy (7)
24 Underground store (6)
25 Matures (of fruit) (6)

Down

1 Large farms (7)
2 Stopped working (7)
3 Deep chasms (5)
4 Standing erect (7)
5 Make fun of someone (5)
6 Doglike mammal (5)
9 Harmful (9)
14 Decorative altar cloth (7)
15 Locked down (7)
16 Boorish (7)
19 Kick out (5)
20 Expel from a country (5)
21 Hank of wool (5)

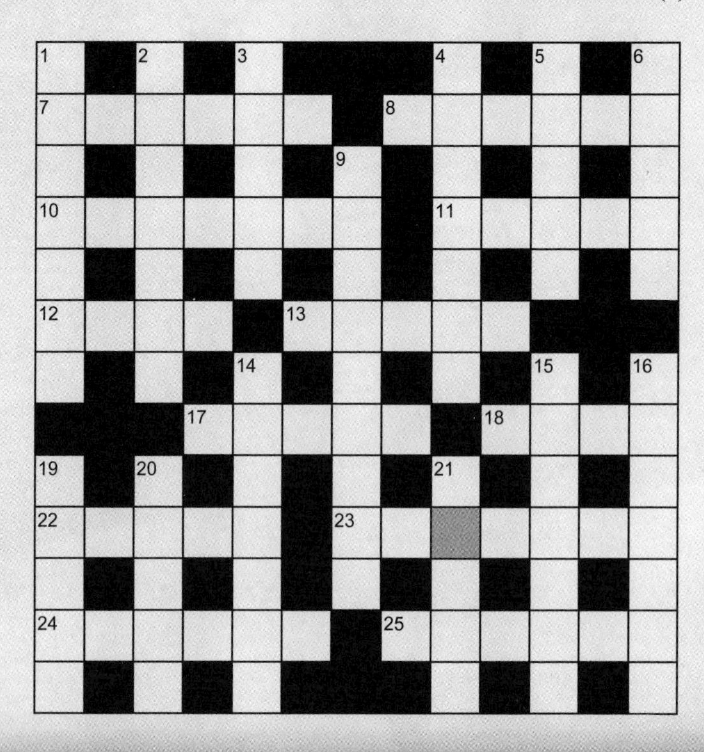

PUZZLE 131

"Soon you'll find your answer and all will make sense."

Pathfinder: Yummy Sandwich Fillings

E	G	A	O	Y	A	M	B	Y	T
E	U	S	N	N	N	N	A	E	U
G	A	O	M	A	E	O	C	K	R
G	S	N	L	I	K	C	I	H	C
S	T	C	A	S	A	C	R	A	M
A	O	A	S	E	N	B	A	P	S
L	R	R	P	T	U	C	N	E	S
A	D	I	M	Y	R	E	I	A	S
T	S	R	H	S	E	L	D	R	S
E	A	K	T	O	M	A	T	O	E

BACON
CARROT
CELERY
CHICKEN
CRAB
EGG SALAD
MAYONNAISE
SALMON
SARDINES
SAUSAGE
SHRIMP
SPAM
STEAK
TOMATOES
TUNA
TURKEY

Transcript of conversation between Detective Sergeant Katie McCrawley and Detective Constable Alex Summers, conducted via text message.

McCrawley: where r u?

Summers: hiding

McCrawley: what?

Summers: hiding with crime Scene techs. The museum people got mad about dummies being moved

Summers: *mummies

McCrawley: u r an idiot. Get bk here. Need u 2 distract the curators while we move things

Summers: why me????

McCrawley: because I said so?

Summers: fine. Easton has found something on the victim's corpse.

McCrawley: tell him we'll b over soon. also, tell him he dropped his scarf in the staff room. Jessops has it.

[END OF TRANSCRIPT]

When the police officers have *carefully* lifted up Mummy A to move it to the correct place, a piece of paper is found stuck to the floor. There's a code on it, but no one has been able to crack it yet. Can you help?

YFSFS OMGBD USGVG RMMNB UNIFJ
IKSDL NSGVD EDRGF DSFSF MILUY
YGHFJ LGHOK IKKLF FSKFF ESKJV
SUOJS ONHMS NERYI OKASS WJLUI
IGMAS TSFFH SSDGD TAWER IKILG
MITTF EDFVB FDBFH OXCVB RCVAS
YDBFB ODFGF UDFGD TDFFG OUILE
PADER AUHKS YDJNB

PUZZLE 133

The keen eyes of the curators notice scuff marks on the floor that weren't there before, indicating that the displays have been moved. A look through the victim's desk uncovers an exhibit plan for the Egyptian area, but unfortunately it is in a code known only to the victim. Can you locate the position of each of the displays listed in the grid? What display covered the giant X marked on the floor?

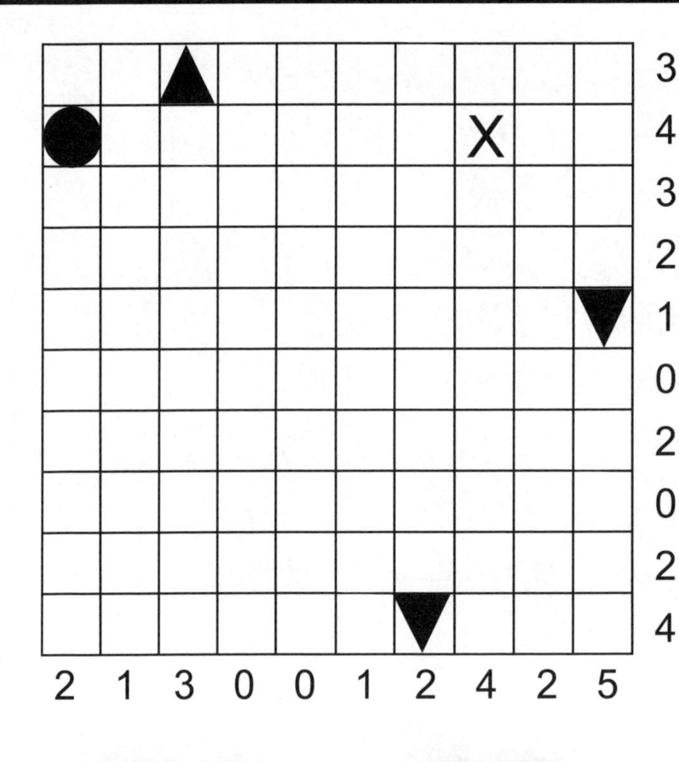

Numbers around the edge are the number of exhibit blocks in each row and column. Exhibits are surrounded on all sides by space, including diagonally.

Golden Mummy Casket

Ancient Egyptian Gold

Farming tools - Early to Late Ancient Egypt

Burial Ceramics

Death Masks

Ancient Egyptian Wedding Customs

Ancient Egyptian medicine

Ancient Egyptian toys

Graven End & Ancient Egypt

Summers points out that someone has scratched hieroglyphs into the side of one of the displays. Is it vandalism, or is someone leaving a message?

A	F	KH	K	E
A	M	KH CH	G	Y
I	N	S Z	T	U W
U W	R	S	TJ	M
B	H	SH	D	N
P	H	K	DJ	L

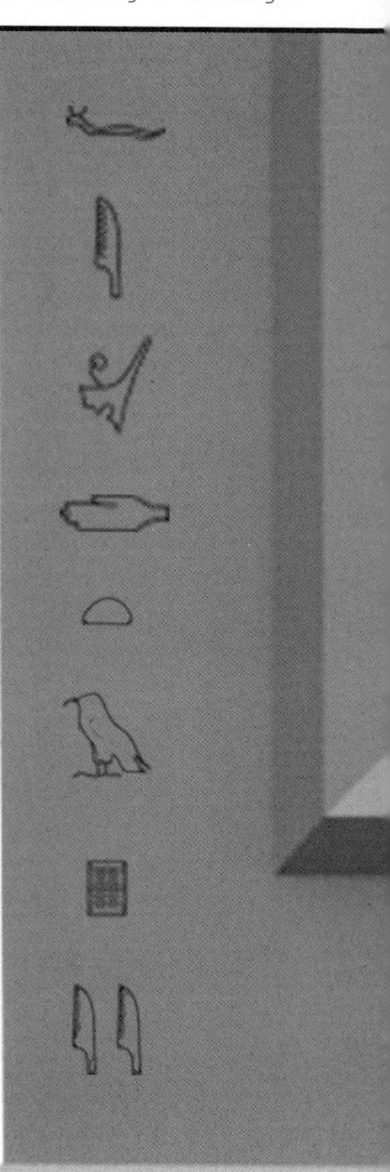

Sara's PUZZLE PAGES

THE BEST-SELLING NEWSPAPER IN GRAVEN END

Word search: Hot Drinks

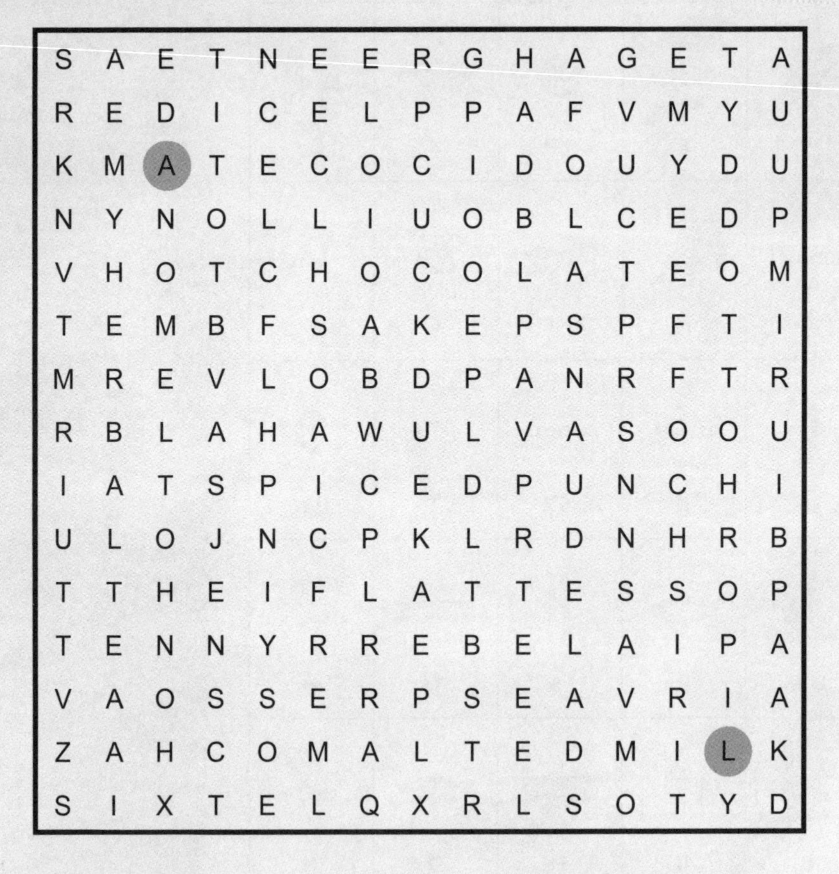

ALEBERRY
APPLE CIDER
BLACK TEA
BOUILLON
CAPPUCCINO
ESPRESSO
GREEN TEA
HERBAL TEA
HOT CHOCOLATE
HOT LEMONADE
HOT TODDY
IRISH COFFEE
LATTE
MALTED MILK
MATE COCIDO
MOCHA
MULLED WINE
POSSET
SAKE
SALEP
SPICED PUNCH

Codebreaker

	11		9		23		23		8		24	
25	19	21	13	23	4	14	5		12	18	14	13
	19		2		9		15		14		20	
15	26	14	25		12	4	15	25	19	12	14	22
	15		4		5		24				25	
9	24	26	14	12	15	12		3	19	14	23	25
			13		12		21		18			
26	15	12	20	15		10	19	23	25	6	15	23
	22				17		12		26		16	
22	4	14	5	26	18	13	7		19	1	9	6
	19		19		19		26		24		22	
12	15	9	26		25	12	9	1	15	23	25	2
	24		5		15		13		24		23	

A B C D E F G H I J K L M N O P Q R S T U V W X Y Z

1	2	3	4	5	6	7	8	9	10	11	12	13
						K						

14	15	16	17	18	19	20	21	22	23	24	25	26
I							W					

CCTV footage from the time of the murder is conveniently missing. However, a still of the Egyptian gold display from before the murder shows discrepancies when compared to a photo taken by a Crime Scene Tech after the murder.

Can you find the **eight** differences between the two photos?

Sara's PUZZLE PAGES

THE BEST-SELLING NEWSPAPER IN GRAVEN END

A - Z

PUZZLE 138

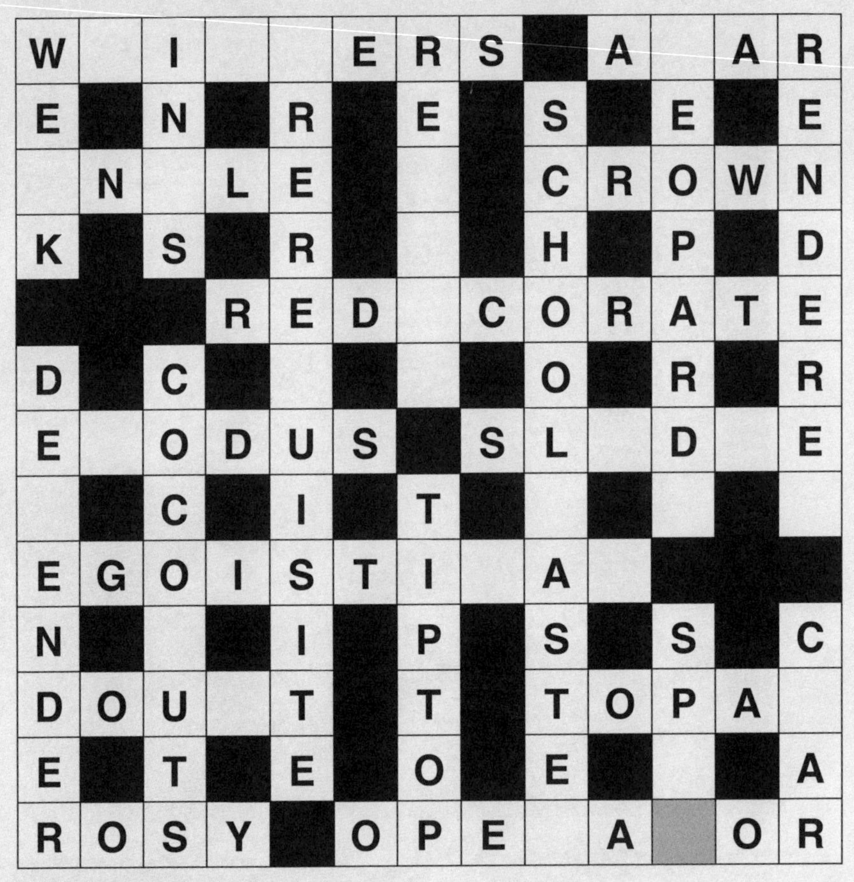

A B C D E F G H I J K L M N O P Q R S T U V W X Y Z

Crossword

Across

1 Country in N Europe (6)
5 ___ Holden: English actress (6)
8 Island of Indonesia (4)
9 Quarrels (8)
10 Whip eggs (5)
11 Mislead on purpose (7)
14 Hidden store of valuables (8,5)
16 Declare to be true (7)
18 Small flexible bag (5)
20 Covered walk in a convent (8)
22 Snatched (4)
23 Subatomic particle such as a nucleon (6)
24 Saying (6)

Down

2 Worn by the elements (9)
3 Salt lake in the Jordan Valley (4,3)
4 Topical information (4)
5 Roused from sleep (8)
6 Standpoint (5)
7 Small numbered cube (3)
12 Full of life (9)
13 Metallic element used in light bulbs (8)
15 Male chicken (7)
17 Oneness (5)
19 Clench (4)
21 Mauna ___ : Hawaiian volcano (3)

Sara's PUZZLE PAGES

THE BEST-SELLING NEWSPAPER IN GRAVEN END

Letter-Doku!

		H	F					D
F			I		H		A	
		D					I	
	G		E	A				
C								I
				I	C		G	
	B					H		
	E		C		D			G
I					B	E		

Daily puzzles brought to you by Graven End's very own Enigmatologist

Kriss Kross

PUZZLE 141

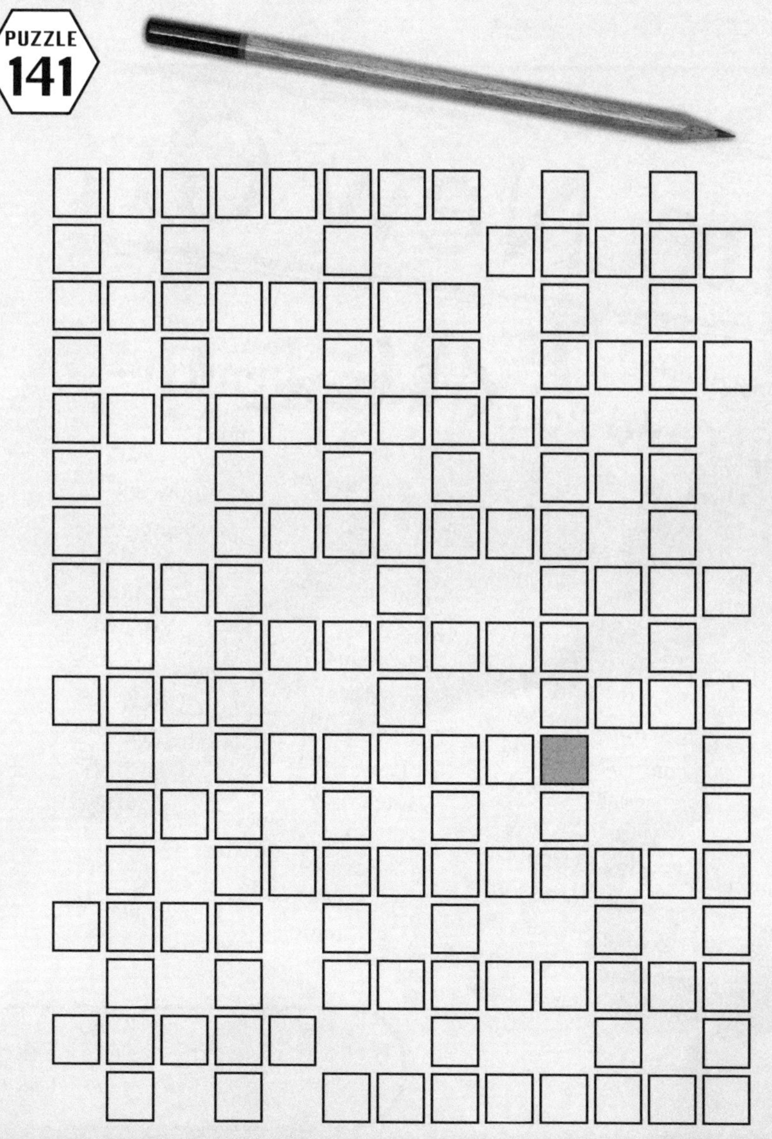

3 letters
Nil
Rot

4 letters
Avid
Honk
Icon
Menu
Stir
Visa

5 letters
Adder
Chain
Hoard
Irons
Largo
Rural
Since

7 letters
Channel
Fanatic
Grounds
Narrate
Nascent

8 letters
Cartoons
Cleanser
Daughter
Enlarged
Escapism
Rearmost

13 letters
Authentically
Manufacturers

Before Dr. Easton and the Crime Scene Techs arrive, McCrawley notices that there is a scrap of newspaper clutched in the victim's hand. Someone has scribbled the word "FAKE" on it.

The New Gra

FAKE!!

Friday, 14th August 2020

Ancient Gold Found in Graven End

A precious hoard of 67 gold coins was unearthed in the grounds of the Graven End Manor by keen metal detectorist and local scientist, Doctor Leo Santana. Each of the coins have the head of a man and a date, 21 BCE, stamped on them, and weigh approximately 60g.

Matthew Jessup, owner of the Graven End Museum, which purchased the hoard from Dr. Santana for a large undisclosed sum, expressed his excitement at the find. "It's amazing to think that these Egyptian coins have been hiding in the grounds of our very own manor house for years with no one knowing."

"There hasn't been a significant gold find in this area for well over a hundred years," Jessup continued. "Not since the builders of the Graven End Theatre found the Kettle of Tunis. So, of course the museum wanted to snap them up".

The coins go on display at the end of the month and a special unveiling event for press and donors is being planned.

How does the victim know the coins were fake?

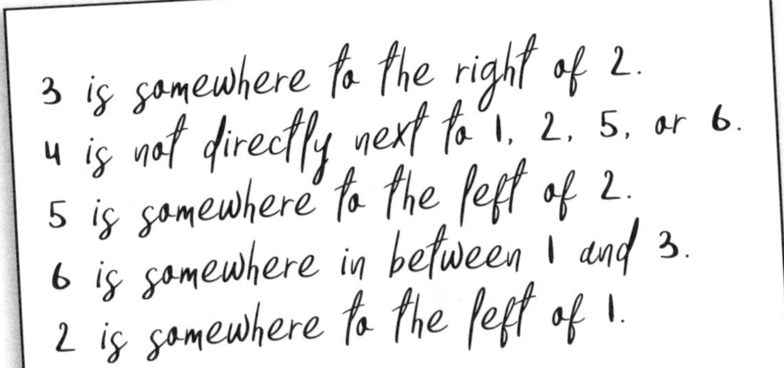

DISPLAY ORDER:

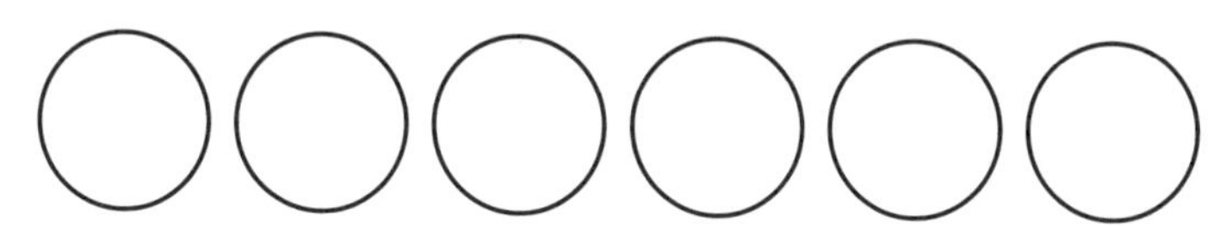

While waiting for Dr Easton to examine the body, something catches the eye of McCrawley: the scarabs on the medicine display are out of order, and a piece of paper has been left beside them. Can you work out what order the scarabs are supposed to be in?

Codebreaker

1		9		22				21		10		23
7	23	5	18	21	7		13	18	17	4	7	19
24		4		18		5		19		3		19
18	24	10	20	5	23	22		24	3	4	26	23
4		4		1		4		7		24		12
7	23	23	12		19	3	24	25	23			
19		18		13		4		24		12		1
			14	24	18	22	1		16	23	7	5
1		3		22		4		1		24		11
16	21	21	1	23		23	8	6	24	3	23	1
23		11		13		1		23		4		4
24	18	11	21	5	18		2	23	24	7	23	12
18		17		3				15		19		23

A B C D E F G H I J K L M N O P Q R S T U V W X Y Z

1	2	3	4	5	6	7	8	9	10	11	12	13

14	15	16	17	18	19	20	21	22	23	24	25	26
K								T				V

Pathfinder: Colours

ALIZARIN
ASPARAGUS
BABY PINK
CADMIUM YELLOW
CAMEL
FUCHSIA
GOLDENROD
JASPER
KHAKI
NAVY BLUE
ORANGE
PERIWINKLE
PURPLE

U	I	M	S	A	J	A	U	F	K
M	A	D	P	E	E	I	C	I	H
Y	C	E	P	R	G	S	H	K	A
E	E	R	D	B	N	A	R	O	E
L	L	I	O	A	N	K	A	L	U
L	K	W	R	B	I	P	S	B	Y
O	N	I	N	Y	P	A	N	A	V
W	C	D	E	S	U	R	N	A	Z
M	A	L	O	G	G	A	I	R	I
E	L	P	U	R	P	L	E	A	L

Use this page to record any notes or answers for this crime. This may help you to determine who you think the killer is at the very end.

PUZZLE	ANSWER
113	
116	
117	
118	
119	
122	
125	
128	
129	
132	
133	
134	
137	
142	
143	

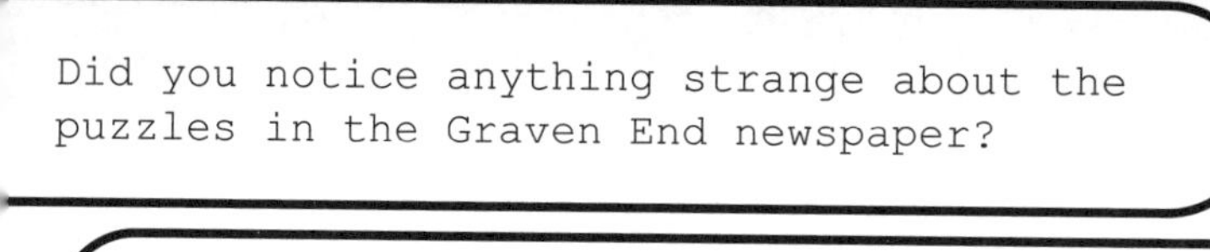

Did you notice anything strange about the puzzles in the Graven End newspaper?

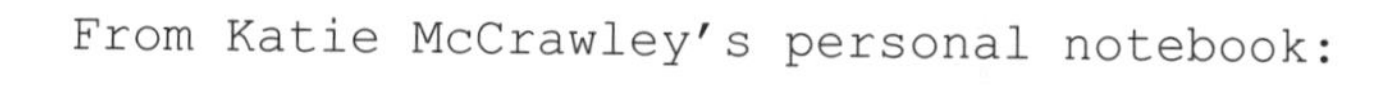

From Katie McCrawley's personal notebook:

The strength it would've taken to shove an amulet down Masterson's throat is interesting. Killer's anger at Masterson may have given them the strength. Anger's powerful.

And the killer is definitely angry at being called a liar again by Masterson.

What's the connection between the two?

They seem to know the area well - knew when no one but the curator would be in the museum. Summers thinks they're local, which looks likely. Leo Santana has appeared again.

I need to dig deeper on this.

CRIME SCENE SIX

CONFIDENTIAL

LOCATION:
Graven End Forensic Laboratory

MURDER WEAPON:
Poison

ELEMENTS OF THE FILE HAVE BEEN REDACTED DUE TO THE HIGHLY CONFIDENTIAL NATURE OF THE CASE. THE FILE AND CONTENTS ARE THE PROPERTY OF THE GRAVEN END POLICE DEPARTMENT. REMOVAL FROM THE BUILDING WILL RESULT IN IMMEDIATE ARREST.

VICTIM: Dr. Josie Denby

The sixth victim was a technician in Graven End Police department's own forensic laboratory. Having moved straight from university to the laboratory as a forensic technician just two months before her death, she was considered to be smart, even "exceptional" at her job by some of her colleagues, often "finding connections that no one else knew existed".

She worked extensively with Dr Easton's Crime Scene Techs, and spent weeks working on the [redacted] and [redacted] with [redacted] in Little Graven.

She had frequent, often-unrelenting migraines, and colleagues mentioned that when she was alone in the lab, she would turn most of the overhead fluorescent lights off, preferring to work in softer lighting than the lab usually had. This could explain how the killer moved through the lab unnoticed by the victim.

The victim was found dead by one of her colleagues the following morning.

A torn print out of a DNA sequence is found underneath the victim's body. Can you determine if it is the same as the DNA the victim was studying at the time of her murder?

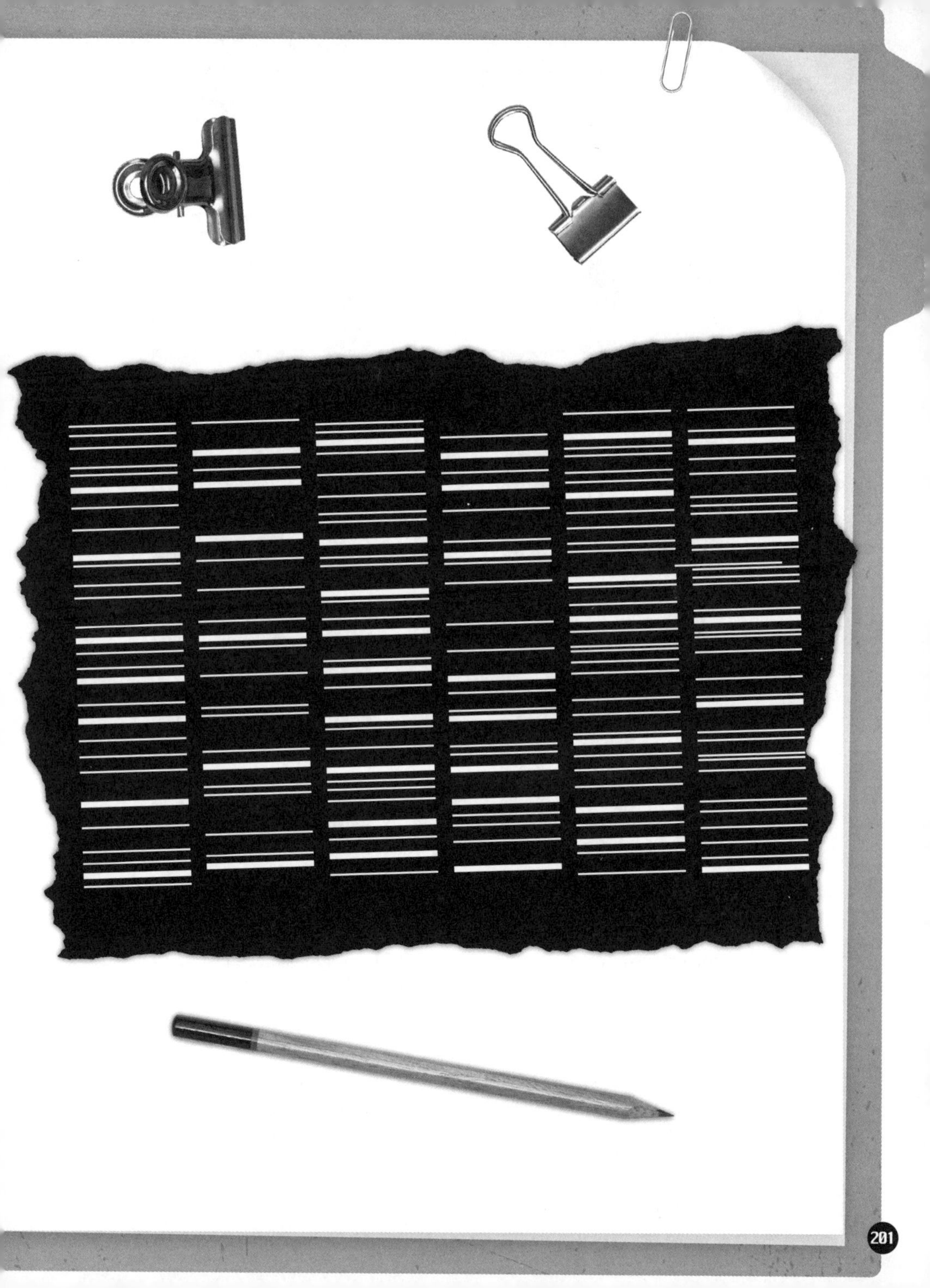

Crossword

Across

7 Peacemaker (8)
8 Cereal grains (4)
9 Passionate desire for something (4)
10 Lacking knowledge (8)
11 Safe places (7)
12 Inferior to (5)
15 Religious groups (5)
17 Go backwards (7)
20 Muttered (8)
22 River in central England (4)
23 Not as much (4)
24 State of being the same (8)

Down

1 Coniferous tree (6)
2 Cause deliberate damage to (8)
3 Hopes to achieve (7)
4 Main stem of a tree (5)
5 Not sweet (4)
6 Causes a sharp pain (6)
13 Capable of being used (8)
14 Necessary (7)
16 Displayed freely (6)
18 Fires a bullet (6)
19 Small container (5)
21 Sentimentality (4)

A - Z

PUZZLE 148

A		A	R	■	D	E		I	R	I		M
P	■		■		■		■	N	■	N	■	I
P	R			I	E	S	■		U	S		
R	■	R	■	S	■	A	■	O	■	I	■	M
O		N	■		■	T	■	S	E	P	I	A
X	■	■	■	U	N				■	I	■	N
I	■	O	■	D	■	■	■	I	■	D	■	
M	■		■	G	R	A	F	T	■	■	■	G
A	D	D	L	E	■	F	■	A	■	P	I	E
T	■		■	M	■		■	B	■	I	■	M
E		A	D	E	■	O	B	L	I		U	E
L	■	L	■		■	R	■	E	■	U	■	N
	U	L	E		I	D	E	■	G		N	T

A B C D E F G H I J K L M N O P Q R S T U V W X Y Z

Even the hardest puzzles have a solution.

Codebreaker

1	10	26	21		12	11	12	14	10	21	18	21
18		10		21		17		15		24		18
25	10	23	22	22	18	9		12	1	17	21	18
10		6		17		7		1		6		22
23	19	3	18	1	13	23	19	12	11	6	8	
3				12		19		14		18		11
12	24	12	1	9	21		21	3	12	19	16	12
6		20		23		18		18				6
	14	17	19	14	18	19	3	1	12	3	18	9
21		6		12		2		23		10		19
7	19	17	6	6		17	11	21	18	1	5	18
10		3		6		23		18		4		21
12	6	6	12	8	23	19	26		12	21	7	21

A B C D E F G H I J K L M N O P Q R S T U V W X Y Z

1	2	3	4	5	6	7	8	9	10	11	12	13
R							Y					

14	15	16	17	18	19	20	21	22	23	24	25	26
C												

Daily puzzles brought to you by Graven End's very own Enigmatologist

Pathfinder: Insurance Words

BACKING
BOND
CERTAINTY
COVER
DEED
INVESTMENT
PROVISION
SAFEGUARD
SECURITY
SUPPORT
TESTAMENT
UNDERWRITER
WARRANTY

C	E	G	U	A	R	R	O	V	I
T	R	E	F	A	D	P	E	T	S
R	T	A	I	S	E	M	S	R	I
O	P	T	N	T	N	A	T	E	O
U	P	Y	D	E	R	I	T	V	N
S	Y	B	N	U	W	R	E	O	I
I	T	O	E	D	N	A	R	C	N
R	U	N	E	Y	T	R	R	E	V
E	C	D	D	B	A	W	A	S	T
S	G	N	I	K	C	T	N	E	M

This word search was found at the back of the victim's notebook. It seems like it's made up of DNA strands, but it also looks odd. Can you solve the word search and work out what's different about it?

Y	T	C	A	A	T	T	A	C	C	C	A	G	A
T	G	A	C	C	G	G	A	T	C	C	C	O	A
C	U	C	G	T	T	G	C	A	A	T	C	G	A
G	A	A	G	T	K	G	A	G	C	G	G	T	C
C	C	T	A	A	A	C	G	G	N	G	T	C	C
A	C	A	G	T	T	C	C	C	G	A	T	C	G
T	G	O	A	C	A	A	A	A	T	A	G	A	T
T	A	C	A	A	W	A	C	A	M	T	A	G	G
A	T	A	T	A	C	T	A	A	G	T	G	G	A
G	T	T	A	A	T	A	G	T	G	T	E	A	G
G	A	W	C	T	A	G	A	C	C	A	T	T	G
A	G	T	A	C	C	C	G	A	A	G	C	T	E
C	C	A	G	C	A	A	T	A	A	C	A	A	L
A	C	C	A	C	L	T	A	C	G	C	A	T	A

CCTGGAATTTA	AGCAATAACA	GTTACCAGATC
CCGATTAGCC	GACCCATTAAC	AATTAACGGAC
AGTTCCCGAT	TATTAGGACC	AAACCGTGAG
TACGATAACCG	TAGTACAAGT	CAGGATTACG
TGACCGGAT		TACCCGAAGC

The top drawer of the victim's desk is locked, and the keypad looks strange - the numbers aren't the typical 1-9, and the last number ism missing. So far, the Crime Scene Techs have worked out that the first three digits are **5, 18** and **9.**

Can you work out the final number?

Letter-Doku!

Asserts to be the case		Standards		21st Greek letter		Phantasm		European country
Legal ambiguity								
Act of getting rid of		17th Greek letter				Under judgement (3,6)		Wife of a knight
Type of savings account (abbrev)		Decorate		Fish				
			Remains preserved in rock		Auction offer			
Hinged barriers	Expect; think that		Repeat something once more		Handsome crow			
					Egyptian goddess		Wicked	Close securely; aquatic mammal
Disperse (anag)								
Mentally sharp								
Pile		___ Keys: US singer						
				Exchange for money				

Daily puzzles brought to you by Graven End's very own Enigmatologist

Letter-Doku!

G					I			
	A							G
E	I	D	B					
		I	F			C		
		C	H	I	G	B		
		H			C	D		
					D	E	B	A
D							C	
			E					D

"

The closer you get, the further away the answer can seem.

The first thing the detectives notice as they finally open the drawer is that a photograph has been placed on top of the contents. On closer inspection, it becomes obvious that it is a photo of the very drawer they are looking in but with a few differences.

Can you find the **six** differences between the two photos?

Kriss Kross

PUZZLE 156

3 letters
Now
Sir

4 letters
Lens
When

5 letters
Astir
Fears
Fungi
Jetty
Khaki
Night
Rigid
Talon
Today
Valid

6 letters
Archer
Impede
Mohair
Sketch
Starch
Tinkle

7 letters
Sandals
Shallot

8 letters
Archival
Hitherto

11 letters
Aggravation
Awkwardness
Heavyweight
Imaginative
Inadvertent
Tetrahedron

Daily puzzles brought to you by Graven End's very own Enigmatologist

Word search: Shades of Green

C	O	M	E	S	A	J	V	L	L	A	Z	J	T	A
N	L	D	I	Q	O	I	H	C	A	T	S	I	P	C
T	E	C	N	N	E	E	R	G	E	L	P	P	A	I
I	M	E	J	E	T	L	S	O	T	Z	A	R	R	D
N	F	O	R	E	S	T	G	R	E	E	N	I	I	G
T	S	S	U	G	A	R	A	P	S	A	K	X	S	R
U	G	H	U	N	T	E	R	G	R	E	E	N	G	E
R	L	O	E	T	I	H	C	A	L	A	M	E	R	E
Q	M	F	V	J	U	N	G	L	E	G	R	E	E	N
U	A	R	I	D	T	G	Y	I	L	L	I	R	E	T
O	N	U	L	I	S	G	O	M	R	K	U	G	N	V
I	T	U	O	K	R	P	H	E	S	B	Z	K	A	R
S	I	I	D	E	I	S	I	R	G	I	D	R	E	V
E	S	U	E	R	T	R	A	H	C	R	T	A	U	I
M	S	N	J	H	Z	E	A	V	O	C	A	D	O	D

ACID GREEN
APPLE GREEN
ASPARAGUS
AVOCADO
BRIGHT GREEN
CHARTREUSE
DARK GREEN
FOREST GREEN
HUNTER GREEN
JUNGLE GREEN
KELLY GREEN
LIME
MALACHITE
MANTIS
MINT
OLIVE
PARIS GREEN
PISTACHIO
TEAL
TURQUOISE
VERDIGRIS

12:34

100%

9 11 14 15 23 23 8 1 20 25 15 21
4 9 4.

25 15 21 4 15 14 ' 20 11 14 15 23
1 14 25 20 8 9 14 7.

9 11 14 15 23 5 14 15 21 7 8. 9 4
15 14 ' 20 21 14 4 5 18 19 20 1 14
4 23 8 25 23 15 21 12 4 25 15 21
4 15 20 8 9 19.

2 5 3 1 21 19 5 9 3 1 14.

6 9 14 5. 9 6 25 15 21 1 18 5 14
15 20 7 15 9 14 7 20 15 20 5 12
12 13 5 25 15 21 3 1 14 20 5 12
12 20 8 5 16 15 12 9 3 5.

An initial search of the top drawer reveals the victim's missing phone. Using the victim's thumbprint, McCrawley manages to unlock the phone. However, as she scrolls through the messages, she notices that one message thread looks completely different from the rest.

Can you work out what the messages say?

A final sweep of the victim's top desk drawer reveals a sticky note with familiar handwriting on it. The officer on duty correctly identifies it as another riddle left by the killer, but is unable to find a solution. Can you?

Josie has 2 bottles of identical-looking tablets. She must take one tablet from each bottle every day: if she forgets to take one or takes more than one of either, she might be ill. When she has two days' supply left, she drops all four tablets on the floor, mixing them up.

What should poor Josie do?

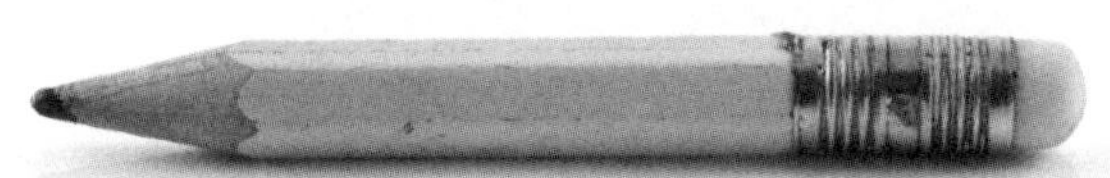

Partial transcript of conversation between Detective McCrawley and Doctor Alan Easton, taken from the laboratory's autopsy room recorder.

McCrawley: So, anything for us, Doc?

Easton: Well, the body was found with minimal signs of trauma. A bruise on the back of the head, probably from where she collapsed, and Doctor Asher reported a faint odour present on the body at the scene. Internally, there were more extensive signs. Vomit was found in her lungs, and her pharynx was found partially collapsed. There were visible changes to the lining of the stomach and microscopic analysis revealed the start of cell death in her organs.

McCrawley: Right. What's your guess at cause of death?

Easton: I'd say poisoning, but we haven't had the toxicology screening back yet, I'm afraid.

McCrawley: Fits with the riddle we found. What's your best stab in the dark?

Easton: She worked with poisons, so mercury, potassium cyanide, warfarin or arsenic trioxide would be my guess.

[END OF TRANSCRIPT]

These 4 entries are from the Poisons Formulary, describing the physical effects of overdose. Can you use the information to work out the most likely poison used to kill the victim?

Mercury
Side effects: erythematous rash; slight hepatic enlargement with mild constriction of the blood vessels causing delayed refill and blanching; damage to the muscosal membrane of the stomach, leading a change in colour to slate grey.

Arsenic Trioxide
Side effects: emanation of garlicky odour from the skin and muscosal linings; vomiting; significant constriction of the pharyngeal passageway; stomach muscosal membrane damage, evidenced by white particles in the membrane; organ failure.

Potassium Cyanide
Side effects: vomiting; erythematous rash; significant pulmonary odema causing asphyxiation, myocardial infarction and cardiac cell death; emanation of bitter almond odour emanating from the skin and muscosal linings.

Warfarin
Side effects: significant internal bleeding leading to exsanguination and pulmonary collapse; bursting of epidermal blood vessels causing a petechiae rash; damage to the muscosal membrane of the stomach evidenced by yellowing.

Sara's PUZZLE PAGES

THE BEST-SELLING NEWSPAPER IN GRAVEN END

Codebreaker

21		24		10		17		17		15		15
20	6	3	5	12	20	6	6	20		17	20	2
26		24		17		15		20		3		18
20	14	15	2	6		6	7	18	1	15	13	7
4		1		3		12		17				1
	17	6	12	8	8	20	13		3	13	4	25
11		3		25				22		3		23
20	15	2	16		21	18	3	20	8	4	25	
25				23		20		13		12		18
9	3	1	21	15	4	4		4	3	6	18	20
15		20		12		3		7		3		12
13	7	6		19	3	19	15	2	3	7	12	17
17		17		20		20		11		1		20

A B C D E F G H I J K L M N O P Q R S T U V W X Y Z

1	2	3	4	5	6	7	8	9	10	11	12	13
	C											

14	15	16	17	18	19	20	21	22	23	24	25	26
	A			R								

Crossword

■	1	2		3		■	4	5		6		■
7	■		■		■	8	■		■		■	9
10							■	11				
	■		■		■		■		■	■	■	
12				■	13					14		
	■		■	15	■		■		■		■	■
16						■	17					18
■	■		■		■	19	■		■		■	
20								■	21			
	■	■	■		■		■	22	■		■	
23		24			■	25						
	■		■		■		■		■		■	
■	26					■	27					■

Across

1 ___ White: popular snooker player (5)
4 Covers in paper (5)
10 Become husky (of a voice) (7)
11 Juicy fruit (5)
12 Travelled by horse (4)
13 Airport checking devices (8)
16 Large terrestrial monkey (6)
17 Lofts (6)
20 Deep ditches (8)
21 Assist (4)
23 Acknowledged; assumed (5)
25 Ice statues with coal for eyes (7)
26 Block of wood (5)
27 Timber framework (5)

Down

2 Impossible to hear (9)
3 Wire lattice (4)
5 Chew cud (8)
6 Joke (3)
7 Winged child (6)
8 Bump (5)
9 Plant containers (4)
14 Layer of cells covering an organism (9)
15 Explosively unstable (8)
18 Lying on the back (6)
19 Robbery (5)
20 Pulls at (4)
22 Grey-haired with age (4)
24 Vessel (3)

This is a photo of the victim's desk taken just after the body is found. Does anything look strange to you?

HG AW EV VE
TY SO LU AT
ER MI NE DE
LS OU XO KP
FI LN SG YU
MN DO SE RL
AT KH WE
DQ ZE BS YK

?

Dr. Easton calls to say that they'd found a piece of paper in the victim's trouser pocket. He sends McCrawley a photo of it and she realises that they've seen this type of puzzle before. Try deleting one letter from each pair to decipher the killer's message.

Transcript of conversation between Detective Sergeant McCrawley and Detective Constable Alex Summers, conducted via text message.

McCrawley:	finished with Easton. he says overdose but i think we go with poisoning
Summers:	ok. found something else. a USB taped underneath her desk
McCrawley:	and???
Summers:	password. need a 4-digit code
McCrawley:	Is there a puzzle?
Summers:	oh yep. a maze
McCrawley:	great. getting sick of puzzles now

[END OF TRANSCRIPT]

Does the maze reveal anything about the password for the USB?

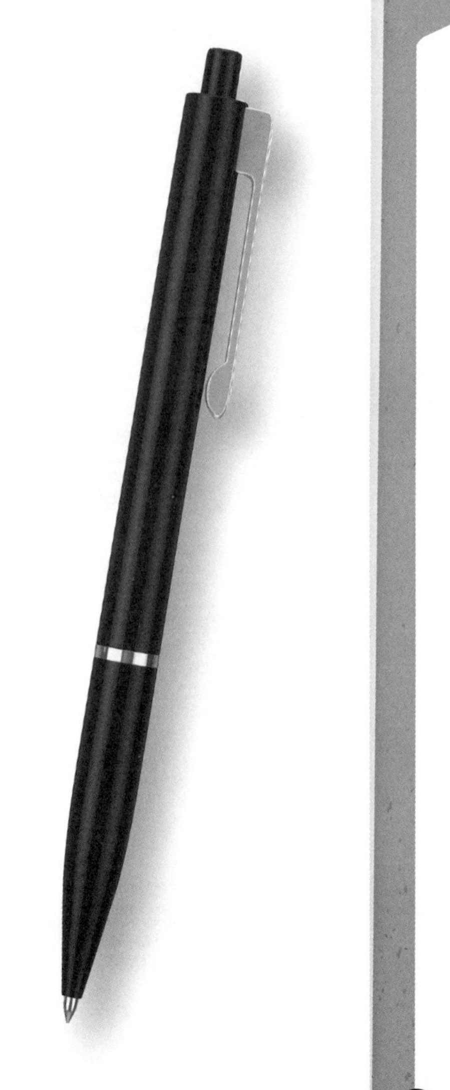

Sara's PUZZLE PAGES

THE BEST-SELLING NEWSPAPER IN GRAVEN END

Arrow Words

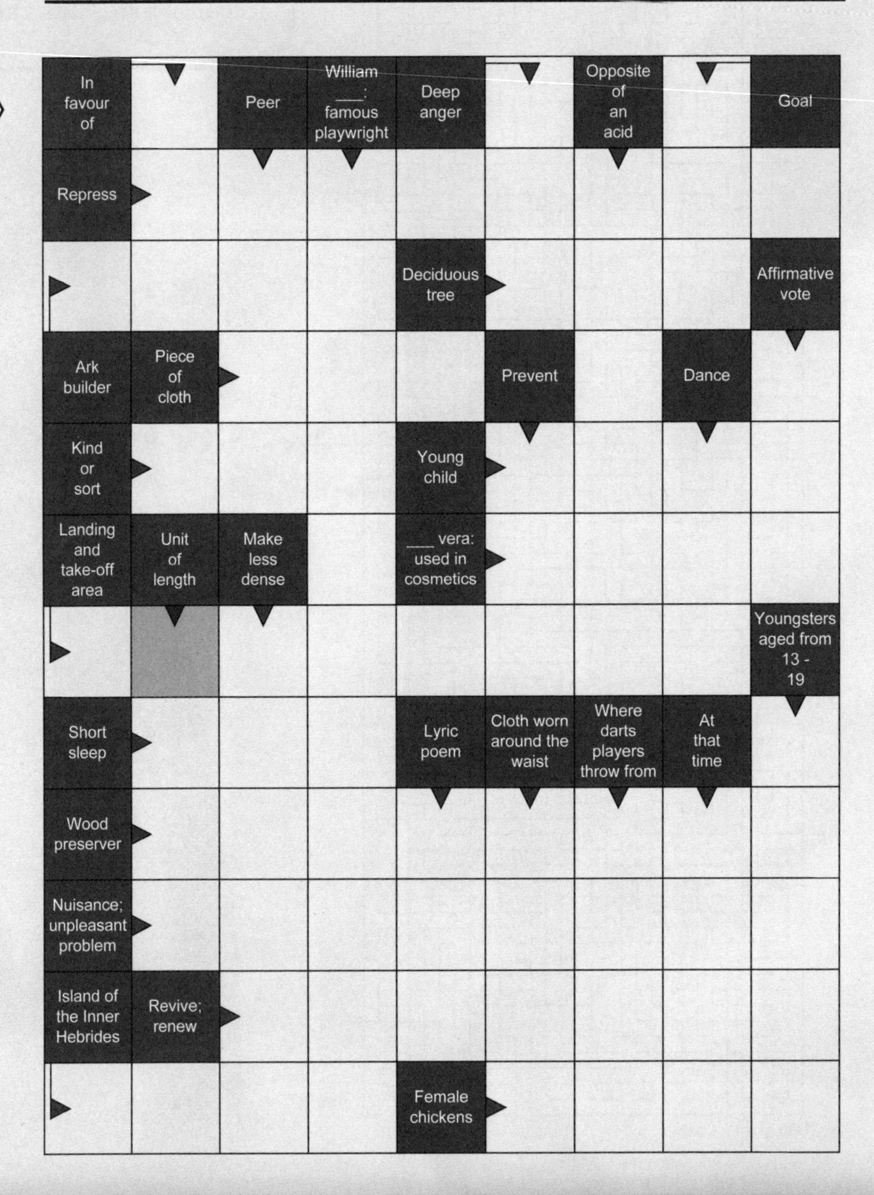

> "When nothing make sense, just keep going."

PUZZLE 167

A - Z

A B C D E F G H I J K L M N O P Q R S T U V W X Y Z

PUZZLE 168

The USB stick contains a single file: a scan of a page from the National Poisons Register, which lists the details of people purchasing restricted substances. It is something the victim would have had access to.

ENTRY NUMBER	NAME / ADDRESS OF PURCHASER	CHEMICAL PURCHASED	QUANTITY (ML)
1071	---- [cipher] / [cipher] [cipher] [cipher]-[cipher] [cipher], [cipher] ------	[cipher]	1500
1072	[cipher] [cipher] / [cipher] [cipher] [cipher]	[cipher] [cipher] [cipher]	125
1073	[cipher] [cipher] / [cipher] [cipher] ----------	[cipher]	2000
1074	[cipher] [cipher] / -------- -- ----------	[cipher] [cipher]	750
1075	[cipher] [cipher] / [cipher] [cipher] [cipher] [cipher] [cipher], [cipher] [cipher]	[cipher]	5000
1076	[cipher] [cipher] / [cipher] --- [cipher]	[cipher]	2000
1077	[cipher] [cipher] / [cipher] [cipher] ----------	[cipher]	2500
1078	[cipher] [cipher] / [cipher] [cipher], [cipher]	[cipher] [cipher] ([cipher])	200
1079	----- [cipher] / [cipher] [cipher] [cipher] [cipher], ------ [cipher]	[cipher] [cipher] ([cipher])	5000

Unfortunately, the file is corrupted and only parts of it are able to be restored. Unrecoverable data has been replaced with a -. The Techs recover what they can, but can you work out the rest?

A B C D E F G H I J K L M

N O P Q R S T U V W X Y Z

ENTRY	NAME ON REGISTER	CHEMICAL/S PURCHASED
1071		
1072		
1073		
1074		
1075		
1076		
1077		
1078		
1079		

Piece by piece, the answer becomes clear.

Word search: London Road Names

R	T	E	E	R	T	S	D	N	O	B	R	O	T	D
S	T	I	H	A	T	T	O	N	G	A	R	D	E	N
P	E	P	A	V	A	H	W	S	P	Y	D	A	E	C
T	E	E	R	T	S	Y	N	A	B	L	A	O	R	H
E	R	C	L	F	D	A	I	V	L	I	O	R	T	E
E	T	A	E	R	A	W	N	O	I	S	R	E	S	Y
R	S	L	Y	I	O	S	G	Y	N	R	S	D	N	N
T	N	P	S	T	R	N	S	P	D	O	G	Y	O	E
S	Y	N	T	H	N	E	T	L	R	A	N	L	T	W
D	M	A	R	S	I	E	R	A	O	D	I	C	X	A
R	R	G	E	T	G	U	E	C	A	V	K	E	A	L
O	E	O	E	R	L	Q	E	E	D	R	M	X	C	K
F	J	D	T	E	E	R	T	S	T	N	E	G	E	R
X	B	A	K	E	R	S	T	R	E	E	T	Y	Z	T
O	Z	C	G	T	E	N	A	L	Y	R	U	R	D	C

ALBANY STREET
BAKER STREET
BAYLIS ROAD
BOND STREET
CAXTON STREET
CLYDE ROAD
CADOGAN PLACE
CHEYNE WALK
DOWNING STREET
DRURY LANE
ELGIN ROAD
FRITH STREET
HARLEY STREET
HATTON GARDEN
JERMYN STREET
KING'S ROAD
LIND ROAD
OXFORD STREET
QUEENSWAY
REGENT STREET
SAVOY PLACE

Kriss Kross

3 letters
Era
Van

4 letters
Auks
Chic
Dewy
Lost

5 letters
Aside
Gulfs

6 letters
Alcove
Bobcat
Erases
Hazier
Houses
Iguana
Lyrics
Novels
Pallid
Picnic

7 letters
Abolish
Animate
Cameras
Sawyers

8 letters
Niceness
Nominate

9 letters
Distances
Leasehold
Newsreels
Paintings

10 letters
Felicitous
Rendezvous

Use this page to record any notes or answers for this crime. This may help you to determine who you think the killer is at the very end.

PUZZLE	ANSWER
146	
151	
152	
155	
158	
159	
163	
164	
165	
168	

Did you notice anything strange about the puzzles in the Graven End newspaper?

Damn it. I liked Josie.

Another overdose, this time with her own migraine medication. The killer must have medical knowledge to have known how much cyanide would be enough to kill.

Where does Leo Santana fit it in to all this?

There's something I'm missing...

I think we're getting closer, though. The clues are a mess, but we think it definitely has to be someone who knew and, possibly, worked with Josie, though we're not sure about that last bit yet.

I need to go over all the evidence one last time and start making connections.

It's time to end this.

Case Notes

Use these pages to record any notes or observations you have about the case.

Transcript of a group conversation between the members of the Graven End Homicide Team, conducted via text message.

Turner:	Summers, please refrain from wasting our time with ridiculous "memes".
Summers:	Sorry, sir. was just excited that we're closing in on the puzzle killer
Charlton:	nice job, guys
Nielson:	wtg :)
Charlton:	so, who is it???
Summers:	all will b revealed!
McCrawley:	its not a circus, summers
Turner:	I'm not entirely sure about that...
McCrawley:	Oh, ur funny, sir.
McCrawley:	Ok Summers, lets catch this SOB.
Turner:	Excuse me?
McCrawley:	Oops. sorry, sir. lets catch this terrible person?
Turner:	Go do your job, McCrawley.
Turner:	And, Summers? Any more "memes" and you're suspended. I don't care what HR says.

[END OF TRANSCRIPT]

You've read through every case file related to the Puzzle Murders that the Graven End Police Department has. You've worked through each puzzle and read every taunting note, pored over all the statements and the discussions between members of the investigating team.

Some detectives will talk about "their gut feeling" and there is scientific evidence that suggests a gut feeling is a very real thing. *You* may have had a gut feeling early on, a sneaking suspicion that one person's actions and words don't quite add up, or that someone may not be what they seem. **Do you still have that gut feeling now?**

Other detectives are more analytical, eschewing emotion, choosing to focus purely on what the evidence says. Perhaps some of the evidence has been consistently pointing at a particular person. Maybe this evidence, when viewed within the context of all six murders, spells out the killer. **What is the evidence telling *you*?**

Now is the time for you to put your skills to the ultimate test: **decide who you think is the The Puzzle Killer.**

I think the killer is:

____

CONCLUSION

It was Leo Santana who killed all these people. But Leo Santana doesn't exist any more.

There was once a man called Leo Santana. He was born and raised in Little Graven by Jorge and Michelle Santana. He was an excellent student and went to university in Graven End, where he studied biology with a view to eventually becoming a doctor. However, in Santana's last year, the university discovered that a lot of his final thesis had been stolen from an old scientific journal. It was a scandal. Leo Santana was kicked out of university for plagiarism. The notoriety drove him and his parents out of Little Graven, far away from all who knew them.

Secretly, Leo vowed revenge against the university and everyone who mocked him. Enter Doctor Alan Easton, forty-five years later. If you haven't already, look carefully at his name: it's an anagram of Leo Santana. The years had not been kind to Santana and his mental state had suffered greatly.

A wrong pizza order, delivered by Josh Harker, was the starting point for this senseless murder spree. Once Josh had died, Santana finally started to take revenge on those who had wronged him.

Daniel Jones was part of the team who discovered Santana's plagiarism (see the newspaper article on page 9) and Santana blamed him for destroying his life.

Hetty Merryweather, like Josh, was simply in the wrong place at the wrong time.

Sydney Blackstone, aka Joe Fraiser, was the other student involved in the scandal, although his name was never released. His fraudulent ways continued into adulthood, and Santana discovered his sideline in fake champagne. Still angry that Fraiser got to remain anonymous when Santana's name was smeared across the paper, Santana killed him.

When the coins were brought to the museum, Dr Anthony Fraiser remembered the name "Santana", put two and two together, realised the coins were fake and confronted Santana in the museum. Unfortunately, that didn't end well for him.

The last victim, Josie Denby, was the closest to the killer, having worked with him since her transfer to the Graven End Laboratory. She handled all the evidence and realised who the killer was before anyone else. Her attempt to reach out to Santana, to understand, meant that her death was inevitable.

FOR YOUR EYES ONLY:

SOLUTIONS

CONFIDENTIAL

CRIME 1: JOSH HARKER

PUZZLE 1

The blacked-out letters spell
I DONT LIKE MUSHROOMS

PUZZLE 2

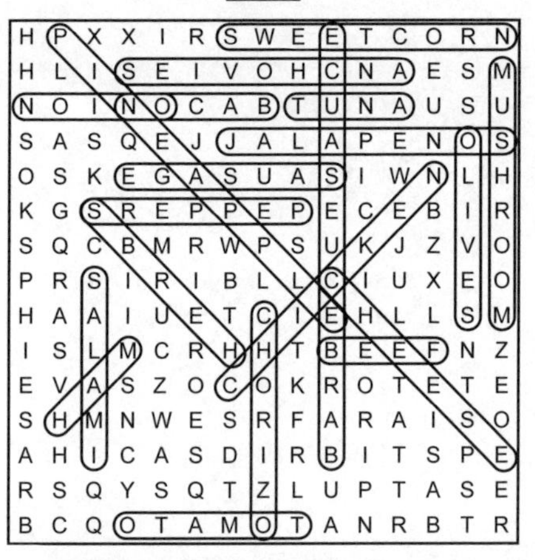

PEPPERONI is in the list of words to find, but is not in the word search.

PUZZLE 3

C	H	A	C	H	A		D		A		G	
R		L			W	H	I	S	P	E	R	S
A	B	I			A		G		I		O	
V		B	E	C	K	O	N		A	L	U	M
A		I			E		I		R		S	
T	U	S	K	S		S	T	R	I	P	E	D
			I		C		Y		S			
E	V	O	L	V	E	D		S	T	A	K	E
	I		O		N		R			D		L
A	V	O	W		T	E	A	S	E	D		E
	A		A		R		I			L	I	V
S	C	O	T	L	A	N	D			E		E
	E		T		L		S	E	A	S	O	N

PUZZLE 4

PUZZLE
5

PIZZA

3	2	6	9	4	1	8	7	5
8	4	3	7	5	2	6	1	9
1	7	5	6	2	8	9	3	4
4	9	7	5	1	6	2	8	3
6	8	2	3	7	9	4	5	1
5	1	9	8	3	4	7	2	6
2	5	1	4	6	7	3	9	8
7	6	8	1	9	3	5	4	2
9	3	4	2	8	5	1	6	7

8.25 - **Meat Feast** to **Short Lane**
8.30 - **Pepperoni (with mushrooms)** to **Polaris Road**
8.40 - **Meat Feast and Vegetarian** to **Avonvale Rise**
8.45 - **2 BBQ** to **Graven Meadows**
8.50 - **2 Vegetarian, Vegan, Margherita, and 2 Meat Feast** to **Rhoilla Close**
9.15 - **Hawaiian (with Bacon), Margherita, and 2 Meat Feast** to **Church Lane East**
9.25 - **2 Margherita and 2 BBQ** to **Makkah Close**
9.35 - **BBQ (no Pepperoni)** to **Orchardside**
9.40 - **Meat Feast and 2 Pepperoni** to **Fairfield Square**
9.45 - **Vegetarian and Pepperoni** to **Fairfield Square**
10.05 - 3 Pepperoni, 2 Vegetarian, 4 BBQ, and 2 Vegan to **Campus Avenue**
10.15 - **2 Margherita, Pepperoni, and Hawaiian** to **Manor Road**
10.25 - **Pepperoni (with bacon and mushrooms) and Pepperoni** to **Avonvale Rise**
10.30 - **Pepperoni and Meat Feast** to **Dawes Close**

The murder was committed around **8.50pm.**

PUZZLE
11

The number 8. On its side it's the symbol for infinity; cut in half, it's 0.

8

9

8; it's the number of letters in the number's word.

8

PUZZLE
12

The killer wants us to pay attention to the word **POLARIS.** There is a Polaris Road on the map at the beginning, and Dr Alan Easton lives on it.

PUZZLE 13

The Morse code message is **I WILL BE BACK VERY SOON BUT I WONT BE THE SAME PERSON.**

PUZZLE 14

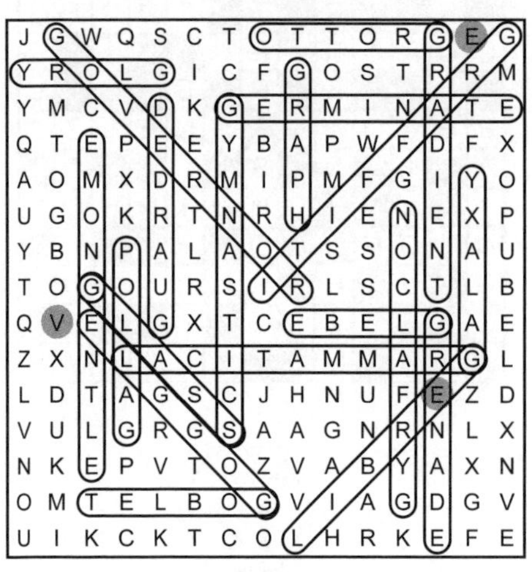

PUZZLE 15

PUZZLE 16

PUZZLE 17

	7	1			2	3		
		4		2	3	5	1	
		2	7	8	9		2	1
			2	1		8	7	9
	1	9	8		1	3		
	2	3		8	6	7	9	
		1	3	4	2		7	9
			2	3		9	8	7
	7	2	1		2	1		
	9	7		7	9	8	3	
		9	8	4	7		2	7
			3	1			1	9

PUZZLE 18

T	E	G	R	O	E	G	Y	D	N
O	U	R	N	K	N	B	G	S	A
W	B	G	A	L	I	I	I	B	R
N	S	F	R	P	M	R	C	V	E
L	R	E	I	H	E	M	H	I	R
A	V	Y	S	M	T	T	W	C	K
R	E	D	L	I	E	L	O	U	D
G	U	T	L	I	R	T	O	N	A
N	G	A	R	N	A	B	D	R	Y
E	F	A	R	G	T	O	N	S	M

PUZZLE 19

30	29	28	27	26	22	21	10	9	8
31	33	34	40	41	25	23	20	11	7
32	35	39	42	50	51	24	19	12	6
36	38	43	49	55	54	52	18	13	5
37	44	48	58	57	56	53	17	14	4
45	47	59	87	86	85	83	16	15	3
46	60	88	93	94	96	84	82	1	2
61	67	89	92	95	99	97	81	79	77
62	66	68	90	91	100	98	80	78	76
63	64	65	69	70	71	72	73	74	75

The next clue is in square **61**.

PUZZLE 20

Key number 2 is the correct key to the door. The order (from left to right) is: 3, 1, 5, 2, 4.

PUZZLE 21

PUZZLE 22

PUZZLE 23

Make the **number three** with the buttons, leaving **four** of them untouched.

1	2	3
4	5	6
7	8	9
10	11	12
13	14	15

PUZZLE 24

Delete one letter from the pair to make the following message: **IVE SAID NO MUSHROOMS SO MANY TIMES IT WAS HIS OWN FAULT**

PUZZLE 25

PUZZLE 26

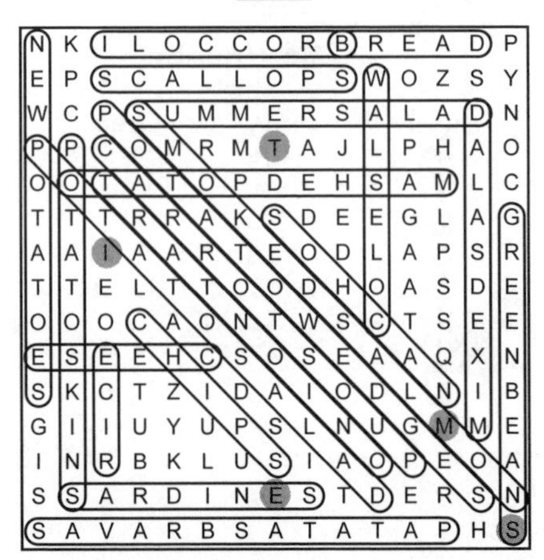

MESSAGE IN THE GRAVEN END NEWSPAPER PUZZLES:

PAY ATTENTION 2 WHAT EVERY 1 IS SAYING AT ALL TIMES

CRIME 2: DANIEL JONES

casipnmurt = **manuscript**
oilsfcstniacai = **classification**
lietts = **titles**
slhscroa = **scholars**
aiailbrrn = **librarian**
vhriscae = **archives**
oxetbtkos = **textbooks**
gnenldi = **lending**

The only location listed is the **archives.**

The correct time of death is **9 pm.**

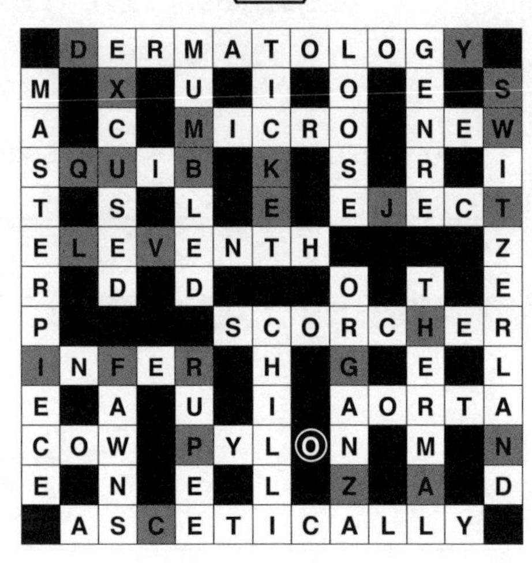

PUZZLE 31

Use the first letter of each book title to spell out **I COULD HAVE BEEN GREAT.**

PUZZLE 32

PUZZLE 33

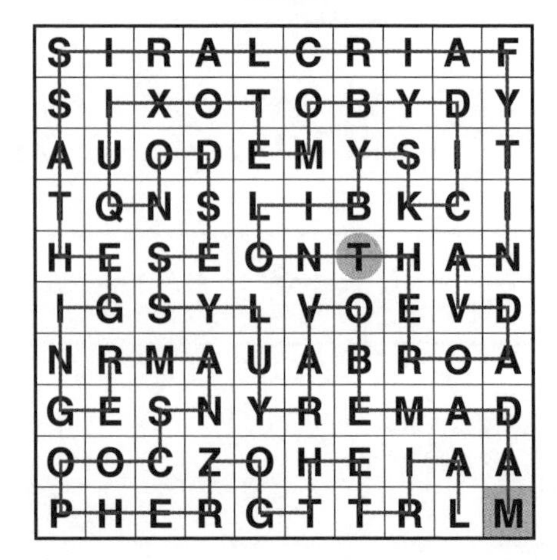

Vol. 46 (4), 2014, pp. 465-472
International Journal of Evidence-Based Justice Reform

The key is in the stomach - rethinking current PMI estimations and methods of taking temperatures from cadavers

Leo Santana
Department of Biology, Graven End University
leo.santana@geu.edu

Abstract: Currently, "PMI estimation approach holds little value when applied to human remains in real criminal investigation," (Sutherland, et al., 2003), but a review of the current methods, both controversial and widely accepted, of determining cadaveric temperature immediately post-mortem reveals new ways of calculating PMI estimations, allowing forensic teams to better assist law enforcement.

Keywords: thermoregulation, soup, tissue dehydration, cadaveric spasm, PMI

1. INTRODUCTION

The body maintains a constant internal temperature of approximately 37°C (98.6°F), the optimum temperature for the thousands of chemical reactions needed for life. As brain-death occurs, so does the cessation of autonomic body functions. The hypothalamus, which controls the homoeostatic feature of thermoregulation, ceases to function, and the temperature of the cadaver in question begins to warm up, syncing with the ambient temperature of the area in which death occurred. This cooling is known as algor mortis.

Research carried out by Al-Alousi, et al. in 2002, shows that there can be a delay of up to three hours post-mortem before the temperature of the cadaver begins to drop, which contrasts with the widely accepted rate of a 1°C (33.8°F) decrease per hour. Also, this accepted measurement does not take into account external factors: the position of the cadaver (is it in the foetal position?), the location (bodies in subzero temperatures will reach an environmental equilibrium at a faster rate than those in humid climates), the presence of clothing (temperature difference can be caused by the cadaver being clothed in a shirt or a well-insulated jacket), and the condition of the cadaver pre-mortem (an emaciated body is less insulated than an obese one).

It also does not account for the pre-mortem temperature of the cadaver, as someone who has been out in the elements for hours during a snowy December would have a lower internal temperature than one who had been indoors during the same period. Newton's Law of Cooling is inefficient, as these factors can not be input into the equation. The accuracy with which post-mortem temperature can currently be calculated remains less than is preferred for a reliable forensic pathological opinion.

This article will look at various methods that can be applied to cadavers in order to obtain a much more accurate temperature at the time of death. By gaining more knowledge in this area, we will be able to offer more precise COD recommendations and give better assistance to law enforcement officials.

2. THE SOUP METHOD

One controversial but widely used way of obtaining cadaveric temperature is the soup method. The pathologist uses a 23 cm (9 in) glass needle and carefully inserts it

PUZZLE 35

H	U	M	P	B	A	C	K		S	K	U	A
O		O		U		H		C		I		C
S	P	O	R	T		I		O	W	N	E	R
E		N		T		N		N		D		I
			J	E	T	T	I	S	O	N	E	D
N		E		R		Z		E		E		I
E	X	P	O	S	E		P	R	E	S	E	T
W		I		C		R		V		S		Y
C	O	L	L	O	Q	U	I	A	L			
O		O		T		S		T		M		F
M	A	G	I	C		S		O	R	I	B	I
E		U		H		I		R		N		N
R	E	E	K		L	A	D	Y	L	I	K	E

PUZZLE 36

Y	D	L	Z	I	A	R	Y	L	X	Z	D	L	C	L
X	I	R	E	L	A	N	D	N	A	L	O	P	S	T
W	L	F	B	U	L	G	A	R	I	A	L	S	P	P
Y	R	C	N	X	C	A	Y	D	F	T	L	K	A	A
C	A	C	Z	E	C	H	R	E	P	U	B	L	I	C
O	Y	W	L	M	T	E	R	N	K	P	C	A	N	C
H	X	P	R	B	E	H	I	M	M	R	E	G	A	E
V	M	V	R	O	A	I	E	A	E	A	U	U	I	B
S	L	U	A	U	N	P	L	R	V	I	S	T	K	T
F	C	A	I	R	S	T	K	K	L	T	E	R	A	I
R	H	U	N	G	A	R	Y	L	R	A	C	O	V	X
S	X	M	N	I	L	D	R	I	B	O	N	P	O	P
S	G	R	E	E	C	E	A	I	L	R	A	D	L	E
T	M	R	P	S	T	A	B	M	L	C	R	T	S	T
U	D	E	A	G	N	E	D	E	W	S	F	K	M	Y

PUZZLE 37

The riddle is pointing to **The Elephant's Castle.**

PUZZLE 38

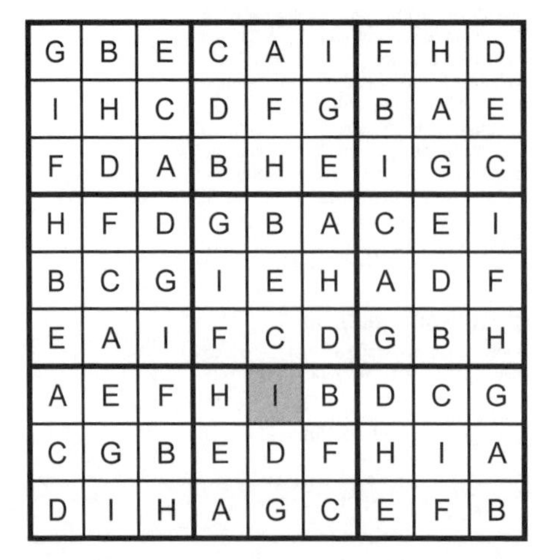

G	B	E	C	A	I	F	H	D
I	H	C	D	F	G	B	A	E
F	D	A	B	H	E	I	G	C
H	F	D	G	B	A	C	E	I
B	C	G	I	E	H	A	D	F
E	A	I	F	C	D	G	B	H
A	E	F	H	I	B	D	C	G
C	G	B	E	D	F	H	I	A
D	I	H	A	G	C	E	F	B

PUZZLE 39

	K	N	I	T	S		C	R	A	F	T	
A		O		E		A		E		O		P
D	E	C	O	R	U	M		M	O	G	U	L
O		T		M		U		O				U
R	O	U	T		A	S	S	U	M	I	N	G
E		R		L		E		N		N		
S	E	N	S	E	S		S	T	A	G	E	D
		A		S		S		S		E		E
D	E	L	U	S	I	O	N		S	N	I	P
O				E		L		D		U		O
G	R	A	I	N		A	I	R	P	O	R	T
S		Y		E		R		N		U		S
	W	E	E	D	S		B	O	O	S	T	

PUZZLE 40

PUZZLE 41

When reorganized, the letters from PUZZLE 40 spell out **The Codex Chrisicus**, which was one of the titles on the shelf of PUZZLE 31.

PUZZLE 42

PUZZLE 43

B E W A
NANNY LASAGNE
L T A T U A
CLARINET TACK
P A N A H O
SAMPLE GREENS
R X E N D
SKIDDED STRAY
E E S C I E
CARVE CONCEPT
I E S M R
SLALOM PRISES
M O E U R D
HELP LITTORAL
N E L E N T
STUDIED PILOT
S D C R

The correct ISBN is **9784677834221.** It is in the list of ISBNs to find, but it is not in the word search.

6	5	3	8	2	4	9	7	1
9	8	2	7	1	6	3	5	4
1	4	7	9	5	3	6	2	8
3	9	4	5	8	7	1	6	2
7	6	8	2	4	1	5	3	9
2	1	5	3	6	9	8	4	7
5	7	9	4	3	8	2	1	6
4	2	6	1	9	5	7	8	3
8	3	1	6	7	2	4	9	5

The numbers in the highlighted squares are 1, 9, and 4. The next clue is on **page 194**.

PUZZLE 46

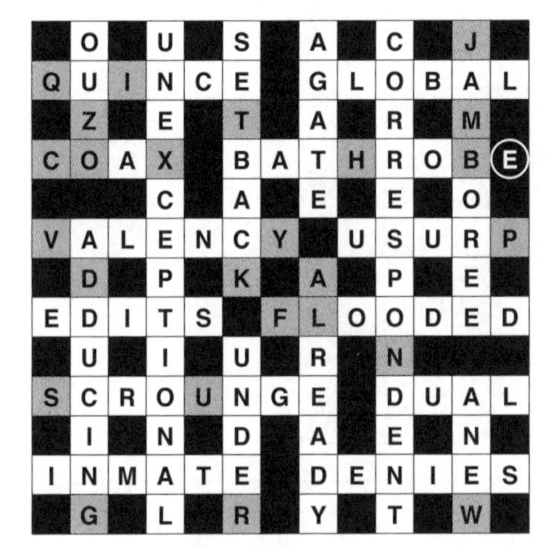

PUZZLE 47

PUZZLE 48

37	36	35	34	33	32	2	3	4	5
38	40	41	76	77	78	31	1	7	6
39	42	75	96	89	88	79	30	9	8
43	74	95	97	99	90	87	80	29	10
44	73	94	100	98	91	86	81	28	11
45	69	72	93	92	85	82	62	27	12
46	68	70	71	84	83	63	61	26	13
47	53	67	66	65	64	60	25	20	14
48	52	54	57	58	59	24	21	19	15
49	50	51	55	56	23	22	18	17	16

The next clue is on **page 95.**

PUZZLE 49

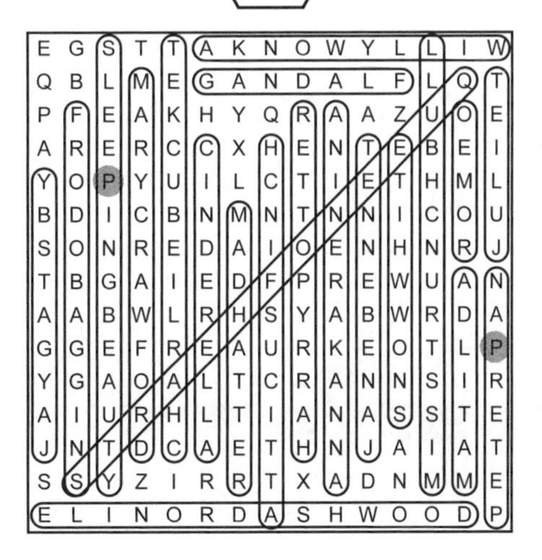

PUZZLE 50

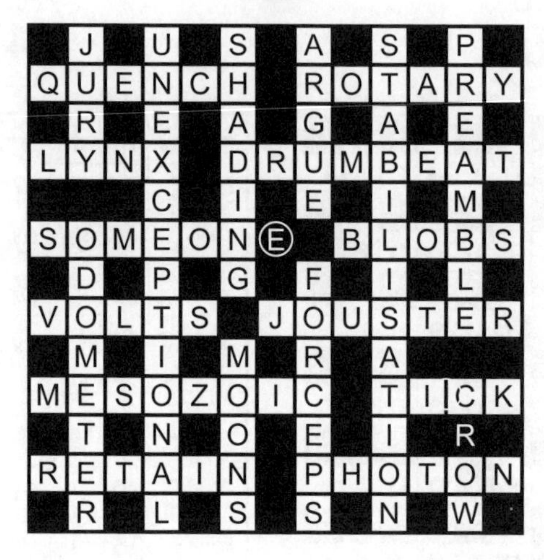

PUZZLE 51

Decrypting the passage of The Codex Chrisicus reveals the following message: **YOU HELPED TO RUIN MY FAMILY YOU DESERVE ALL OF THIS.**

PUZZLE 52

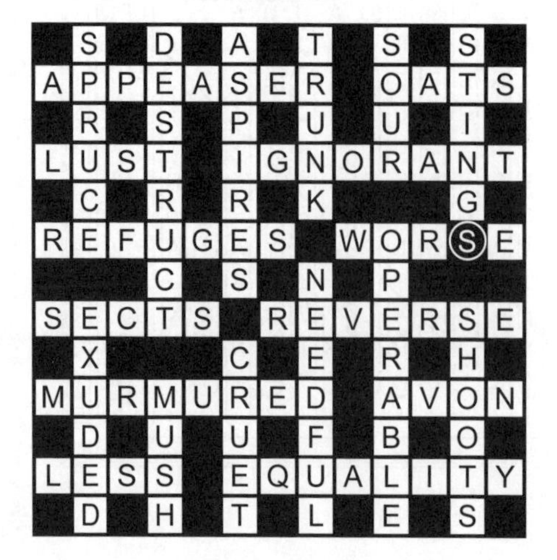

PUZZLE 53

PUZZLE
54

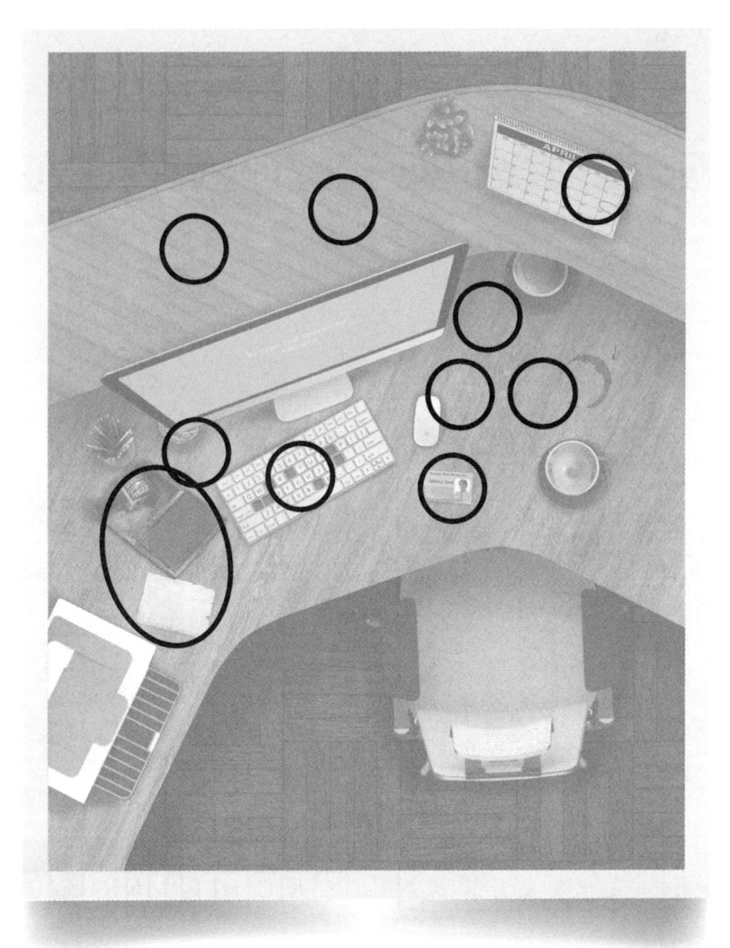
APRIL

MESSAGE IN THE GRAVEN END NEWSPAPER PUZZLES:

LEO SANTANA IS A MIXED UP PERSON

CRIME 3: HETTY MERRYWEATHER

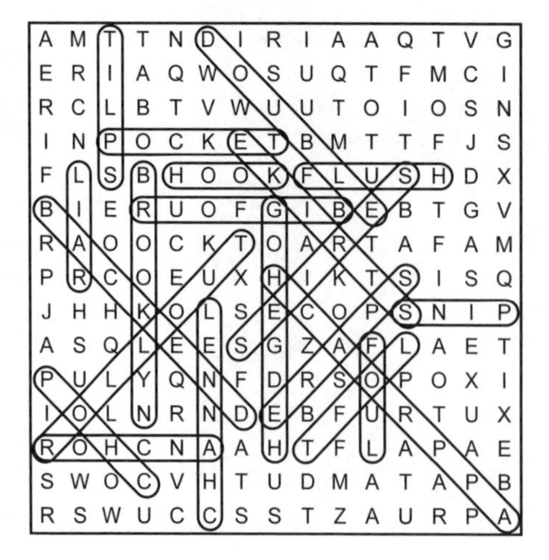

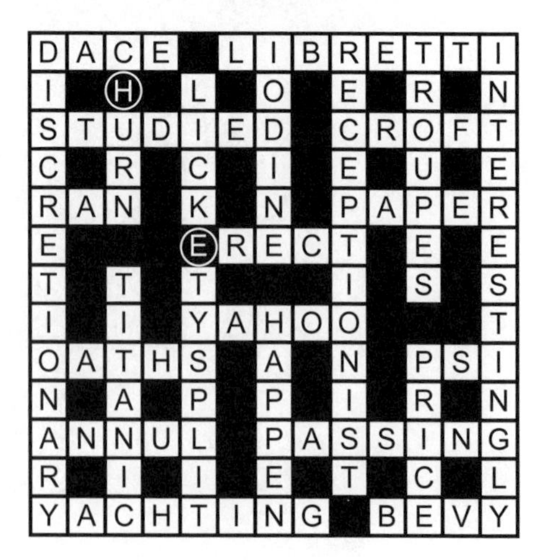

PUZZLE 57

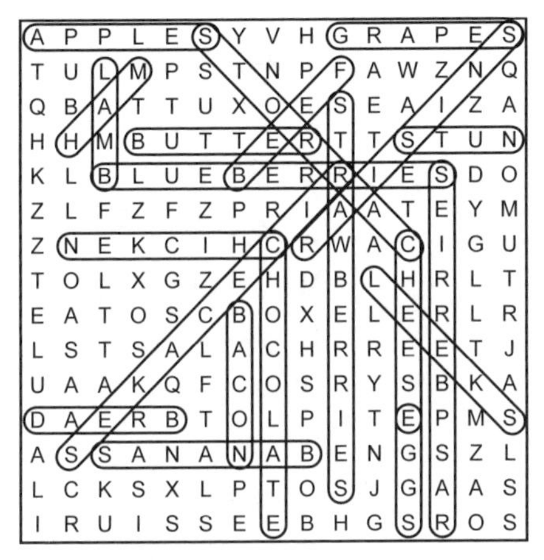

Yes, all of the items on the receipt can be found in the word search.

PUZZLE 58

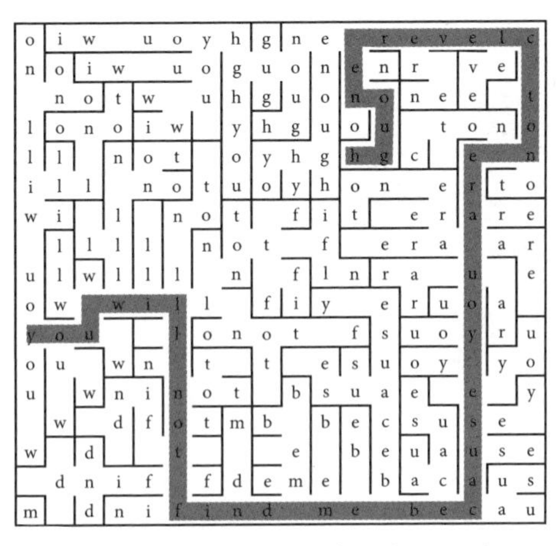

The correct path through the maze spells out the following message: **YOU WILL NOT FIND ME BECAUSE YOU ARE NOT CLEVER ENOUGH**

PUZZLE 59

C	O	W	E	D		Y	T	T	R	I	U	M
U		O		R		O		O		N		I
R	O	O	F	I	N	G		W		F		N
R		D		V		A		P		U		S
E		C		E			T	A	N	S		T
N		H		S	U	P		T		E	A	R
T	A	U			S		O	H	M	S		E
S		C	A	S	E							L
		K			S	A	G			O		
P							A	U	K	S		O
L		S	A	S	H		P			C	U	B
A	S	K		T		M	E	T		I		D
T		I	B	I	S			H		L		U
F		D		M		S		E		L		R
O		D		U		C	A	N	T	A	T	A
R		E		L		U		C		T		C
M	U	D	D	I	E	D		E	M	E	R	Y

PUZZLE 60

G	F	D	B	H	C	A	E	I
H	A	E	I	F	D	G	C	B
B	I	C	A	E	G	D	F	H
E	C	A	H	B	I	F	D	G
F	D	B	G	A	E	I	H	C
I	H	G	D	C	F	E	B	A
D	E	H	C	G	A	B	I	F
C	G	F	E	I	B	H	A	D
A	B	I	F	D	H	C	G	E

PUZZLE 61

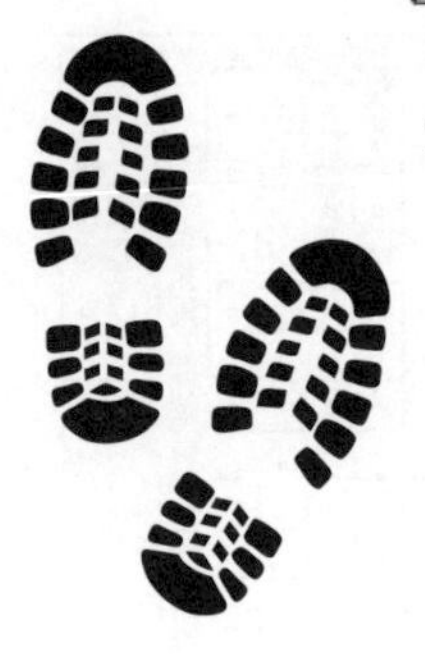

These footprints are not in the list of identified people. They must belong to the killer.

PUZZLE 62

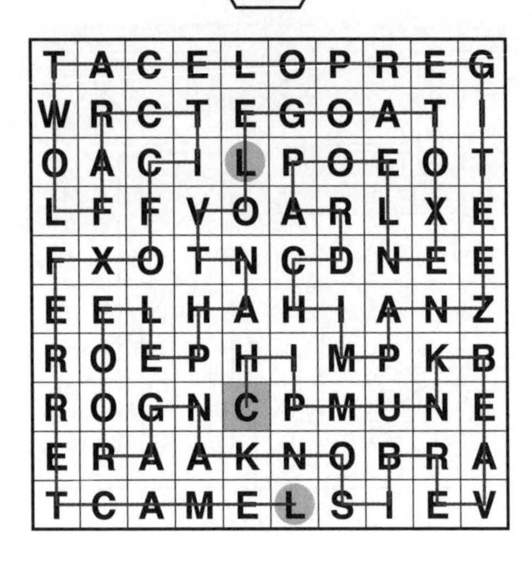

PUZZLE 63

PUZZLE 64

5	4	3	2	1	25	26	27	28	29
6	8	9	10	24	97	100	33	32	30
7	12	11	23	96	99	98	92	34	31
13	15	16	22	95	94	93	91	83	35
14	17	21	61	88	89	90	84	82	36
18	20	60	62	87	86	85	81	72	37
19	59	63	77	78	79	80	73	71	38
55	58	64	66	76	75	74	70	45	39
54	56	57	65	67	68	69	46	44	40
53	52	51	50	49	48	47	43	42	41

PUZZLE 65

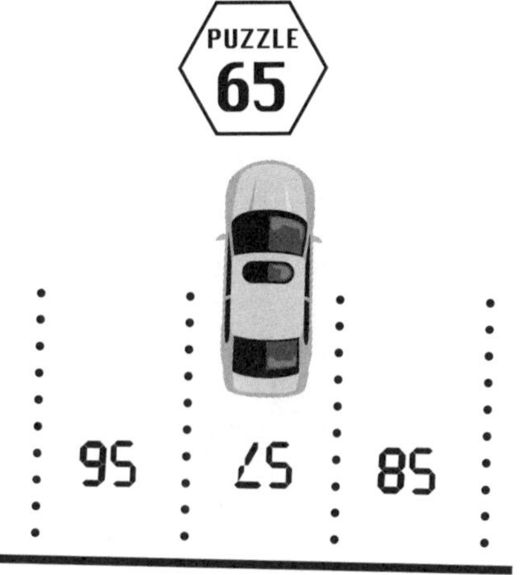

The car is parked in **space 57**. Turn the book upside down and the numbers read 61, 60, 59, 58, 57 and 56.

PUZZLE 66

C		R		B				P		F		A
O	V	E	R	L	Y		B	O	X	I	N	G
R		W		U		I		C		Z		L
D	I	A	G	R	(A)	M		K	A	Z	O	O
I		R		T		P		E		Y		W
A	I	D	E		Q	U	I	T	S			
L		S		P		D		S		C		L
			S	H	E	E	T		J	U	D	O
S		S		A		N		F		T		U
M	O	T	O	R		C	A	J	O	L	E	D
I		A		A		E		O		A		E
L	E	S	S	O	N		E	R	A	S	E	S
E		H		H				D		S		T

PUZZLE 67

		(I)						F
O	W	N		L	A	T	E	R
	A	L	P	A	C	A		E
A	X	E		D	R	I	V	E
		T		S	O	L	I	D
	C		H		S	O	(S)	O
G	O	B	I		T	R	A	M
	U		S		I			S
P	R	O	T	O	C	O	L	
	S	M	O	G		G	E	L
P	E	A	R	L		R	I	O
		R	Y	E		E	A	T

PUZZLE 68

6.

Tire track **number 6** matches the victim's car.

PUZZLE 69

There are a number of missing letters in the article which spell out **I AM CLOSER THAN YOU THINK.**

PUZZLE 70

PUZZLE 71

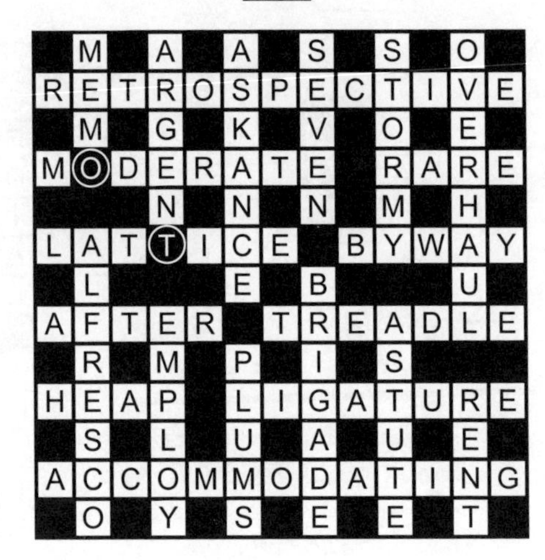

PUZZLE 72

Key **number 7** matches the lock on the victim's car.

PUZZLE 73

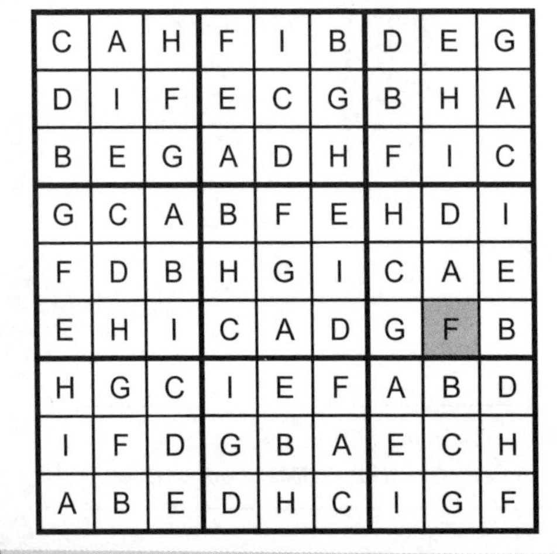

C	A	H	F	I	B	D	E	G
D	I	F	E	C	G	B	H	A
B	E	G	A	D	H	F	I	C
G	C	A	B	F	E	H	D	I
F	D	B	H	G	I	C	A	E
E	H	I	C	A	D	G	F	B
H	G	C	I	E	F	A	B	D
I	F	D	G	B	A	E	C	H
A	B	E	D	H	C	I	G	F

PUZZLE 74

O	U	T	O	F	A	F	R	I	C	A	O	O	R	I
D	Y	N	Q	A	H	S	H	T	I	C	E	N	O	G
L	S	R	A	W	R	A	T	S	S	K	V	T	R	O
C	V	U	M	Y	Y	K	H	I	U	J	E	H	E	I
U	F	H	A	D	G	X	E	L	M	P	T	E	P	N
C	O	N	D	A	I	R	S	S	F	I	U	W	M	G
O	R	E	E	L	J	C	T	R	O	H	O	A	E	M
R	R	B	U	R	H	A	I	E	D	D	B	T	T	Y
P	E	G	S	I	T	T	N	L	N	N	A	E	S	W
A	S	R	C	A	E	O	G	D	U	A	L	R	A	A
T	T	A	I	F	R	O	A	N	O	G	L	F	L	Y
T	G	V	I	Y	A	K	M	I	S	I	A	R	E	S
O	U	I	O	M	B	S	D	H	E	G	V	O	H	K
N	M	T	I	T	A	N	I	C	H	I	R	N	T	K
S	P	Y	O	P	C	S	W	S	T	X	N	T	K	Z

PUZZLE
75

= 1 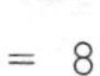 = 8 = 5

185 + 185 + 185 = 555

The code to unlock the phone is **555.**

The letters A to Z have been replaced with the numbers 1 to 26.

Sender: Unknown

SHE WAS A RUDE BITTER OLD WOMAN WHO DESERVED EVERYTHING SHE GOT. I'D DO IT AGAIN IF I COULD.

Received: 04:36

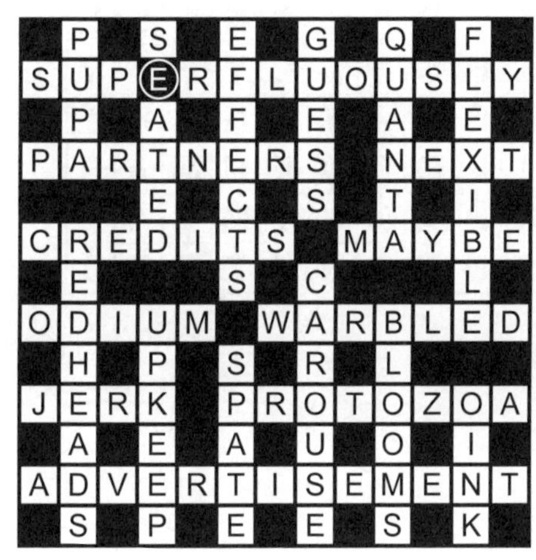

MESSAGE IN THE GRAVEN END NEWSPAPER PUZZLES:

THE KILLER IS NOT FEMALE

CRIME 4: JOE FRASIER

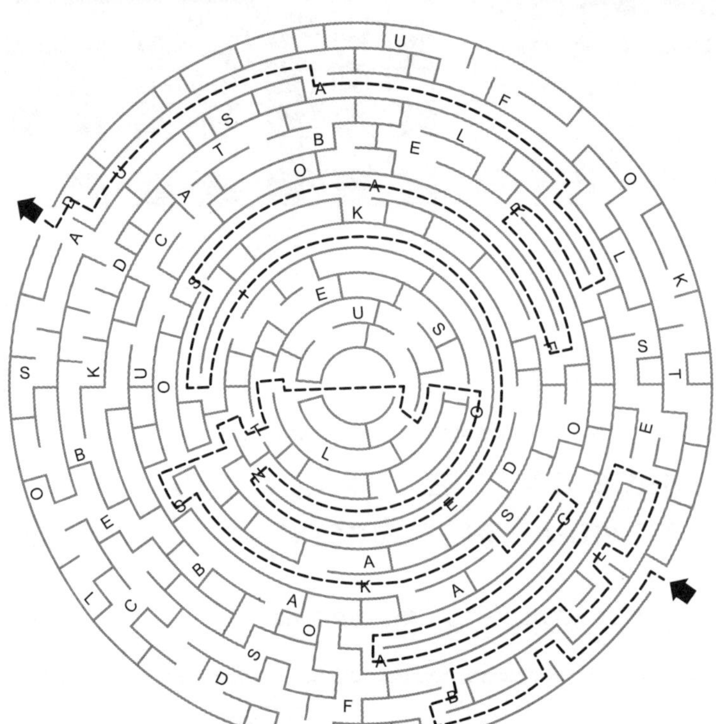

PUZZLE
84

By following the correct path through the maze, you reveal the following message:
BLACKSTONE IS A FRAUD

PUZZLE 85

This clue was found underneath the *phone*. If you tap out the numbers on an old-fashioned phone with letters on the buttons exactly as they are shown on the note, it reveals the following message: **YOU NEED TO LOOK IN THE SAFE.**

PUZZLE 86

	Z		M			L		
	E	N	A	C	T	I	N	G
	P	E	R			C	O	O
	H	A	R	M		E	W	E
S	Y	R	I	A		N		S
	R		A	B	A	S	H	
	S	A	G		R	E	A	(D)
			E		M	E	M	O
O	P	T			Y			M
	A	W	E	S		P	(H)	I
	C	I	T	A	T	I	O	N
	K	N	A	P		T	W	O

PUZZLE 87

G	D	B	H	F	E	C	I	A
I	E	A	C	B	G	F	D	H
F	H	C	A	D	I	E	B	G
H	I	G	B	E	A	D	C	F
C	B	G	D	G	F	A	H	I
A	F	D	I	H	C	G	E	B
E	A	I	G	C	H	B	F	D
D	C	G	F	A	B	I	G	E
B	G	F	E	I	D	H	A	C

PUZZLE 88

By studying the cards on the right, you will see that there are four cards missing: the 2 of clubs, the 4 of diamonds, the 7 of spades, and the 10 of hearts. If you sort these four cards into the order shown on the front of the safe, the code is **41072.**

PUZZLE 90

E		E			A		B			W		A
M	A	L	A	Y	S	I	A		B	R	A	N
B		E			S		G			E		O
A		V			E		P	I	N	T		D
T		A			S	K	I			C	O	Y
T	U	T	O	R	S		P	O	S	H		N
L		O			E		E			E		E
E	A	R	T	H	S		R	U	E	D		
D			U						L			E
		E	B	B	S		T	I	L	I	N	G
N		S			U		H			N		O
I		C	L	U	B		A	N	O	I	N	T
B	O	A			T	O	N			T		I
B		P	I	E	R		K			I		S
L		I			A		I			A		T
E	L	S	E		C	O	N	F	E	T	T	I
D		T			T		G			E		C

PUZZLE 91

This thumbprint does not appear in the "Prints on File" list but has been seen already: **it is listed under Dr. Alan Easton's photo** on the "Meet the Team" profile pages (4-5).

PUZZLE 92

PUZZLE 93

PUZZLE 94

50	51	52	58	60	61	62	63	64	65
49	53	57	59	79	80	94	95	67	66
48	54	56	78	81	93	99	97	96	68
40	47	55	77	82	92	100	98	89	69
39	41	46	76	83	85	91	90	88	70
35	38	42	45	75	84	86	87	71	25
34	36	37	43	44	74	73	72	26	24
14	33	32	31	30	29	28	27	22	23
13	15	16	17	18	19	20	21	1	3
12	11	10	9	8	7	6	5	4	2

The puzzle is directing the police to dig up the paving stone **number 83.**

PUZZLE 95

The safe in the floor can be opened using the code **9876.**

PUZZLE 96

P	O	L	E	D		W	A	R	B	L	E	D
R		A		E		R			R		X	
E		U		F		A		G	A	M	U	T
V	A	N	Q	U	I	S	H		Z		L	
I		D		N		S		J	E	S	T	S
S	T	R	I	C	K	E	N		N			E
I		Y		T				A		S		P
O			C		O	P	E	R	E	T	T	A
N	I	G	H	T		O		T		O		R
	R		A		E	T	H	I	O	P	I	A
M	O	R	P	H		E		C		P		T
	N		E			N		L		E		E
C	Y	C	L	I	S	T		E	R	R	E	D

PUZZLE 97

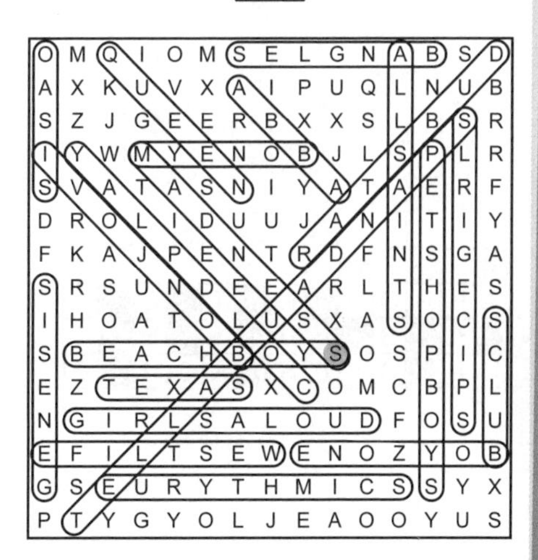

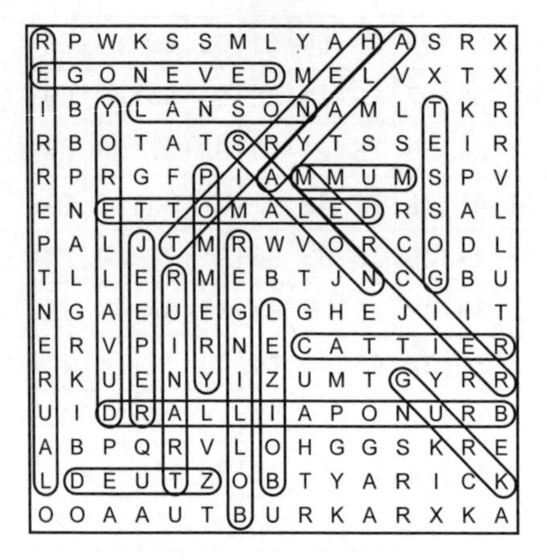

POL ROGERS is in the list of words to find, but it is not in the word search.

F	L	I	R	T		P	I	M	P	L	E	S
L				R		L		I				A
O	X	I	D	I	S	E		L	E	A	S	T
W		N		C		T		I		B		I
E	M	E	R	Y		H		T	U	B	E	S
R		X		C	O	O		A		R		F
P	O	P		L		R		N	E	E	D	Y
O		E	L	E	G	A	N	T		V		
T	O	R								I	V	Y
		I		G	O	R	I	L	L	A		A
D	W	E	L	L		I		U		T	I	C
I		N		O		G	A	S		I		H
O	C	C	U	R		H		C	R	O	F	T
R		E		I		T		I		N		S
A	U	D	I	O		F	L	O	T	S	A	M
M				U		U		U				A
A	B	Y	S	S	A	L		S	E	D	A	N

PUZZLE
100

I	N	S	E	T		G	R	O	W	I	N	G
N		C		R		O			I		A	
S		H		U		K		F	L	A	M	E
O	V	E	R	D	R	A	W		T		E	
L		M		G		R		L	E	A	D	S
E	L	E	V	E	N	T	H		D			U
N		R		S				G		D		R
C			A		S	U	P	E	R	I	O	R
E	N	A	C	T		R		L		V		O
	E		R		D	A	M	A	G	I	N	G
A	P	R	O	N		N		T		D		A
	A		S			U		I		E		T
U	L	Y	S	S	E	S		N	O	R	S	E

PUZZLE
101

The letters A to Z have been replaced with the numbers 1 to 26.

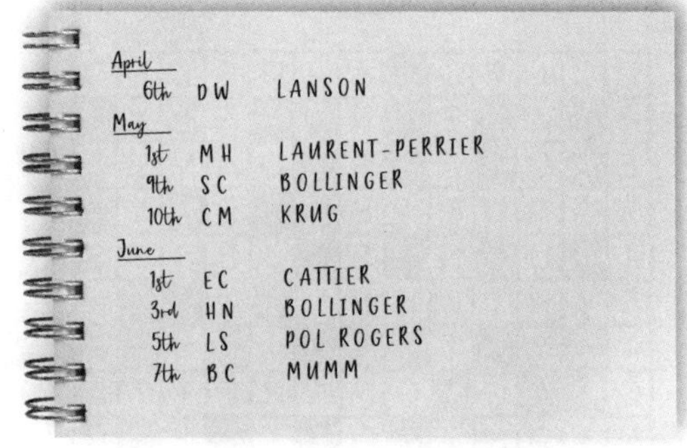
April
6th DW LANSON
May
1st MH LAURENT-PERRIER
9th SC BOLLINGER
10th CM KRUG
June
1st EC CATTIER
3rd HN BOLLINGER
5th LS POL ROGERS
7th BC MUMM

The initials all represent the names of people listed in Wonderment's ledger and which bottle of champagne they bought from the victim.

PUZZLE 102

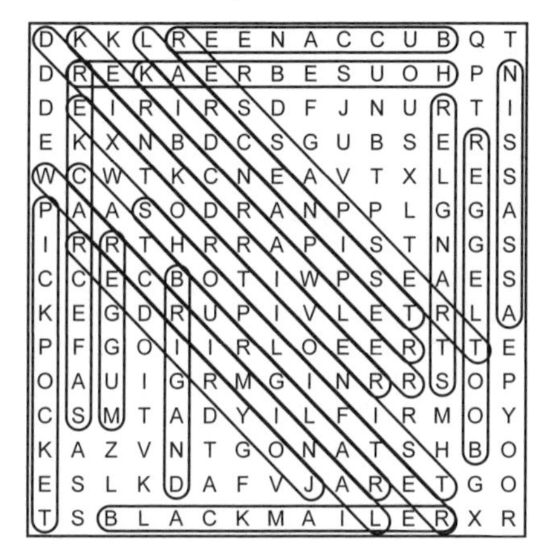

FORGER is in the list of words to find, but it is not in the word search.

PUZZLE 103

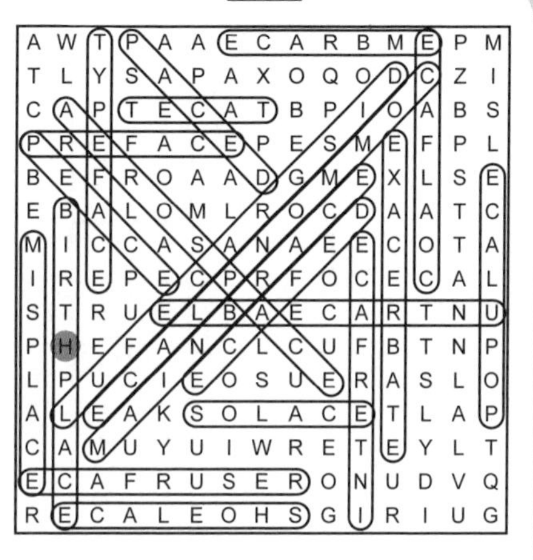

PUZZLE 104

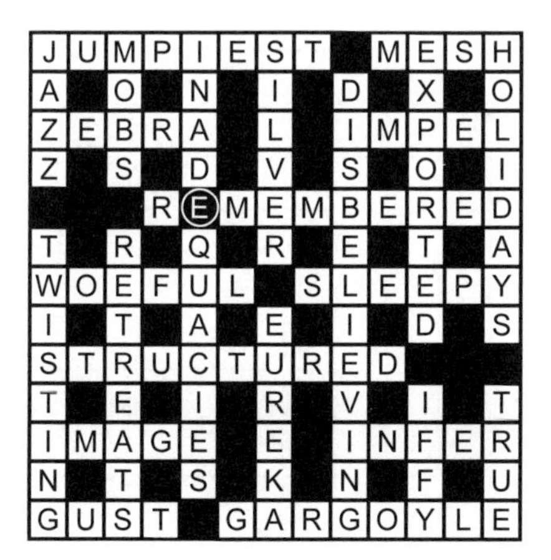

PUZZLE 105

The control sample has 4 black, 6 grey and 7 white elements. None of the chemical samples of champagne match the control sample. **All the champagnes are fake.**

D	C	H	A	F	G	I	E	B
E	G	B	H	I	D	F	A	C
F	A	I	C	B	E	D	H	G
G	H	D	B	E	A	C	I	F
A	E	C	I	D	F	B	G	H
I	B	F	G	C	H	E	D	A
H	I	E	F	G	B	A	C	D
C	F	A	D	H	I	G	B	E
B	D	G	E	A	C	H	F	I

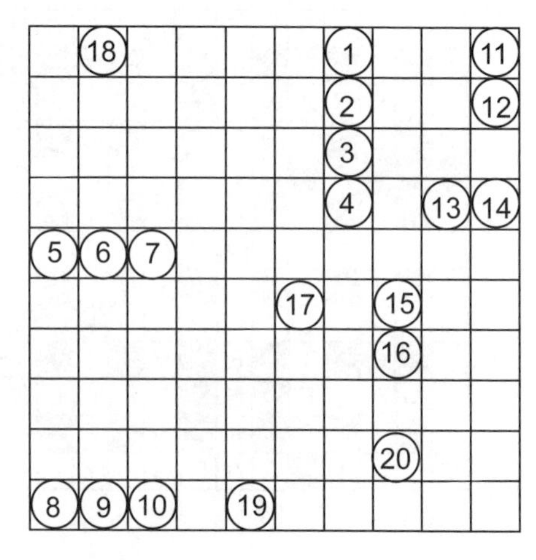

This is one possible solution to the puzzle

They looked through the hole in the ceiling to tell when it was night, then left through the glass tunnel, which wasn't then hot.

MESSAGE IN THE GRAVEN END NEWSPAPER PUZZLES:

AND HE IS NOT WHO HE SAYS HE IS

CRIME 5: DR. ANTHONY MASTERSON

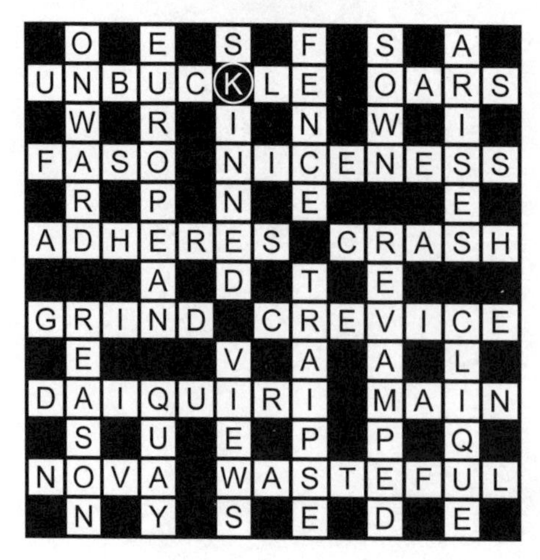

	A		S			G		
	S	C	H	O	L	A	R	S
S	H	O	(E)			T	O	P
		P	L	A	C	E	B	O
		E	L	F		W	O	K
D	I	S	S	I	P	A	T	E
				E		Y		N
P	E	A	R	L	S		U	
	P	R	E	D	I	C	T	S
	E	M	U		L	A	T	(E)
B	E	E	S		O	P	E	N
		D	E	S	S	E	R	T

PUZZLE 113

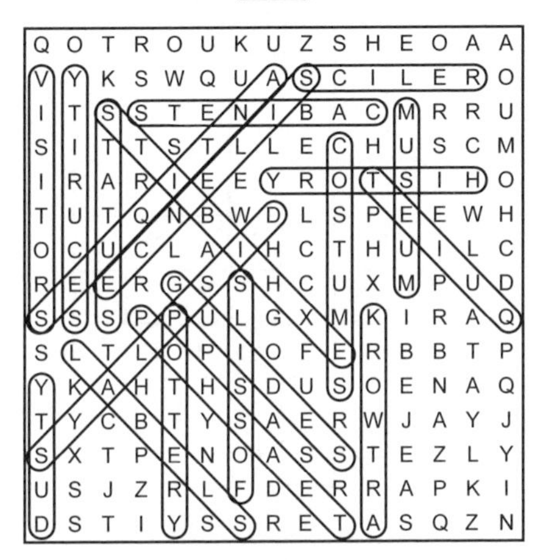

CURATOR is in the list of words to find, but it is not in the word search.

PUZZLE 114

T	A	K	E	S		T	W	I	N	I	N	G
U		N		U		U			U		E	
M		O		P		S		A	Z	U	R	E
E	S	C	A	P	I	S	T		Z		V	
S		K		O		L		F	L	O	E	S
C	H	E	R	R	I	E	S		E			Q
E		D		T				S		J		U
N			I		A	L	L	E	L	U	I	A
T	H	I	N	G		O		A		J		W
	A		D		J	O	Y	S	T	I	C	K
P	I	X	I	E		S		O		T		I
	R		G			E		N		S		N
B	Y	G	O	N	E	S		S	W	U	N	G

PUZZLE 115

C	A	F	E		A	B	N	O	R	M	A	L
R		O		N		U		U		A		I
A	G	I	L	E	L	Y		T	E	N	E	T
F		S		V		I		S		M		T
T	I	T	R	E		N	E	T	B	A	L	L
S				R		G		R		D		E
M	I	G	H	T	Y		R	E	D	E	E	M
A		R		H		P		T				E
N	E	A	T	E	N	S		C	I	D	E	R
S		D		L		Y		H		O		M
H	O	U	S	E		C	A	E	S	U	R	A
I		A		S		H		D		S		I
P	O	L	I	S	H	E	D		W	E	E	D

PUZZLE 116

2	6	5	9	1	7	3	4	8
8	4	7	6	5	3	9	1	2
9	1	3	4	8	2	5	6	7
5	9	4	2	3	1	7	8	6
7	2	6	8	4	5	1	3	9
3	8	1	7	6	9	4	2	5
4	5	9	1	2	6	8	7	3
1	7	2	3	9	8	6	5	4
6	3	8	5	7	4	2	9	1

The highlighted squares are 6 and 4.

PUZZLE 117

3	9	7	2	4	6	5	1	8
8	1	4	3	5	9	6	2	7
6	2	5	1	7	8	4	3	9
2	7	6	8	3	5	1	9	4
4	8	3	9	1	2	7	6	5
9	5	1	7	6	4	2	8	3
1	3	9	4	2	7	8	5	6
5	4	2	6	8	3	9	7	1
7	6	8	5	9	1	3	4	2

The highlighted squares are **1** and **3**.

PUZZLE 118

2	7	3	6	9	1	8	4	5
8	1	4	7	5	2	3	6	9
9	6	5	3	4	8	2	7	1
4	3	6	9	1	7	5	8	2
7	8	1	5	2	3	4	9	6
5	9	2	8	6	4	7	1	3
6	4	8	1	3	5	9	2	7
3	2	9	4	7	6	1	5	8
1	5	7	2	8	9	6	3	4

The highlighted squares are **9** and **5**.

The full code to get in the door is **641395**.

PUZZLE 119

The letterboard is missing letters, which spell out **U DARE TO CALL ME A LIAR AGAIN.**

PUZZLE 120

PUZZLE 121

```
LEAPFROG  MUCK
 L O A  E  I O
GALLIC  CASING
 S E E  K D  T
STOMP  TOPIARY
 I I  B   R A
ANECDOTE  EELS
R L  U  X C  T
COMMUNICATION
 B A  C E  C O
AJAR  EMPLOYED
 E G   T C  R
ECUADOR  STERN
 T R L  E A  A
TIDIED  PIGSTY
 N N  E I O  U
OGRE  NICKNAME
```

Each employee will change the status of all lockers that have a number that is a multiple of that employee's number. Conversely, every locker will have its status changed by the employees that are numbered by one of the locker's factors.

Locker 1, which has one factor, will be open at the end, as the only employee who touches it is employee 1, who opens it. Locker 2, with two factors, will be closed, since the only two employees to touch it are employee 1, who opens it, and then employee 2, who closes it.

Locker 3, also with two factors, will also be closed at the end. On the other hand, Locker 4, which has three factors (1, 2, and 4), will be open, shut, and open again.

As the lockers are closed to begin with, any time a locker number has an even number of factors, it will end up closed. Numbers with an odd number of factors will end up open. All perfect squares have an odd number, which is why the lockers with these numbers end up open.

The lockers left open are 1, 4, and 9 and, therefore the code to the combination lock is **149**.

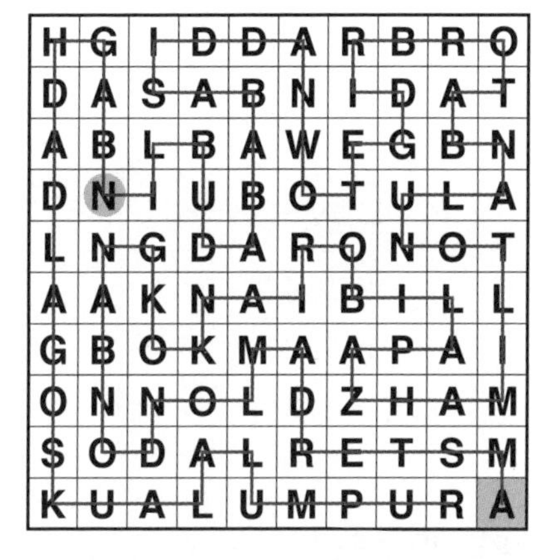

PUZZLE
124

B	I	H	F	G	C	A	E	D
C	G	E	A	D	H	I	B	F
D	A	F	B	E	I	G	H	C
F	E	I	D	C	B	H	A	G
G	C	D	E	H	A	B	F	I
H	B	A	G	I	F	D	C	E
I	F	G	H	B	E	C	D	A
A	H	C	I	F	D	E	G	B
E	D	B	C	A	G	F	I	H

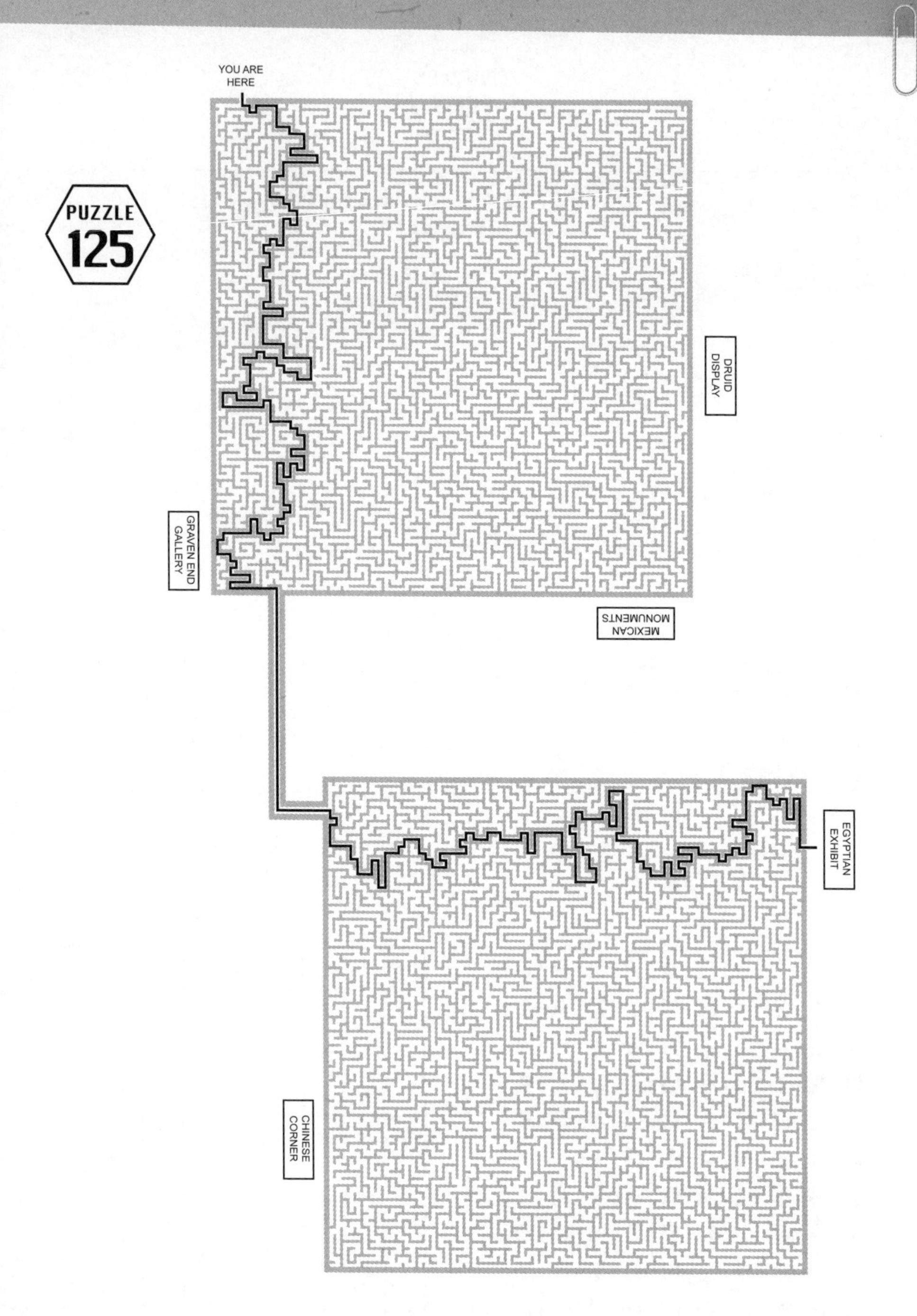

The next clue is in the **Egyptian Area** of the museum.

PUZZLE 126

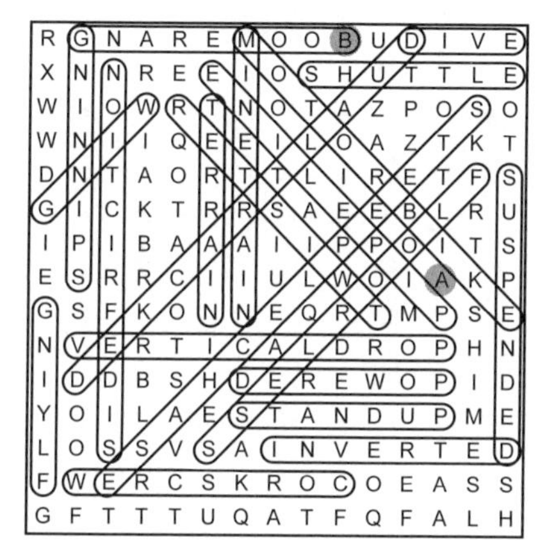

PUZZLE 127

G	A	D	F	B	H	I	E	C
H	C	B	I	A	E	F	D	G
I	F	E	D	G	C	H	A	B
D	B	A	E	F	I	C	G	H
F	E	H	G	C	B	D	I	A
C	G	I	H	D	A	E	B	F
E	D	F	B	H	G	A	C	I
B	H	C	A	I	D	G	F	E
A	I	G	C	E	F	B	H	D

PUZZLE 128

23	22	21	20	19	18	17	11	10	9
24	26	27	54	55	56	16	14	12	8
25	28	53	60	59	58	57	15	13	7
29	52	61	63	64	65	66	1	6	5
30	51	62	95	94	74	73	67	2	4
31	50	96	99	100	93	75	72	68	3
32	42	49	97	98	92	89	76	71	69
33	41	43	48	91	90	88	85	77	70
34	37	40	44	47	87	86	84	81	78
35	36	38	39	45	46	83	82	80	79

The next clue can be found in **square 78.**

PUZZLE 129

1 = Mummy A
2 = Mummy D
3 = Mummy E
4 = Mummy B
5 = Mummy C
6 = Mummy F

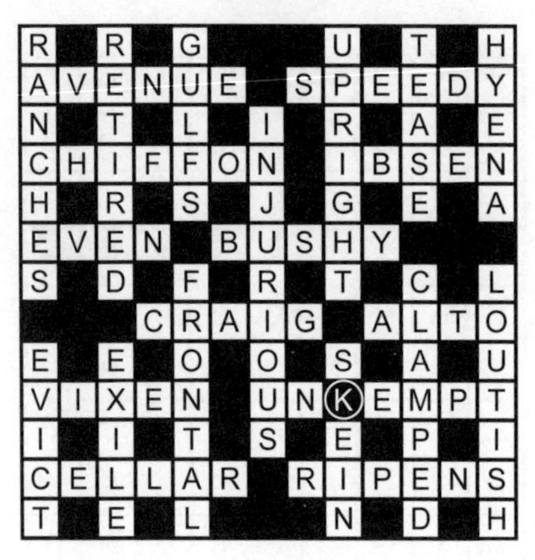

PUZZLE 132

Take the first letter from each of the 5-letter groups to spell out the following sentence: **YOU RUINED MY LIFE SO NOW ITS TIME FOR YOU TO PAY.**

PUZZLE 133

The Egyptian **gold display** would be covering the X.

The hieroglyphs scratched into the side of the display cabinet spell out **FIND TAPE.**

PUZZLE 135

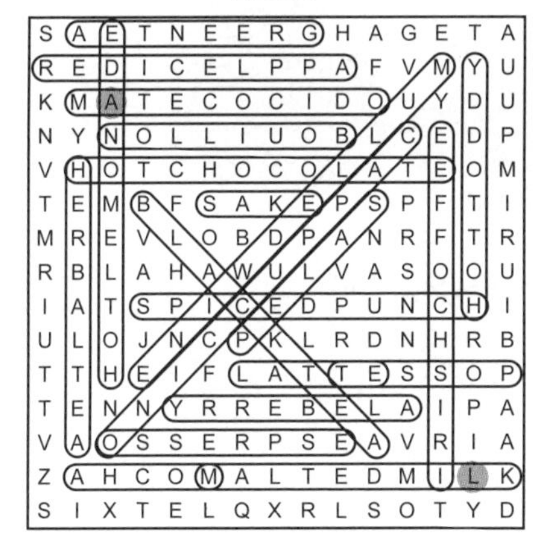

PUZZLE 136

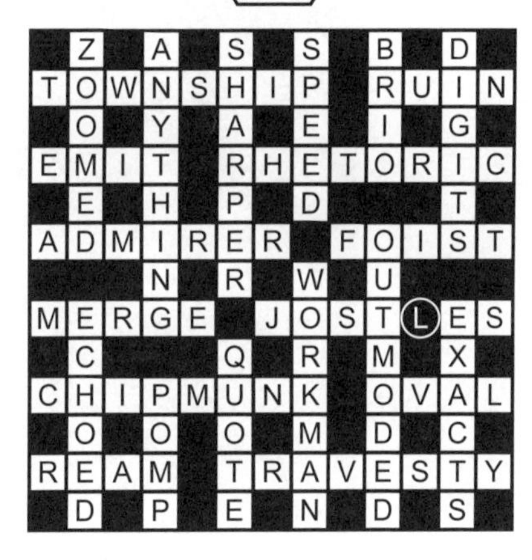

PUZZLE
137

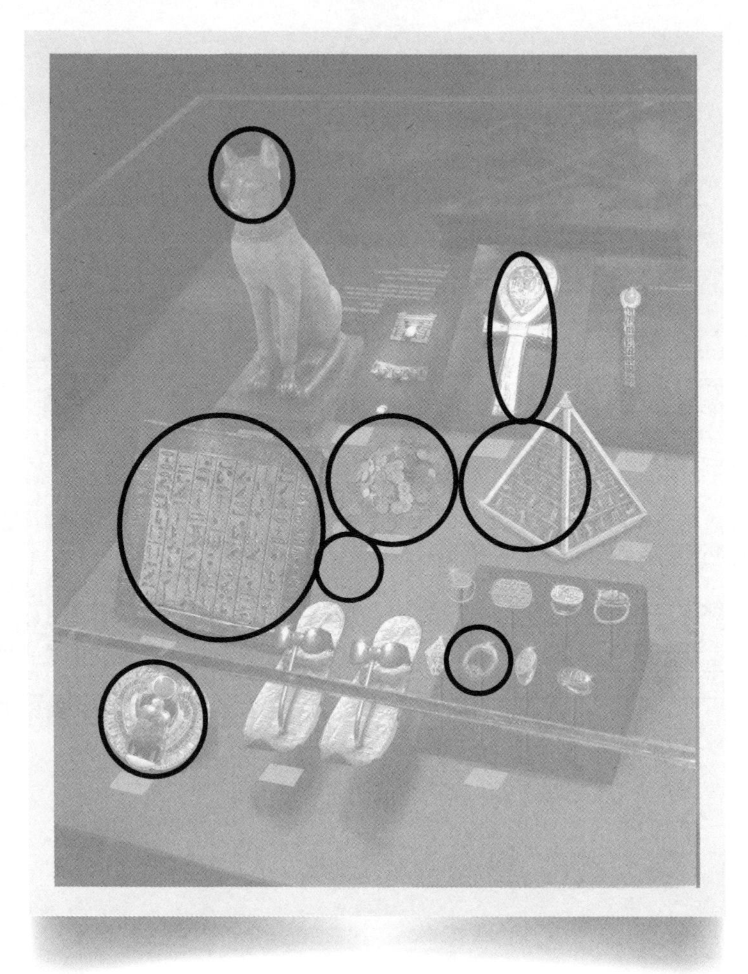

PUZZLE 138

PUZZLE 139

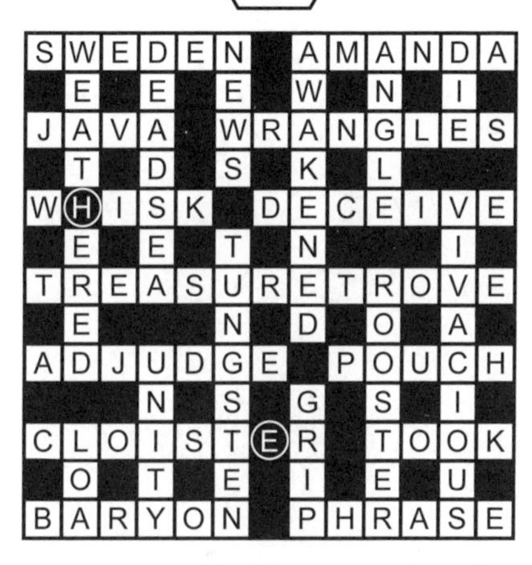

PUZZLE 140

E	I	H	F	B	A	G	C	D
F	C	G	I	D	H	B	A	E
B	A	D	G	C	E	F	I	H
D	G	I	E	A	F	C	H	B
C	F	B	D	H	G	A	E	I
A	H	E	B	I	C	D	G	F
G	B	F	A	E	I	H	D	C
H	E	A	C	F	D	I	B	G
I	D	C	H	G	B	E	G	I

PUZZLE 141

E	N	L	A	R	G	E	D		A		C	
S		A			R			R	U	R	A	L
C	A	R	T	O	O	N	S		T		N	
A		G			U		I		H	O	N	K
P	R	O	M	I	N	E	N	C	E		E	
I			A		D		C		N	I	L	
S			N	A	S	C	E	N	T		L	
M	E	N	U			H			I	C	O	N
	M		F	A	N	A	T	I	C		N	
V	I	S	A			I			A	V	I	D
	G		C	H	A	N	N	E	L			A
	R	O	T		D		A		**L**			U
	A		U	N	D	E	R	L	Y	I	N	G
S	T	I	R		E		R			R		H
	I		E		R	E	A	R	M	O	S	T
H	O	A	R	D			T			N		E
	N		S		C	L	E	A	N	S	E	R

PUZZLE 142

Genuine coins could have had a date but **NOT** BCE inscribed on them.

PUZZLE 144

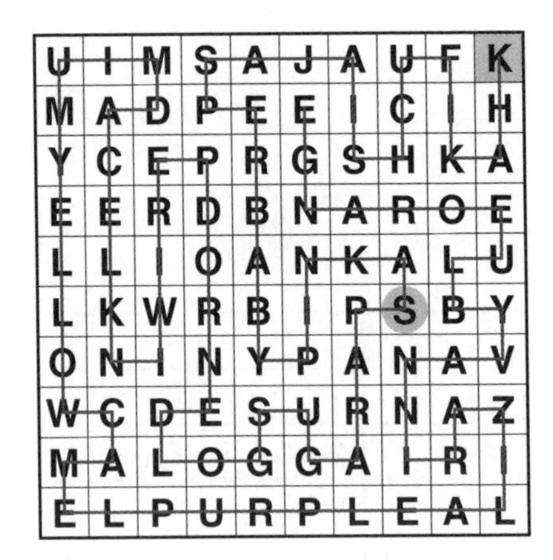

MESSAGE IN THE GRAVEN END NEWSPAPER PUZZLES:

KEEP LOOKING BACK AT ALL THE CLUES

CRIME 6: DR. JOSIE DENBY

PUZZLE 146

Yes, the printout does match the DNA sequence the victim was looking at – it's upside down.

PUZZLE 147

	S		D		A		T		S		S	
A	P	P	E	A	S	E	R		O	A	T	S
	R		S		P		U		U		I	
L	U	S	T		I	G	N	O	R	A	N	T
	C		R		R		K				G	
R	E	F	U	G	E	S		W	O	R	S	E
			C		S		N		P			
S	E	C	T	S		R	E	V	E	R	S	E
	X				C		E		R		H	
M	U	R	M	U	R	E	D		A	V	O	N
	D		U		U		F		B		O	
L	E	S	S		E	Q	U	A	L	I	T	Y
	D		H		T		L		E		S	

PUZZLE 148

PUZZLE 149

PUZZLE 150

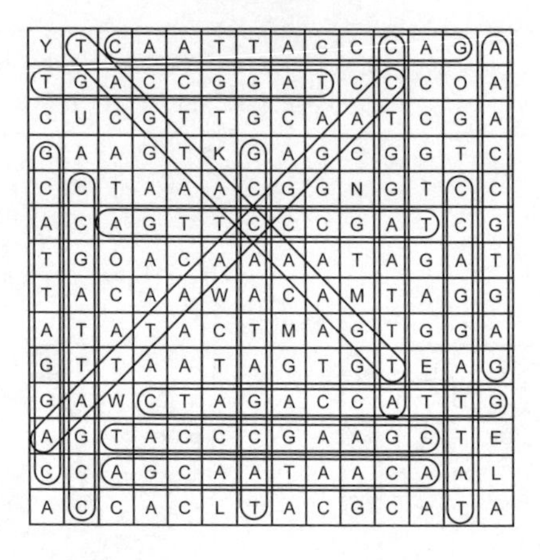

The unused letters in the puzzle (that aren't C, T, A OR G) spell out **YOU KNOW ME WELL.**

PUZZLE 152

The missing number is **45**. In each column, each number is 3 times the one above.

PUZZLE 153

PUZZLE 154

G	C	F	D	A	I	H	E	B
H	A	B	C	F	E	I	D	G
E	I	D	B	G	H	A	F	C
A	E	I	F	D	B	C	G	H
F	D	C	H	I	G	B	A	E
B	G	H	A	E	C	D	I	F
C	F	G	I	H	D	E	B	A
D	H	E	G	B	A	F	C	I
I	B	A	E	C	F	G	H	D

PUZZLE
155

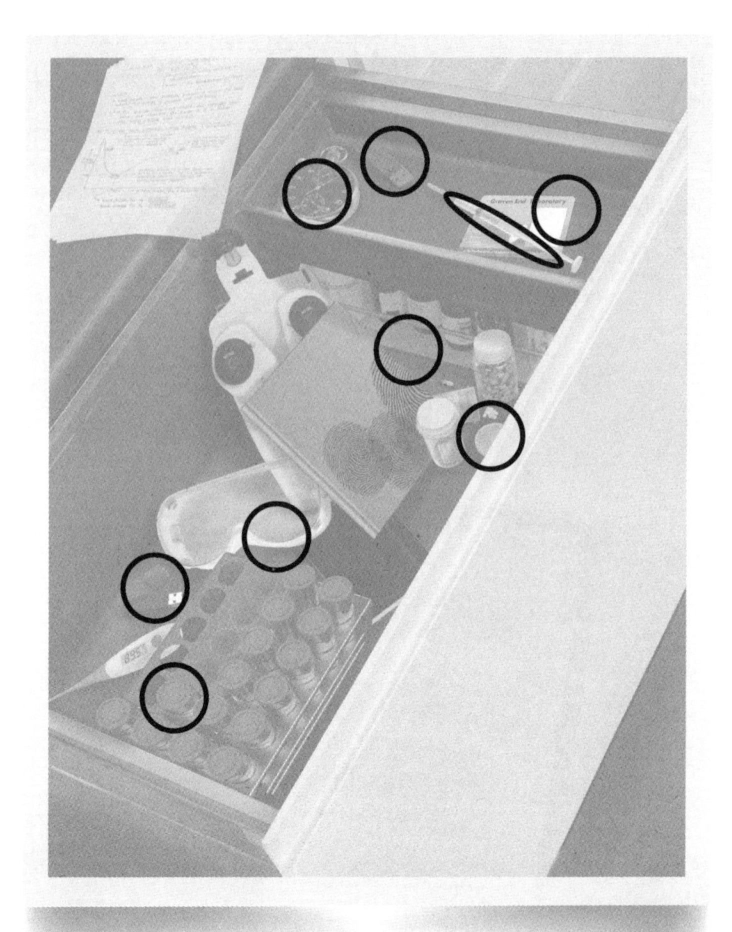

PUZZLE
156

PUZZLE
157

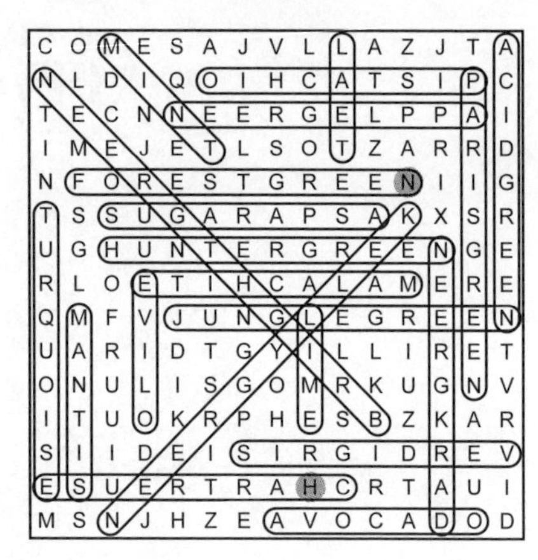
C O M E S A J V L L A Z J T A
N L D I Q O I H C A T S I P C
T E C N N E E R G E L P P A I
I M E J E T L S O T Z A R R D
N F O R E S T G R E E N I I G
T S S U G A R A P S A K X S R
U G H U N T E R G R E E N G E
R L O E T I H C A L A M E R E
Q M F V J U N G L E G R E E N
U A R I D T G Y I L L I R E T
O N U L I S G O M R K U G N V
I T U O K R P H E S B Z K A R
S I I D E I S I R G I D R E V
E S U E R T R A H C R T A U I
M S N J H Z E A V O C A D O D

PUZZLE 158

12:34
100%
I KNOW WHAT YOU DID
YOU DON'T KNOW ANYTHING
I KNOW ENOUGH. I DON'T UNDERSTAND WHY YOU WOULD DO THIS.
BECAUSE I CAN
FINE. IF YOU ARE NOT GOING TO TELL ME YOU CAN TELL THE POLICE

PUZZLE 159

Josie should take half of each tablet today, then the other halves tomorrow.

PUZZLE 160

The symptoms Dr Easton described match **potassium cyanide** poisoning.

PUZZLE 161

PUZZLE 162

PUZZLE 163

The letters of the keyboard have been rearranged to spell **SHE GOT TOO CLOSE.**

PUZZLE 164

Delete one letter from the pair to make the following message: **HAVE YOU TRIED LOOKING UNDER THE DESK.**

The path through the maze reveals the password for the USB drive: **2019.**

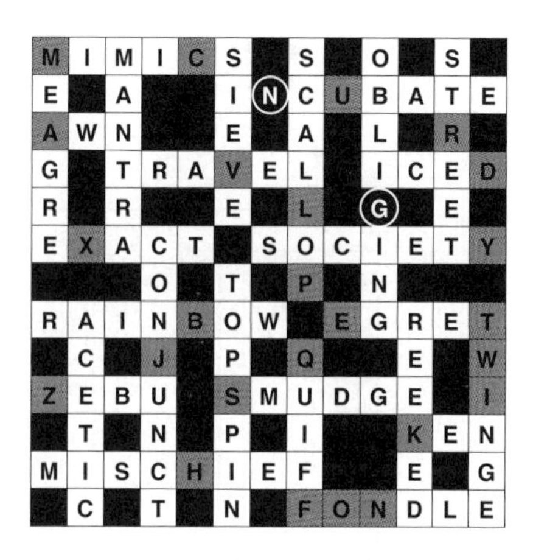

ENTRY	NAME ON REGISTER	CHEMICAL/S PURCHASED
1071	---- DURRANT	AMMONIA
1072	STUART RIGGS	AQUEOUS SODIUM HYDROXIDE
1073	JOSIE DENBY	FORMALDEHYDE
1074	LEO SANTANA	POTASSIUM CHLORIDE
1075	SALLY RICHARDSON	ACETONE
1076	ALAN EASTON	FORMALDEHYDE
1077	JOSIE DENBY	FORMALDEHYDE
1078	JOHN AVERY	OXALIC ACID (RECONSTITUTED)
1079	----- CATT	YELLOW PHOSPHORUS (RECONSTITUTED)

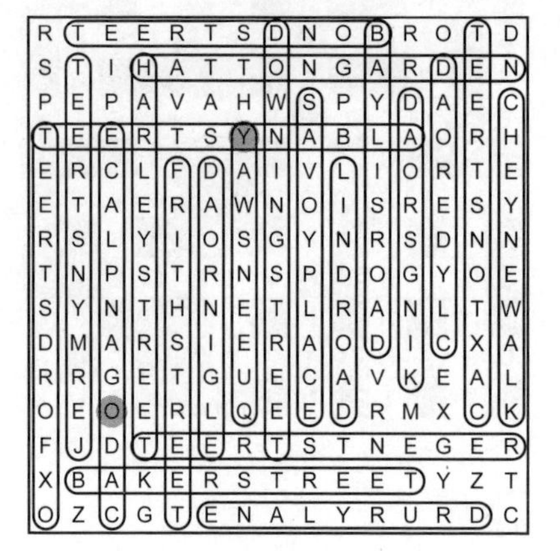

P	I	C	N	I	C		L	Y	R	I	C	S
A		H			A		E		E			A
I		I			M		A		N			W
N	I	C	E	N	E	S	S		D	E	W	Y
T			R		R		E		E			E
I	G	U	A	N	A		H	A	Z	I	E	R
N					S		O		V			S
G	U	L	F	S		A	L	C	O	V	E	
S			E		D		D		U			N
	P	A	L	L	I	D		A	S	I	D	E
A			I		S		A					W
B	O	B	C	A	T		N	O	V	E	L	S
O			I		A		I		A			R
L	O	S	T		N	O	M	I	N	A	T	E
I			O		C		A			U		E
S			U		E		T			K		L
H	O	U	S	E	S		E	R	A	S	E	S

MESSAGE IN THE GRAVEN END NEWSPAPER PUZZLES:

THE KILLER HAS BEEN HELPING YOU

Thinking Through History

Black Peoples of the Americas

Kiaran Sexton

FOLENS

Acknowledgements

The British Library pp6, 7 (bottom)
The British Museum p5 (top)
Carl Iwasaki / Time & Life Pictures / Getty Images p15
Charles Moore / Black Star / Alamy p18 (both)
Donald Uhrbrock / Time & Life Pictures / Getty Images p17 (top)
Greg Villet / Time & Life Pictures / Getty Images p16 (top)
Hulton Archive / Getty Images pp19, 65 (top)
STRANGE FRUIT Music and Words by Lewis Allan - © 1939 - Edward B Marks Music Company - Copyright renewed; extended term of copyright derived from Lewis Allan assigned and effective July 21, 1995 to Music Sales Corporation - all rights for the world outside of USA controlled by Edward B Marks Music Company - All Rights Reserved - Lyric reproduced by kind permission of Carlin Music Corp., London NW1 8BD p65
'I have a dream' speech: Copyright 1967 by Martin Luther King Jr., copyright renewed 1991 by Coretta Scott King. Reprinted by arrangement with the Heirs to the Estate of Martin Luther King Jr., c/o Writers House as agent for the proprietor New York, NY. p20
Mary Evans Picture Library pp5 (bottom), 8, 9, 72 (top), 89, 90 (both)
The History of Mary Prince: A West Indian Slave by Mary Prince (1831) Penguin Classics p8
Paul Schutzer / Time & Life Pictures / Getty Images p17 (bottom)
Paul Slade / Hulton Archive / Getty Images p16 (bottom)
Phil Yasili p43
TopFoto p7 (top)
Topical Press Agency / Getty Images p72 (bottom)

UK: Folens Publishers, Apex Business Centre, Boscombe Road, Dunstable, LU5 4RL.
www.folens.com

Ireland: Folens Publishers, Greenhills Road, Tallaght, Dublin 24

Editors: Joanne Mitchell and Nina Randall
Layout artist: Neil Hawkins, ndesign
Illustrations: Tony Randell
Cover design: Richard Jervis Design
Cover image: Giving Thanks, c.1942 (oil on panel) by Pippin, Horace (1888–1946) ©The Barnes Foundation, Merion, Pennsylvania, USA / The Bridgeman Art Library Nationality / copyright status: American / out of copyright

First published 2007 by Folens Limited.

British Library Cataloguing in Publication Data. A catalogue record for this publication is available from the British Library.

ISBN 978-1-85008-207-1

1. Slave trade
2. Plantation Life
3. Slave resistance
4. The Underground railroad.
5. The abolitionists
6. The American Civil War
7. Jim Crow Laws
8. Ku Klux Klan
9. Mary Seacole
10. Civil Rights

Contents

Introduction

An active and thematic approach to History at Key Stage 3

This file covers a very important and popular option for the Key Stage 3 National Curriculum. It complements the core units and takes a similar thematic approach. It picks out six key themes and considers the important enquiries within each theme. This allows students to draw conclusions about change, continuity and causation while also deepening their understanding of chronology and sequencing. Using the materials from the section on Communication, for example, students begin by studying the methods employed by the abolitionists in the 18th and 19th centuries. They then consider the methods used by the Civil Rights Movement in the 20th century, including photo journalism and television. Students are therefore encouraged to compare across the time period and to note not only the ways in which communication has changed but also the elements that have remained constant.

This file provides ready-to-go materials for lessons that can be 'dropped' into existing schemes of work. It is not intended to replace textbooks but it does form the basis for teaching the whole unit.

As well as providing a new way for students to look at History, this file also brings a new way of learning to Key Stage 3. As far as is possible, an active learning approach is followed. By using a wide variety of visual and active materials, students will be able to arrive at their own learning with minimal guidance from the teacher. An 'at a glance' chart on page vi shows which learning styles are potentially addressed by each lesson.

Finally, it should be stressed that these materials, whilst following an active and thematic approach, do follow the National Curriculum requirements. A National Curriculum checklist on page v shows which objectives can be addressed by each lesson.

National Curriculum and learning style references

These references are intended to help you to incorporate the materials in this file into your schemes of work. The first shows which elements of the National Curriculum for History are particularly addressed by each section of the materials (though the materials can be extended to cover almost any element). The second set of references shows which of the five learning 'styles' are potentially addressed by the materials in each section as they stand. This will help to enable curriculum planners to ensure that all the different learning styles are addressed within a programme of study.

National Curriculum: knowledge, skills and understanding

	1	2a	2b	2c	2d	2e	3a	3b	4a	4b	5a	5b	5c
The abolitionists						✓			✓	✓	✓		✓
Civil rights						✓			✓	✓	✓		✓
Slave resistance	✓	✓			✓	✓					✓		✓
The American Civil War			✓	✓			✓	✓			✓		✓
Black Americans and the World Wars	✓	✓				✓					✓	✓	✓
Runaways		✓	✓			✓					✓	✓	
Jim Crow Laws		✓	✓						✓	✓	✓	✓	
The Ku Klux Klan		✓	✓			✓			✓	✓	✓		✓
The slave trade					✓	✓	✓	✓					✓
Plantation life		✓	✓						✓	✓	✓		✓
Mary Seacole	✓						✓	✓	✓	✓		✓	✓
Empire	✓	✓		✓								✓	✓
Emancipation	✓	✓			✓	✓					✓	✓	
Independence	✓			✓	✓	✓						✓	✓

	Verbal	Visual	Kinaesthetic	Interpersonal	Intrapersonal
The abolitionists	✓	✓		✓	
Civil rights		✓		✓	✓
Slave resistance			✓	✓	✓
The American Civil War	✓		✓	✓	
Black Americans and the World Wars		✓	✓	✓	✓
Runaways	✓		✓	✓	
Jim Crow Laws	✓	✓	✓	✓	
The Ku Klux Klan		✓		✓	✓
The slave trade			✓	✓	✓
Plantation life	✓	✓		✓	
Mary Seacole			✓	✓	✓
Empire		✓	✓	✓	
Emancipation			✓	✓	✓
Independence	✓			✓	✓

Brief definitions

Verbal: learning through the hearing and vocalisation of information.

Visual: learning through seeing and pictorially representing information.

Kinaesthetic: learning through movement; this might include rearranging information through role-play or board games and so on.

Interpersonal: learning through exchanging information with other students, for example, paired or group work.

Intrapersonal: learning through working alone with information.

Progression map: a journey through History

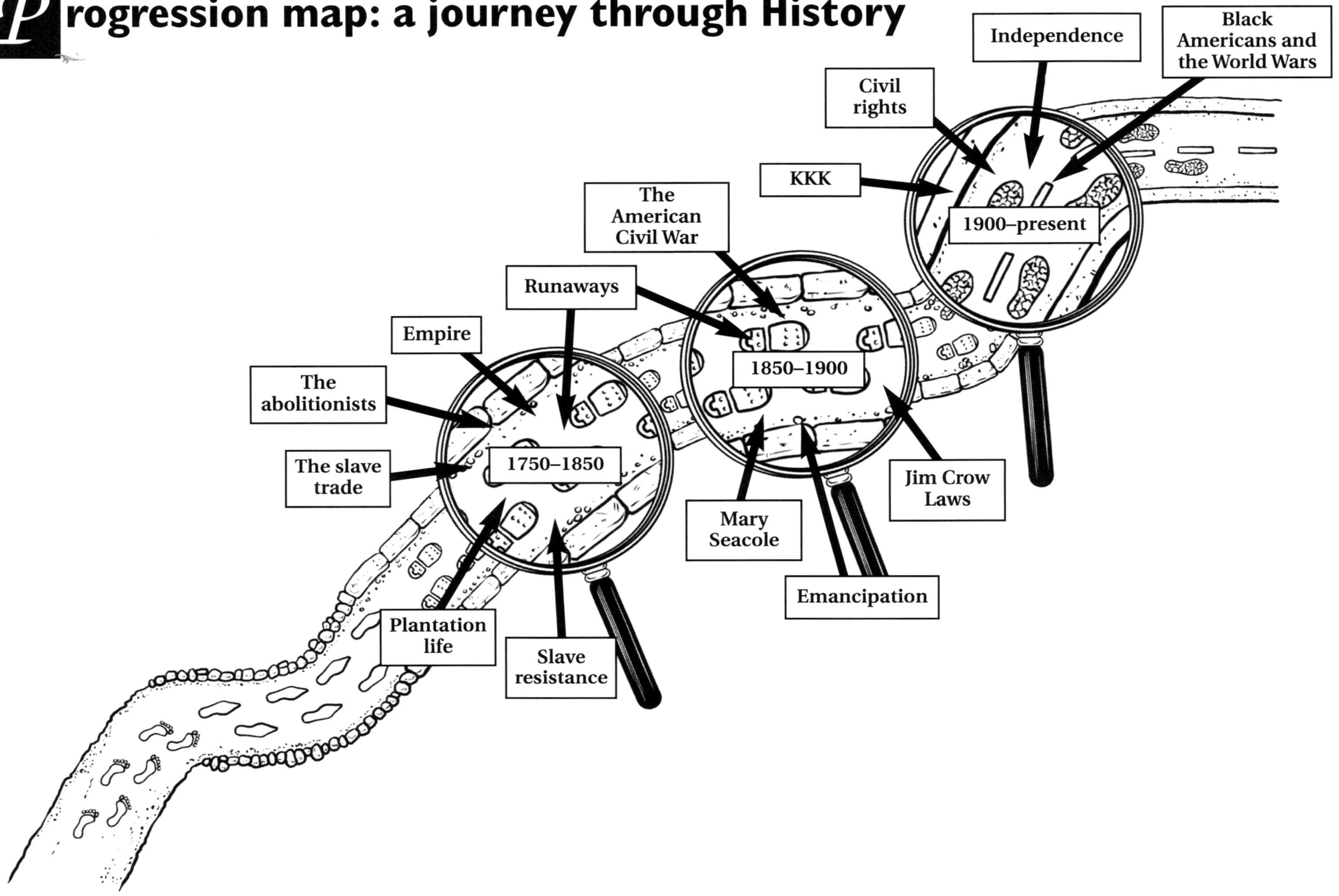

1750–1850

The slave trade

The abolitionists

Empire

Runaways

Plantation life

Slave resistance

1850–1900

The American Civil War

Mary Seacole

Emancipation

Jim Crow Laws

1900–present

KKK

Civil rights

Independence

Black Americans and the World Wars

Theme map: Communication

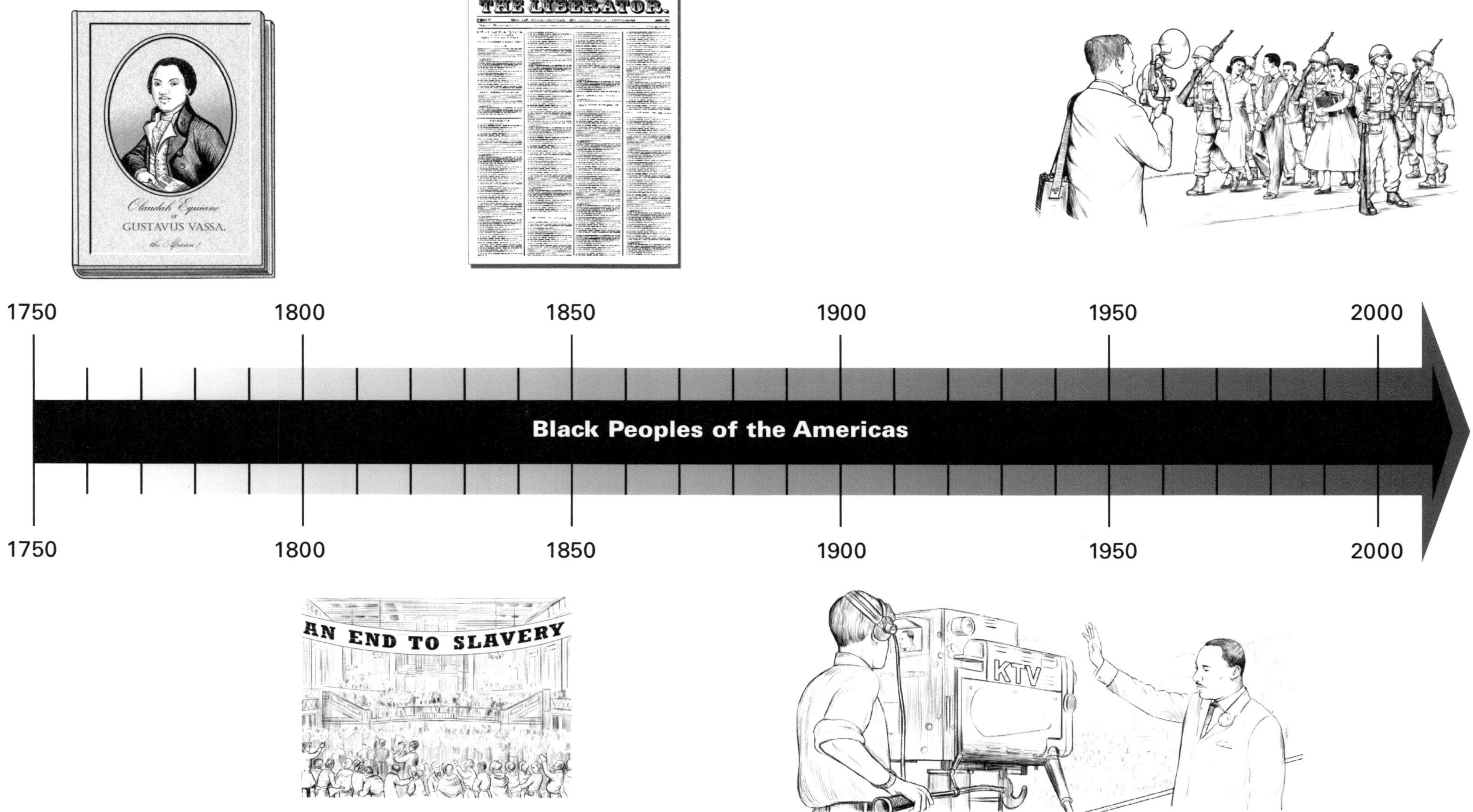

Theme map: Warfare

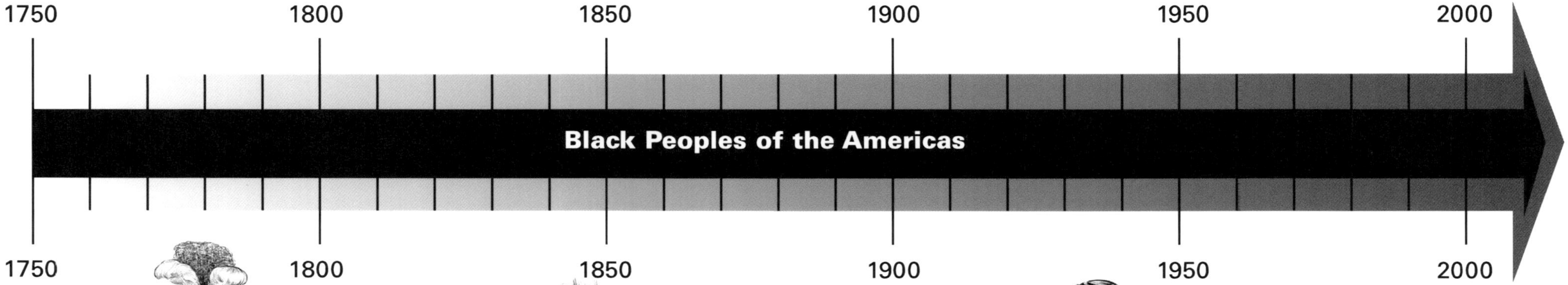

Theme map: Crime and Punishment

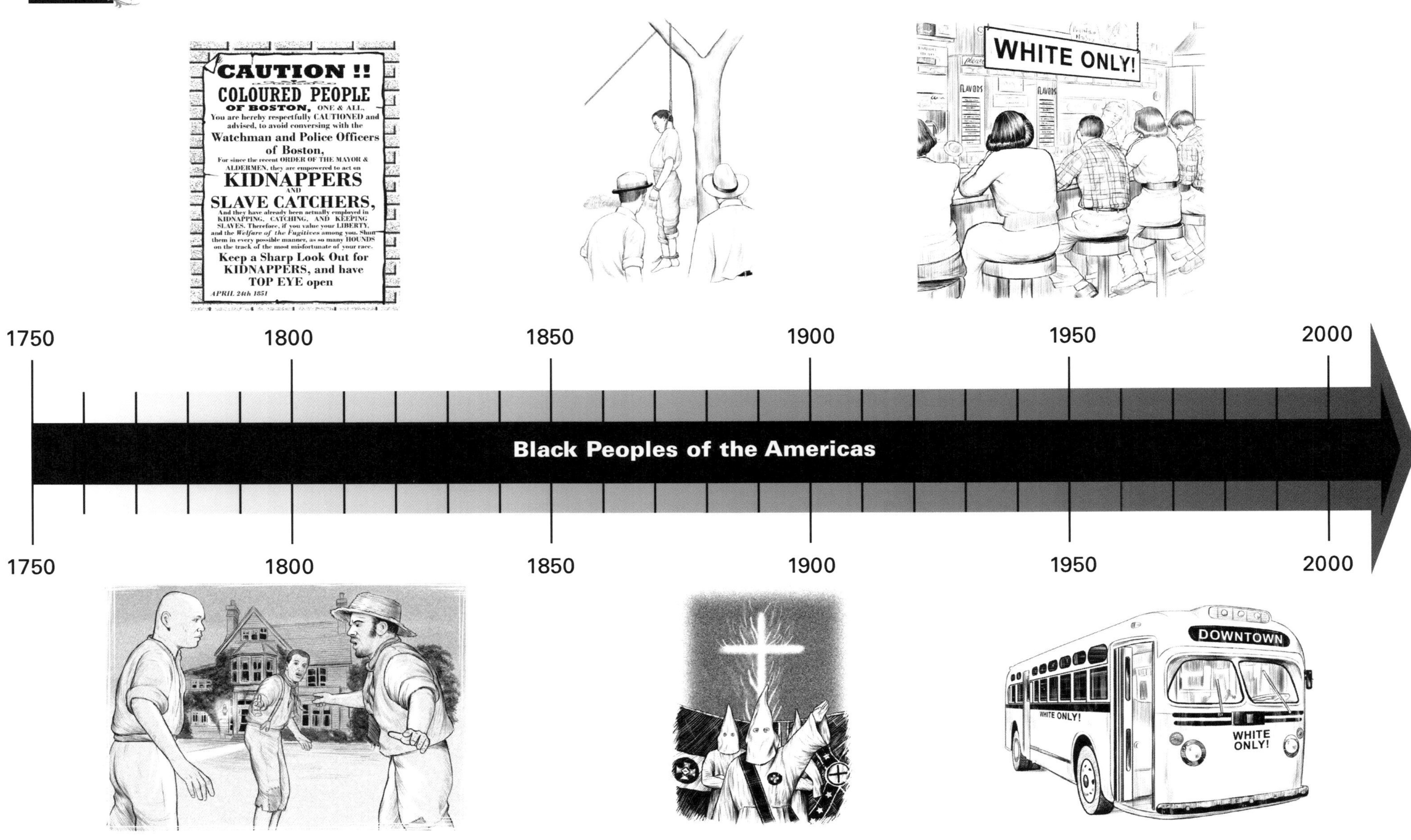

Theme map: Town and Country

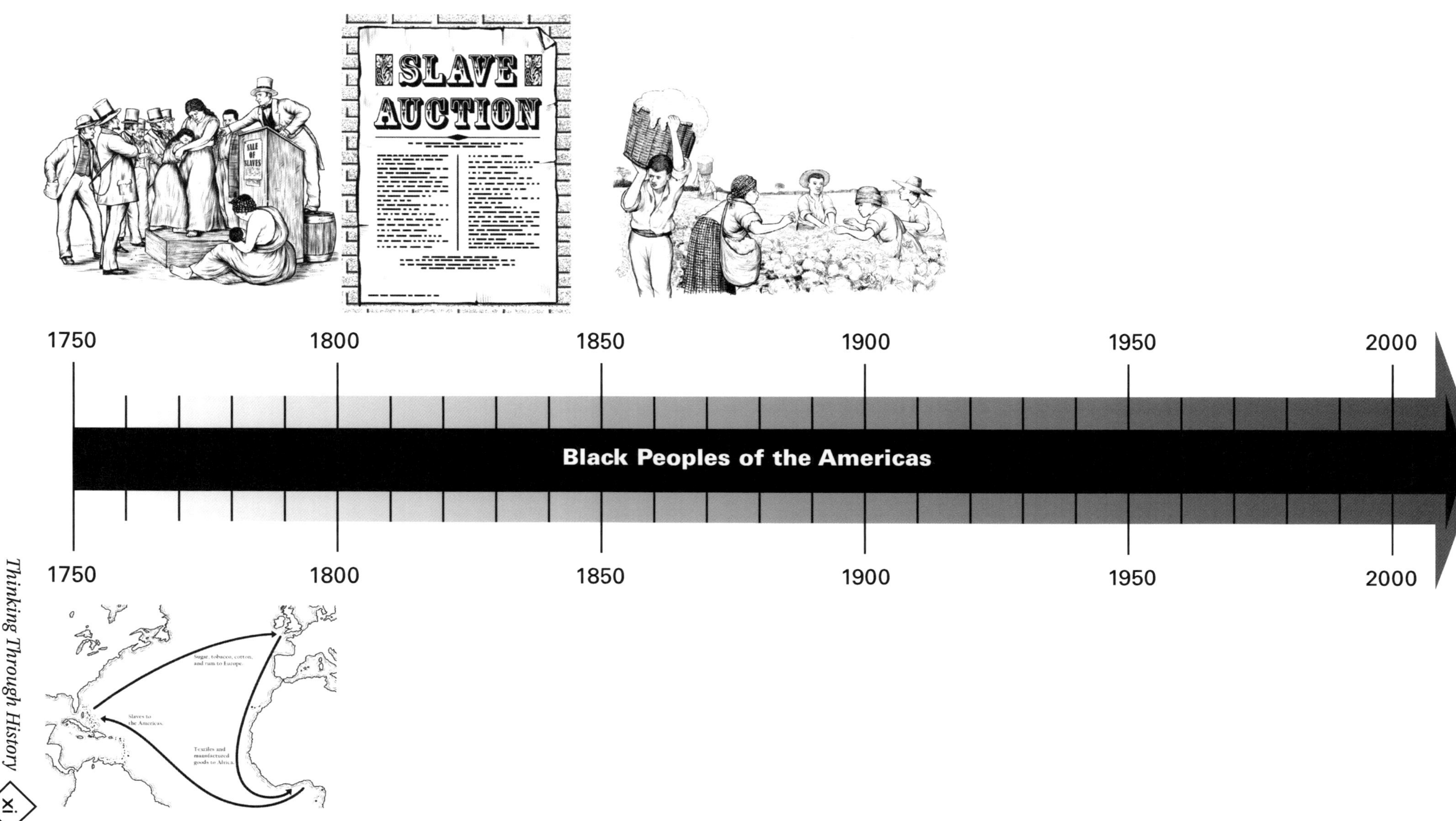

Theme map: Health and Medicine

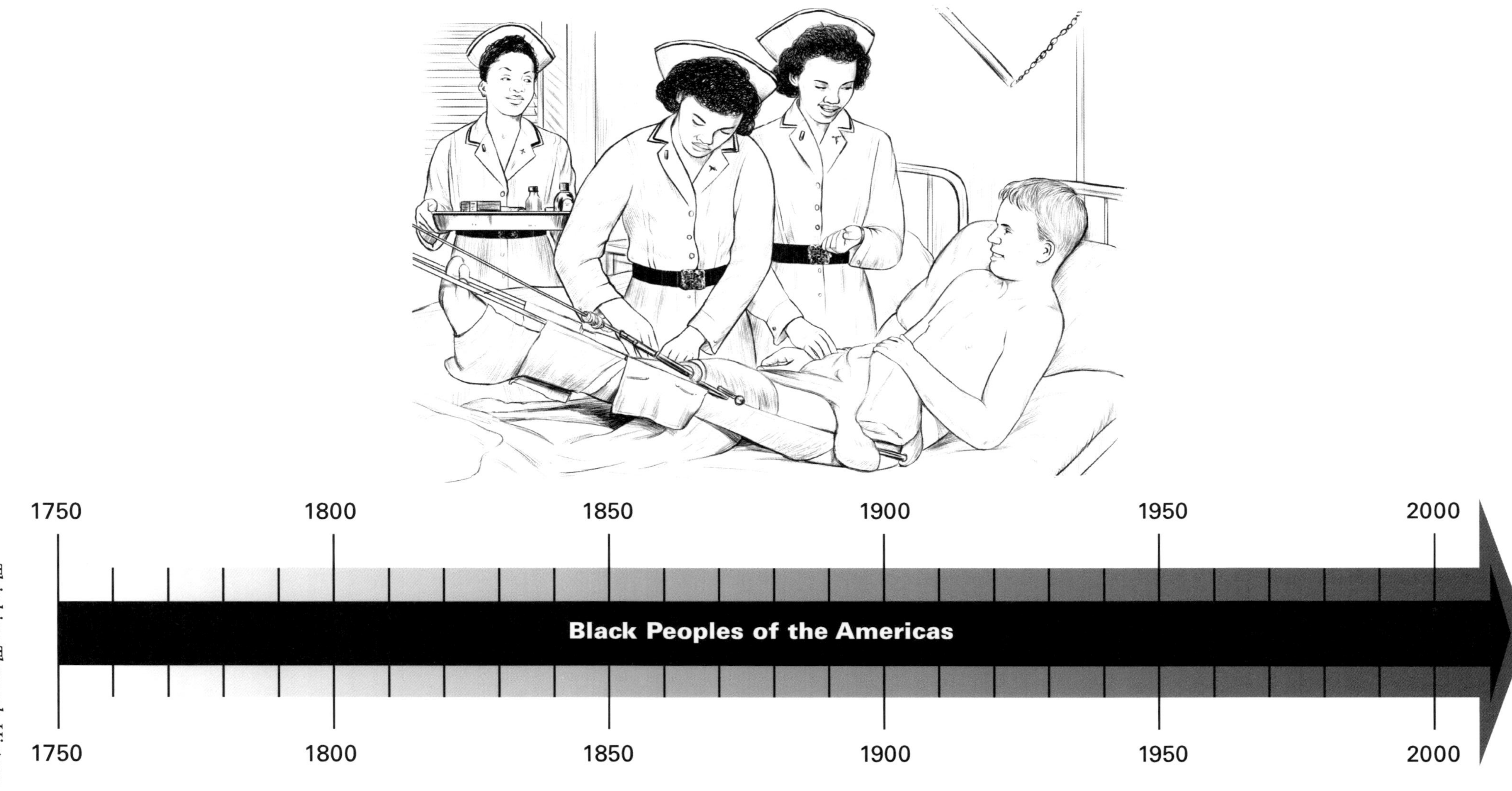

Theme map: Government

THE NEWS
1833
Slavery in Empire
ended by Parliament

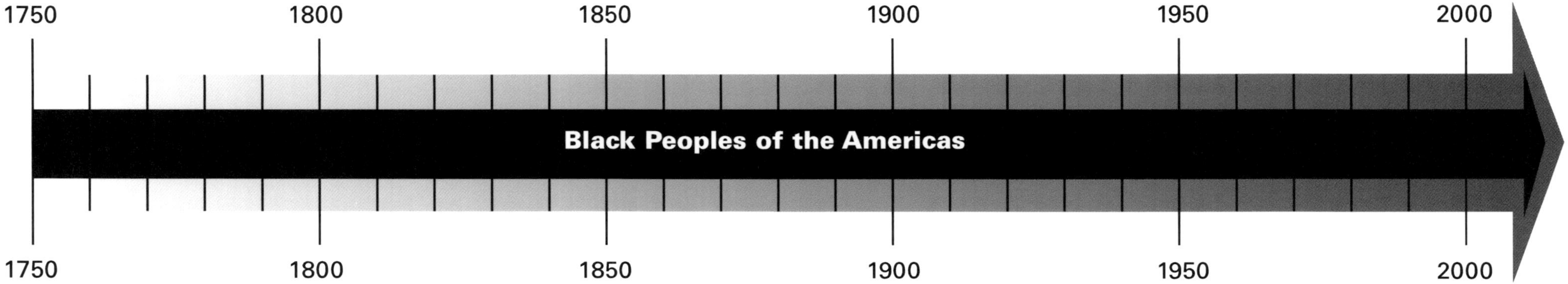

1750 1800 1850 1900 1950 2000

Black Peoples of the Americas

1750 1800 1850 1900 1950 2000

Key: areas owned by Britian

FREEDOM NOW!
FREEDOM NOW!
FREEDOM NOW! CORE
FREEDOM NOW CORE

Writing for Freedom
Eyes on the Prize

The abolitionists

Aims and objectives

These activities are designed to allow students to consider the different methods of communication used by the anti-slavery movements. This will help them to communicate their ideas and, more importantly, to select relevant information and organise it in response to a specific question.

Background

The movement against slavery in Britain began at the end of the 18th century and achieved the abolition of the slave trade in 1807, followed by the end of slavery in the British Empire in 1833. It was the first mass protest movement of the modern age. The success of the movement encouraged abolitionists in the USA to organise and communicate their ideas. Slavery ended in the USA in 1865.

Activity 1: *What methods of communication could be used?*

- Initial preparation: photocopy the worksheets entitled 'What methods of communication could be used?' (page 3) and 'Methods of communication spider diagram' (page 4) for students to work in pairs or small groups.
- Introduce the task and explain the objectives.
- Students should read through the introduction and consider what methods the movements against slavery could try to use to achieve their objectives.
- Students should list as many different methods as they can think of on the worksheet.
- Discuss findings with the class and allow them to modify their worksheets accordingly.
- For each method on the spider diagram, students should try to think of one advantage and one disadvantage. They should write these on the spider diagram.

Activity 2: *Abolitionist movements in Britain and the USA*

- Initial preparation: photocopy the sheets 'Abolitionist methods of communication' (pages 5–9) and the worksheet 'Analysing methods of communication record sheet' (pages 10–11) for all students.
- Introduce the task and model how the worksheet should be completed.
- Students should work in pairs to examine the various sources and complete the worksheet.

Activity 3: *Consolidation into a written response*

- Initial preparation: photocopy the writing frame entitled 'What methods of communication were used by the abolitionists?' (page 12) for all students.
- Students should use the activities and discussion to complete the writing frame and to write an essay.

General notes

Students may come to different conclusions as to the most significant points and their overall evaluation. This is to be encouraged as long as the points are effectively supported. Extension activities could include research into different groups or a comparison between roles played by black and white individuals, or by men and women, or by Britain and the USA.

What methods of communication could be used?

We live in a world of instantaneous communication through television and the Internet. News travels vast distances immediately. We also have access to information from a wide range of viewpoints. Two hundred years ago, communication was much slower. There was no television, radio, cinema or Internet. Newspapers did exist but few people could read them.

Communication was still very important. Groups and individuals needed to communicate to get support for their ideas on how their society should be run and what changes should be made. They needed to communicate with each other, with the government, with their supporters, with their opponents and with ordinary people.

The movements against slavery in Britain and the USA wanted to change the law to make slave trading and slavery itself illegal. Slavery had existed for many years and had made fortunes for traders and plantation owners. Many of these people sat in Parliament and in Congress (the American parliament) and were very reluctant to end slavery.

Tasks

To change the law and end slavery, the anti-slavery groups, or abolitionists, needed to communicate with as many people as possible to develop a popular protest movement that would force politicians to act.

On 'Methods of communication spider diagram' (page 4), write a list of all the different methods of communication that could have been used to attack and criticise slavery in order to get more support for Parliament to change the law.

Next, write down why each method of communication would have been helpful and what disadvantages each would have had.

Methods of communication spider diagram

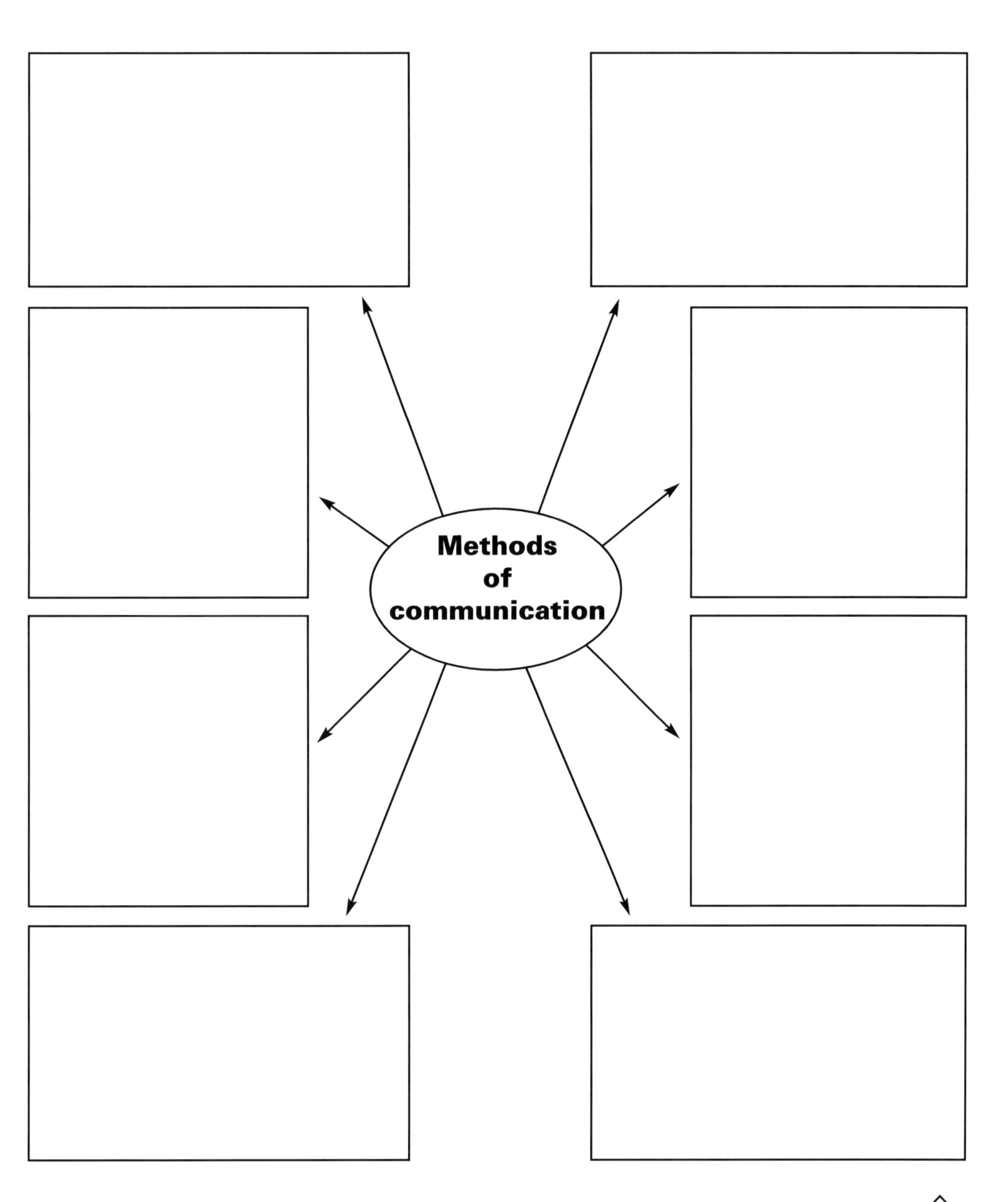

Abolitionist methods of communication

A Am I Not a Man and a Brother?

The image of a slave in chains was originally adopted as the seal of the Society for the Abolition of Slavery in England in the 1780s. It appeared on medallions made by Josiah Wedgwood as early as 1787, and these were sold and worn by abolitionists. A popular image, it often appeared in anti-slavery publications.

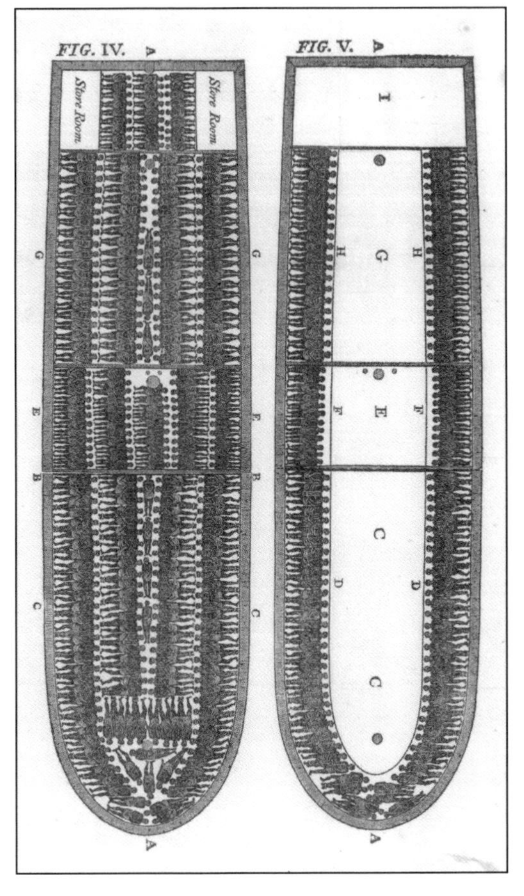

B The storage of slaves on a Liverpool slave ship

In 1787, Granville Sharp and Thomas Clarkson formed the Society for the Abolition of the Slave Trade.

Clarkson gathered evidence from the crew of slave ships about the storage of slaves on ships and the equipment used, which included branding irons.

The evidence, found in written accounts and pictures like this one, was published in pamphlets.

The main white abolitionists

Granville Sharp: helped black people fight test cases in the courts.

Thomas Clarkson: collected evidence from all over Britain of the cruelty of the slave trade.

William Wilberforce: fought for legislation in Parliament.

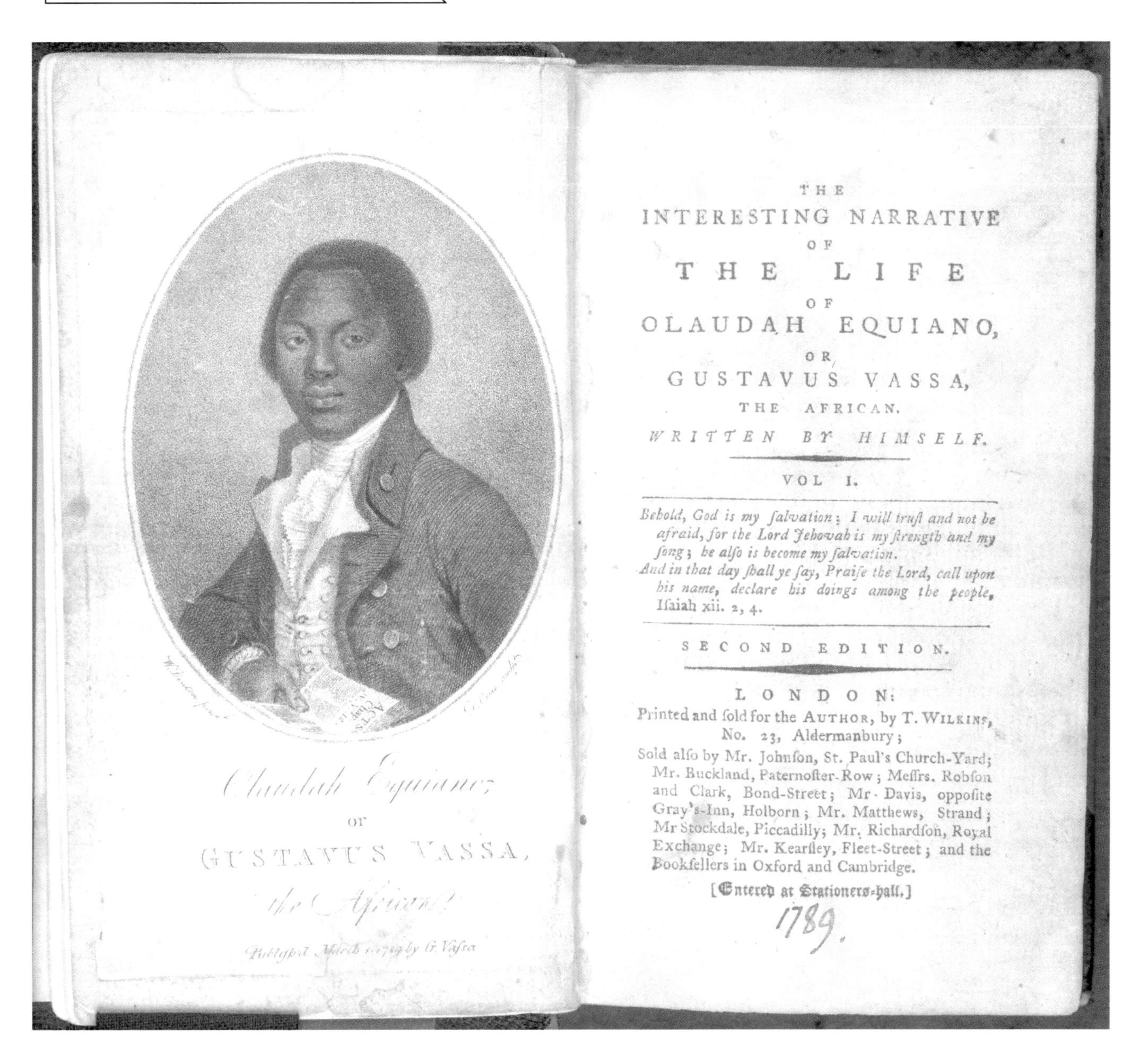

Olaudah Equiano,
or
GUSTAVUS VASSA,
the African.
Published March 1789 by G. Vassa

THE
INTERESTING NARRATIVE
OF
THE LIFE
OF
OLAUDAH EQUIANO,
OR
GUSTAVUS VASSA,
THE AFRICAN.
WRITTEN BY HIMSELF.

VOL I.

Behold, God is my ſalvation; I will truſt and not be afraid, for the Lord Jehovah is my ſtrength and my ſong; he alſo is become my ſalvation.
And in that day ſhall ye ſay, Praiſe the Lord, call upon his name, declare his doings among the people, Iſaiah xii. 2, 4.

SECOND EDITION.

LONDON:
Printed and ſold for the AUTHOR, by T. WILKINS, No. 23, Aldermanbury;
Sold alſo by Mr. Johnſon, St. Paul's Church-Yard; Mr. Buckland, Paternoſter-Row; Meſſrs. Robſon and Clark, Bond-Street; Mr. Davis, oppoſite Gray's-Inn, Holborn; Mr. Matthews, Strand; Mr Stockdale, Piccadilly; Mr. Richardſon, Royal Exchange; Mr. Kearſley, Fleet-Street; and the Bookſellers in Oxford and Cambridge.
[Entered at Stationers-hall.]
1789.

C The autobiography of Olaudah Equiano

Equiano wrote about his capture and transportation from Africa, the horrors of slavery and how he bought his freedom. The book was a best-seller and attracted wide publicity. Equiano helped Granville Sharp in the case of the slave ship *Zong*. In September 1781, the ship had lost its way off the coast of Jamaica and the captain ordered 133 slaves to be thrown over the side. The owners of the ship attempted to claim money from their insurers for 'loss of goods', as slaves were considered cargo. They won their initial case but were later defeated when they were challenged in court by the insurers due to bad cargo management.

THE BLACK MAN'S LAMENT.

THE PETITION FOR ABOLISHING THE SLAVE-TRADE.

COME, listen to my plaintive ditty,
Ye tender hearts, and children dear!
And, should it move your souls to pity,
Oh! try to *end* the griefs you hear.

THE BLACK MAN'S LAMENT. 3

SUGAR-CANE.

There is a *beauteous plant* *, that grows
In western India's sultry clime,
Which makes, alas! the Black man's woes,
And also makes the White man's crime.

* "A field of canes, when standing in the month of November, when it is in arrow or full blossom, (says Beckford, in his descriptive account of the Island of Jamaica,) is one of the most beautiful productions that the pen or pencil can possibly describe. It, in common, rises from three to eight feet, or more, in height; a difference

D ***The Black Man's Lament or How to Make Sugar*** **by Amelia Alderson Opie (1826)**
Amelia Alderson Opie was a poet and Quaker. She was part of the Women's Anti-Slavery Society in Norwich. Together with similar groups from other towns, the society demanded an immediate end to slavery – not the gradual end proposed by the Anti-Slavery Society. They were successful and the policy was changed in 1830.

E The campaign to boycott West Indian sugar by the Peckham Ladies' Friends of Africa Society (1826)
The boycott was taken up by other women's anti-slavery societies across the country.

F ***The History of Mary Prince: A West Indian Slave* by Mary Prince (1831)**

Mary Prince wrote her autobiography with the help of the Anti-Slavery Society in England. Here she tells of how she was sold away from her mother and sisters. She was sued by her former owners who accused her of telling lies but she won the case and received great publicity.

'At length the vendue master, who was to offer us for sale like sheep or cattle, arrived, and asked my mother which was the eldest. She said nothing, but pointed to me. He took me by the hand, and led me out into the middle of the street, and, turning me slowly round, exposed me to the view of those who attended the vendue. I was soon surrounded by strange men, who examined and handled me in the same manner that a butcher would a calf or a lamb he was about to purchase, and who talked about my shape and size in like words – as if I could no more understand their meaning than the dumb beasts. I was then put up to sale. The bidding commenced at a few pounds, and gradually rose to fifty-seven, when I was knocked down to the highest bidder; and the people who stood by said that I had fetched a great sum for so young a slave.

I then saw my sisters led forth, and sold to different owners: so that we had not the sad satisfaction of being partners in bondage. When the sale was over, my mother hugged and kissed us, and mourned over us, begging of us to keep up a good heart, and do our duty to our new masters. It was a sad parting; one went one way, one another, and our poor mammy went home with nothing.'

G The masthead of William Lloyd Garrison's abolitionist newspaper *The Liberator*

This weekly newspaper was launched in 1831 and continued until 1865, by which time slavery in the USA had been abolished and the American Civil War was over. He also launched the American Anti-Slavery Society, encouraged by methods and events in Britain.

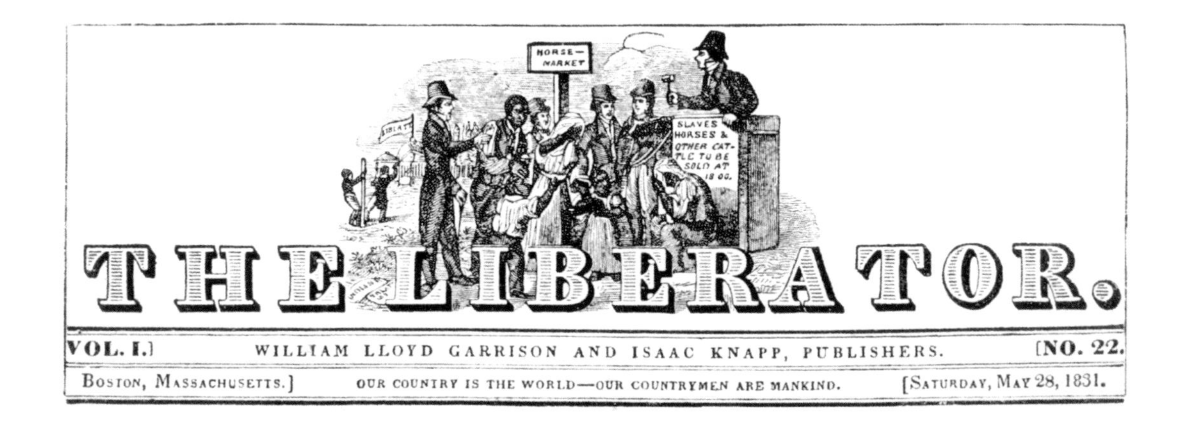

THE LIBERATOR.

VOL. I.] WILLIAM LLOYD GARRISON AND ISAAC KNAPP, PUBLISHERS. [NO. 22.

BOSTON, MASSACHUSETTS.] OUR COUNTRY IS THE WORLD—OUR COUNTRYMEN ARE MANKIND. [SATURDAY, MAY 28, 1831.

Writing for Freedom

Eyes on the Prize

H A mob breaks up an abolitionist meeting in the USA in 1861

nvahissement d'un meeting abolitioniste dans le Michigan. — D'après les croquis de M. W. S., à Charlestowı

I An extract from a speech by Frederick Douglass

Frederick Douglass was an ex-slave and member of the American Anti-Slavery Society. He typically spent about six months of the year travelling extensively, giving lectures.

'This Fourth of July is yours, not mine. You may rejoice, I must mourn.

What, to the American slave, is your 4th of July? I answer; a day that reveals to him, more than all other days in the year, the gross injustice and cruelty to which he is the constant victim. To him, your celebration is a sham; your boasted liberty, an unholy license; your national greatness, swelling vanity; your sounds of rejoicing are empty and heartless; your denunciation of tyrants brass fronted impudence; your shout of liberty and equality, hollow mockery; your prayers and hymns, your sermons and thanks-givings, with all your religious parade and solemnity, are to him, mere bombast, fraud, deception, impiety, and hypocrisy – a thin veil to cover up crimes which would disgrace a nation of savages. There is not a nation on the earth guilty of practices more shocking and bloody than are the people of the United States, at this very hour.'

Analysing methods of communication record sheet

Nature of the source (for example, newspaper)	Origin of the source (where/ when produced)	Purpose of the source (what it is trying to achieve)	Use of the source (what understanding does it give us?)
A			
B			
C			
D			
E			

Writing for Freedom

Eyes on the Prize

Nature of the source (for example, newspaper)	Origin of the source (where/ when produced)	Purpose of the source (what it is trying to achieve)	Use of the source (what understanding does it give us?)
F			
G			
H			
I			

What methods of communication were used by the abolitionists?

Use your record sheets and notes from discussions to complete the writing frame. Then use the frame to construct an extended written response to the question above.

Introduction
The abolitionist movement was the first mass protest movement in the modern age...

Abolitionists wanted to build a mass movement because...

The most important method of communication was...

The next most important method was...

They also...

They were successful because...

Writing for Freedom
Eyes on the Prize

Civil rights

Aims and objectives

These activities focus on the means of communication used by the Civil Rights Movement in the USA in the 1950s and 1960s. They enable students to consider why these means were chosen and what impact they had. Students can also compare these methods with those used by the abolitionists and suggest reasons for similarities and differences.

Background

In the 1950s and 1960s, the Civil Rights Movement began a national campaign to tackle segregation in the southern states of the US. These states had passed segregation laws after the slaves had been granted freedom in 1863. As well as laws preventing black students attending white schools and universities, black people had separate eating, toilet and washing facilities. They also had to stand on buses and were refused entry to places that served white people. Under the leadership of Martin Luther King, black people and white students from the northern states organised large-scale non-violent protests. They were following the tactics used successfully in India by Gandhi. The violent reactions of white people and the police in the South received nationwide publicity through television and the newspapers.

Congress passed the Civil Rights Act in 1964, which made discrimination illegal, and the Voting Rights Act in 1965, which enabled black people to register to vote.

Activity 1: *How did the Civil Rights Movement achieve national publicity?*

- Initial preparation: photocopy the sheets entitled 'Methods of communication' (pages 15–20) and the worksheet 'Analysing methods of communication record sheet' (pages 21–22) for all students.
- Introduce the task and model how the sheets should be completed.
- Students should work in pairs to examine the various sources and complete the worksheet.
- Discuss the findings with the class and allow them to modify their record sheets accordingly.

Writing for Freedom

Eyes on the Prize

Activity 2: *Living pictures*

- Students, in groups, should be given one of the pictures to recreate.
- Students can then invent dialogue for each of the characters in their picture
- Each group should present their 'living picture' to the rest of the class.
- A discussion should follow on the possible impact of the picture and what they have learned from recreating it.

Activity 3: *What was the impact of these methods of communication?*

- Initial preparation: photocopy the worksheet entitled 'What was the impact of these methods?' (page 23) for all students.
- Introduce the task, emphasising the amount of attention given to the Civil Rights Movement in the USA and throughout the world through television. It will be worth pointing out that each state in the USA had its own government, police force and soldiers as well as the national government having its own army and police force.
- Students should consider the likely impact of different methods of communication on each of the groups in the boxes and jot down their points on the record sheet.
- Carry out a class discussion on the issues raised about the impact of different methods on different groups.

Activity 4: *Consolidation into a written response*

- Initial preparation: photocopy the writing frame entitled 'How important was communication in the success of the Civil Rights Movement?' (page 24) for all students.
- Students should complete the writing frame and use it to construct an extended written response.

General notes

Students may come to different conclusions as to the most significant points and their overall evaluation. This is to be encouraged as long as the points are effectively supported. They should come to a balanced answer and be able to select criteria for their judgements. Extension activities could include research into some of the key individuals and events in the struggle for civil rights.

Methods of communication

A Court cases

Segregation was challenged through the courts in America as being against the Constitution. In 1954, following Brown v Topeka Board of Education, segregation in schools was declared unlawful. In 1955, segregation on buses was declared unlawful.

Students in the Brown v Topeka Board of Education case.

Writing for Freedom

Eyes on the Prize

B Boycotts

In 1955, Rosa Parks was arrested in Montgomery, Alabama, for refusing to give up her bus seat to a white man. Civil rights leaders organized the Montgomery Bus Boycott in which the black population refused to use the buses. The bus companies lost 70 per cent of their income.

The first day of the bus boycott.

C Exercising rights

In 1957, national troops had to escort black high school students into Little Rock school after they were refused entry by state troops and police, and attacked by white protesters. In 1962, two people were killed and over 100 police were injured in riots as James Meredith enrolled at the University of Mississippi.

A student with a broken bicycle is given a lift home from Little Rock school by national troops.

COMMUNICATION

Writing for Freedom

Eyes on the Prize

D Sit-ins

Black and white students organised sit-ins at lunch counters across the southern states in 1960.

The police move in to arrest a student at a lunch counter.

E Freedom Rides

Black and white students travelled by bus across the South, entering places where black people were not allowed to go.

Freedom Riders entering a whites-only waiting room at a bus terminal where they were arrested.

F Protest marches

Thousands of people took part in peaceful protest marches across the southern states, including one in 1965 in Alabama at which the marchers were attacked by state police.

The police attack the peaceful march.

G Speeches

The most famous is Martin Luther King's 'I have a dream' speech at the end of the march to Washington in 1963.

200 000 people gather in Washington at the end of the march to hear Martin Luther King's 'I have a dream' speech. Millions more watched on television.

Writing for Freedom

Eyes on the Prize

H Extract from Martin Luther King's 'I have a dream' speech:

'I have a dream that one day this nation will rise up and live out the true meaning of its creed: "We hold these truths to be self-evident, that all men are created equal."

I have a dream that one day on the red hills of Georgia, the sons of former slaves and the sons of former slave owners will be able to sit down together at the table of brotherhood.

I have a dream that one day even the state of Mississippi, a state sweltering with the heat of injustice, sweltering with the heat of oppression, will be transformed into an oasis of freedom and justice.

I have a dream that my four little children will one day live in a nation where they will not be judged by the color of their skin but by the content of their character.

I have a dream today.

I have a dream that one day down in Alabama, with its vicious racists, with its governor having his lips dripping with the words of 'interposition' and 'nullification', that one day right there in Alabama little black boys and black girls will be able to join hands with little white boys and white girls as sisters and brothers.

I have a dream today.

And if America is to be a great nation, this must become true. So let freedom ring from the prodigious hilltops of New Hampshire. Let freedom ring from the mighty mountains of New York. Let freedom ring from the heightening Alleghenies of Pennsylvania. Let freedom ring from the snow-capped Rockies of Colorado. Let freedom ring from the curvaceous slopes of California.

But not only that: let freedom ring from Stone Mountain of Georgia.

Let freedom ring from Lookout Mountain of Tennessee.

Let freedom ring from every hill and molehill of Mississippi.

From every mountainside, let freedom ring.

And when this happens, and when we allow freedom ring, when we let it ring from every village and every hamlet, from every state and every city, we will be able to speed up that day when all of God's children, black men and white men, Jews and Gentiles, Protestants and Catholics, will be able to join hands and sing in the words of the old Negro spiritual: "Free at last! Free at last! Thank God Almighty, we are free at last!"'

Analysing methods of communication record sheet

Nature of the source (for example, newspaper)	Origin of the source (where/ when produced)	Purpose of the source (what it is trying to achieve)	Use of the source (what understanding does it give us?)
A			
B			
C			
D			

Writing for Freedom

Eyes on the Prize

Nature of the source (for example, newspaper)	Origin of the source (where/ when produced)	Purpose of the source (what it is trying to achieve)	Use of the source (what understanding does it give us?)
E			
F			
G			
H			

What was the impact of these methods?

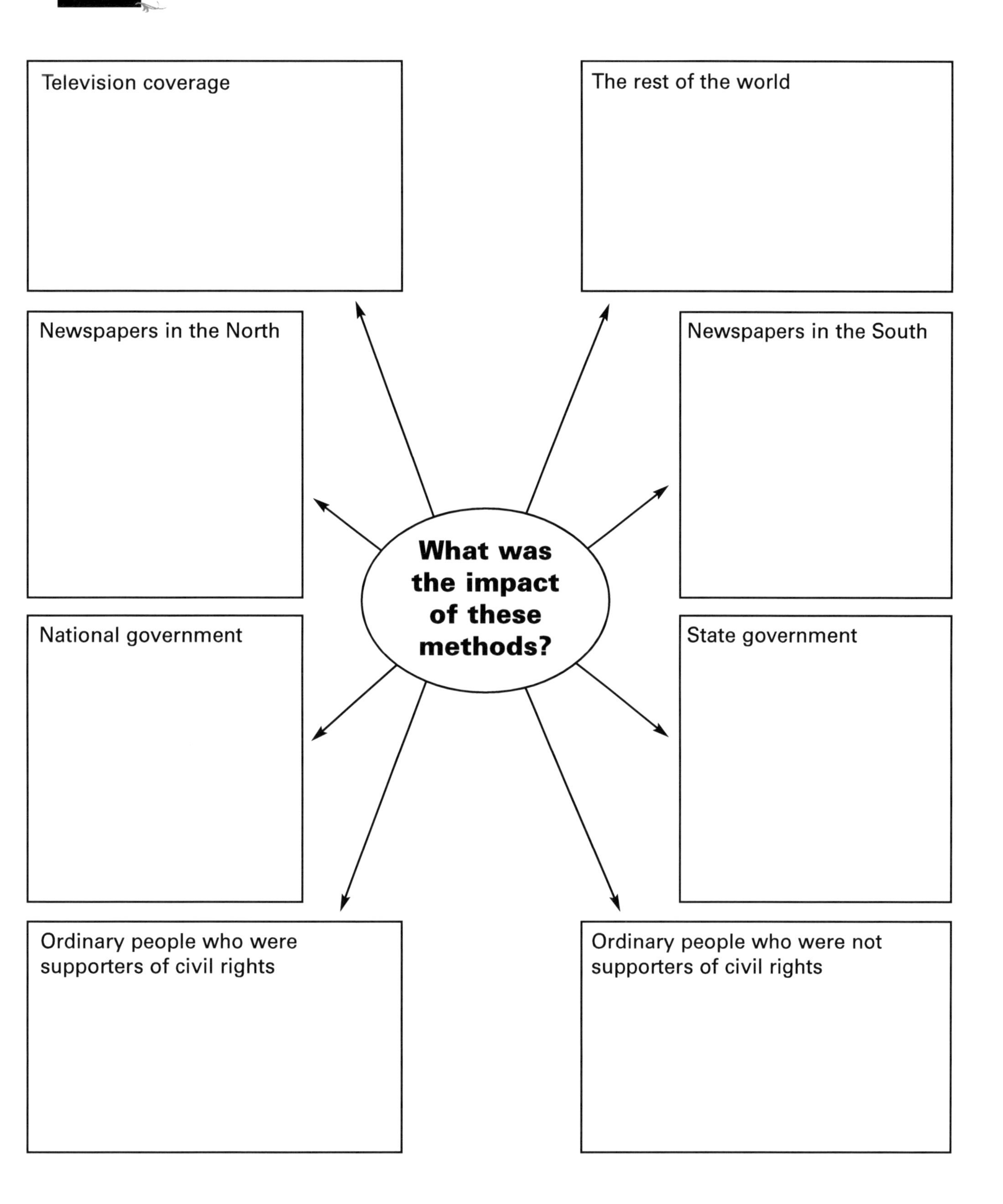

How important was communication in the success of the Civil Rights Movement?

Use your record sheets and notes from discussions to complete the writing frame. Then use the frame to construct an extended written response to the question above.

Introduction
The main goals of the Civil Rights Movement in America were...

The movement had many methods of achieving these goals, which included...

Support was increased because...

There was also opposition from...

Television and newspaper coverage was important because...

The government changed the law because...

Fighting for Freedom
Freedom is Never Given; it is Won

Slave resistance

Aims and objectives

These activities enable students to establish a chronology of slave resistance as well as considering different types of resistance. Students will also be given the chance to evaluate the success and consider the significance of slave resistance in the history of slavery.

Background

For a long time, the abolition of slavery was presented as something that was achieved by white campaigners. As a result, the slaves themselves were portrayed as passively accepting their fate until rescued by the white abolitionists. Now it is recognised that slaves resisted slavery in many different ways and this was very important not only for the ending of slavery, but also for the history of slavery itself.

Activity 1: *A lifeline of slave resistance (card sorting exercise)*

- Initial preparation: provide copies of the 'Slave resistance cards' (pages 27–28) and photocopy the 'Slave resistance lifeline' (page 29) to A3 size for students and encourage them to work in pairs or small groups.
- Introduce the task and explain the objectives.
- Students should place the cards on the lifeline according to the date and the extent of success or failure. Slave resistance that was continuous should be placed in the 'Ongoing resistance' box.
- Students should then record their findings on the record sheet.
- Discuss the findings with the class and allow them to modify their record sheets accordingly.

Activity 2: *Evaluation of slave resistance*

- Initial preparation: Students should be given copies of 'Evaluation sheet 1' (page 30) and 'Evaluation sheet 2' (page 31).
- Students, in pairs or small groups, should evaluate the material from their lifeline and jot down points on the sheets.
- Discuss the findings with the class and allow them to modify their record sheets accordingly.

Activity 3: *Consolidation into a written response*

- Initial preparation: photocopy the writing frame entitled 'How important was slave resistance?' (page 32) for all students.
- Students should complete the writing frame and use it to construct an extended written response.

General notes

Students may come to different conclusions as to the most significant points and their overall evaluation. This is to be encouraged as long as the points are effectively supported. They should come to a balanced answer and be able to select criteria for their judgements.

Slave resistance cards

1839 Amistad Mutiny Slaves killed the captain and took over the Spanish ship *Amistad*. They were captured and put on trial in the USA. They were freed because slave trading between countries was illegal.	Many slaves drowned by throwing themselves off the slave ships taking them from Africa.	Historians have recorded over 250 slave uprisings in the 200 years before 1865.
Many slaves deliberately damaged machinery on the plantations. Owners lost money due to repairs and lost production.	1859 John Brown led a group from the northern states of the USA into Virginia to free the slaves. He was captured and executed.	Many slaves worked deliberately slowly. Owners made less money as a result.
In Haiti, slaves developed their own religion called vodou or voodoo. This was a mixture of Christian and African practice.	Mothers had abortions or killed their babies to stop the owners getting another slave.	1800 A rebellion by a thousand slaves in Virginia failed. Many were executed.
Drums were banned on the island of St Kitts in the West Indies.	Punishments were very severe for everything, from not working hard enough to running away.	Thousands of slaves ran away from their owners. Some escaped to Haiti and others to Canada.

Fighting for Freedom

Freedom is Never Given; it is Won

Many runaway slaves were captured.	In Jamaica, the Maroons (escaped slaves who lived in the mountains) successfully fought against the army. They were given their freedom and allowed to keep their land in 1739.	African names, religion, language, music and stories were all passed down by slaves from generation to generation.
1831 Nat Turner led a revolt of 75 slaves. Over 50 white people were killed. The revolt failed and Turner was executed.	In the West Indies, those who rebelled were tortured and killed as an example to others.	1760 400 people were executed for taking part in a rebellion in Jamaica.
There were revolts on over 150 slave ships.	Many Jamaican slaves ran away to join the Maroons.	In 1801, Toussaint L'Ouverture set up the first independent black state on Haiti in the French West Indies.
1831 Sam Sharpe's Rebellion or the Baptist War. In Jamaica, an uprising lasted ten days and involved 60 000 slaves. Hundreds were executed. The British Parliament freed all slaves in 1833.	1849 Harriet Tubman escaped from slavery. She returned south 19 times and rescued 300 slaves.	1829 Race riots in Cincinnati USA. 1000 slaves ran away to Canada.

Slave resistance lifeline

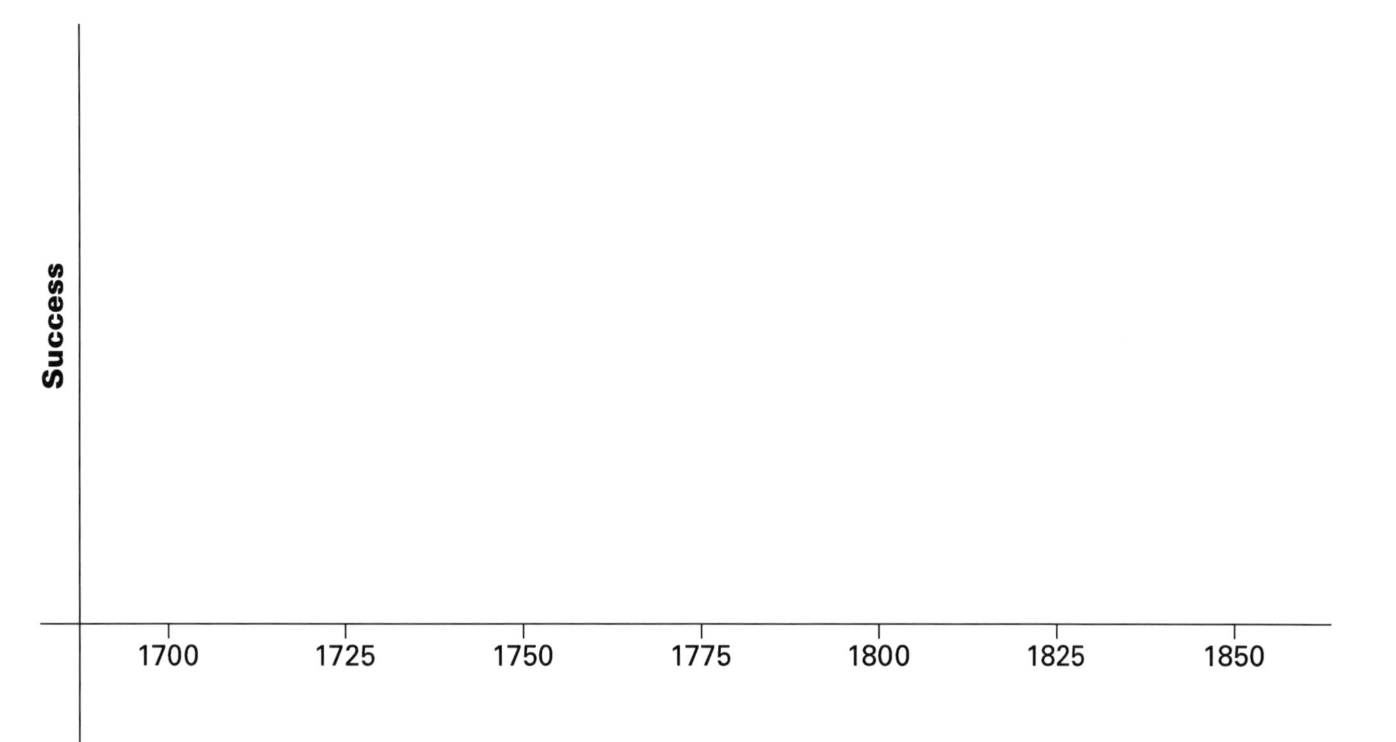

Failure

Ongoing resistance

Evaluation sheet 1

Number of slaves involved

Disadvantages of the slaves

Reasons for the failure of the slave resistance

Advantages of the owners

Role of the government

Evaluation sheet 2

Hope for the slaves

Loss of profit for the owners

Reasons for the significance of the slave resistance

Increased support for abolition

History of black people

Fighting for Freedom

Freedom is Never Given; it is Won

How important was slave resistance?

Use your record sheets and notes from discussions to complete the writing frame. Then use the frame to construct an extended written response to the question above.

Introduction: Slave resistance took many forms. Ongoing resistance included...

The biggest revolts were...

There were many reasons for failure, which included...

Slave resistance was significant because...

Overall, I would say that slave resistance was important because...

Fighting for Freedom

Freedom is Never Given; it is Won

The American Civil War

Aims and objectives

These activities are designed to allow students to investigate different attitudes and beliefs that were held by groups of people in the USA prior to the Civil War. Students can then consider the events leading to war within this context and come to a conclusion as to the inevitability of the conflict.

Background

The USA was set up in 1776 when the different states joined together to defeat Britain and govern themselves. It was a new kind of government. Each state had its own parliament and could make its own laws. Each state also agreed to have a national or federal government with a national parliament (Congress) and an elected President. There were huge differences between the states but it was felt that a union of states would be easier to protect.

The Civil War ended in a victory for the North and the freeing of all slaves in the South.

Activity 1: *How united was the United States?*

- Initial preparation: photocopy the sheets entitled 'Attitudes and beliefs cards' (page 35) and 'American Civil War character cards' (page 36).
- Divide students into groups of four. Give a copy of both sheets to each group.
- The group should then decide which attitudes and beliefs belong to each character. These should be noted down on the character cards. There may be overlaps between the attitudes and beliefs of different characters. This is fine but the group should agree about this.
- There should be time allowed for each group to discuss its findings on the range of conflicting attitudes. What were these differences based on?
- There should then be a whole-class discussion. What were the main issues that divided the USA? Can a country live with such differences? How inevitable was war?
- Comparisons can be made with a modern society as well as looking at the differences that exist over important issues without the threat of civil war.

Activity 2: *When did Civil War become inevitable?*

- Each group should be allocated a character. Ensure there is a balance across the class.
- Students will have to decide how their character will react to each event leading up to the Civil War.
- Each group should be given the worksheet entitled 'Event chart' (pages 37–39).
- Set a time limit for the activity so that each group has time for discussion, but also moves through the decisions at a suitable pace.

Activity 3: *Class debate*

- Pose the question 'What was the turning point in the road to Civil War?' and explain the concept of a turning point.
- Each character (group) should give their response in turn. This allows groups who played each character to give an answer and support their choice.
- This may result in agreement but is more likely to lead to a discussion as to when the Civil War became inevitable.

Activity 4: *Consolidation into a written response*

- Initial preparation: photocopy the writing frame entitled 'Why did America have a Civil War?' (page 40) for all students.
- Students should identify key points arising from the activity and the discussion and then use the frame to write an extended written response.

General notes

Students should be encouraged to research this complex topic further by studying a wide range of individuals and looking at their letters and speeches. Many of these are available on American websites.

Attitudes and beliefs cards

There are more people living in the northern states so they should have more power than the southern states.	Each state should be able to decide if it wants to have slavery or not.	Slaves who run away should be captured and returned.	Slavery is a crime against God.
The northern states have too much power over the President and the Congress.	Slavery is cruel and uncivilised.	The factories in the North are making the USA wealthy.	All men are equal. One man should not be allowed to own another.
Slaves who run away should be helped and protected.	The Union must be preserved. We cannot allow States to leave the Union.	Slaves are property and the US Constitution prevents the property of men being taken from them.	Slavery should not be allowed to spread to new states that join the Union.
Slaves are not allowed to go to school or to church.	The South pays more taxes on imports and exports than the North.	The southern states can govern themselves.	Slaves are protected by their owners and looked after.
Freed slaves would provide factory owners with cheap labour.	Each state should be able to decide if it wants to stay in the Union or not	The economy in the South is based on cotton, plantations and slaves.	Black people in the North face discrimination and violence at work.

American Civil War character cards

A northern politician

An abolitionist

A southern politician

A plantation owner

Fighting for Freedom

Freedom is Never Given; it is Won

Event	Reaction from your character	Civil War is more likely/less likely/inevitable
1800–1810 Northern states abolish slavery. International slave trading is made illegal.		
1820 Missouri Compromise. The USA is increasing in size. A slave state can only join the Union if a free state joins at the same time.		
1830–1840 Nat Turner's slave revolt fails but the South fears more revolts will take place. The Anti-Slavery Society is formed in the North and grows in size.		
1850 Fugitive Slave Law. Slaves who escape to the North must be captured and returned. Helping fugitive slaves is a crime.		

Fighting for Freedom

Freedom is Never Given; it is Won

Event	Reaction from your character	Civil War is more likely/less likely/inevitable
1852 An anti-slavery book called *Uncle Tom's Cabin* is published and becomes a best-seller in the North.		
1854 Kansas-Nebraska Act. New states can decide for themselves if they wish to be slave states. This overturns the Missouri Compromise.		
1857 The Dred Scott Case. Supreme Court rules that Congress cannot stop slavery in new states.		
1859 John Brown enters the South and attempts to start a slave uprising but is stopped and executed.		

Fighting for Freedom

Freedom is Never Given; it is Won

Event	Reaction from your character	Civil War is more likely/less likely/inevitable
1860 Abraham Lincoln is elected President. He has said that he will stop slavery spreading and will stop states leaving the Union.		
1860 Seven southern states leave the Union and set up the Confederate States of America.		
1861 Confederate States attack Fort Sumter. Lincoln blockades Southern ports. Four more States join the Confederacy.		
1861 Civil War begins.		

Why did America have a Civil War?

Use your record sheets and notes from discussions to complete the writing frame. Then use the frame to construct an extended written response to the question above.

Introduction
The American Civil War was between...

The Civil War began when...

Before the war, there were many differences between the North and the South...

The Civil War became more likely when...

The Civil War became inevitable when...

Slavery was an important cause of the war because...

Fighting for Freedom
Freedom is Never Given; it is Won

Black Americans and the World Wars

Aims and objectives

These activities are designed to enable students to consider how historians can rediscover things that have been left out of history or forgotten. They can consider why this is an important part of the historical process.

Background

Britain and the USA in both World Wars called on all their peoples to volunteer and fight for their country. Thousands responded from the black communities but they had to face the enemies of prejudice and bigotry as well as the enemy that they had been asked to fight against. After the war, little or nothing was done to commemorate them and films and history books left their contribution out completely. In recent years, creditable attempts have been made to rediscover the contribution made by black soldiers in both World Wars.

Activity 1: *Walter Tull and the Tuskegee Airmen*

- Initial preparation: provide copies of the two case studies (pages 43 and 44) and the record sheet 'What can we learn from the stories of Walter Tull and the Tuskegee Airmen?' (page 45) for students to work in pairs or small groups.
- Introduce the task and explain the objectives.
- Students should read and discuss the information in the case studies and offer initial thoughts.
- Students can then feed back to the class their observations about the case studies. Encourage consideration as to the significance of the case studies and reasons as to why they were 'forgotten'.
- Students should then record their findings on the record sheet.

Activity 2: *Black soldiers in the World Wars*

- Initial preparation: provide copies of 'Black soldiers in the World Wars' (pages 46–47) and 'What similarities and differences were there for black soldiers in World War I and World War II?' (page 48) for all students.
- Explain the task and objectives.
- Students should complete the similarities and differences worksheet.
- Carry out a class discussion, comparing not only the two World Wars but also the differences between American soldiers and other black soldiers.
- Students should modify their record sheets in the light of the discussion.

Activity 3: *Consolidation into a written response*

- Initial preparation: photocopy the writing frame entitled 'How did black soldiers contribute to the two world wars?' (page 49) for all students.
- Students should complete the writing frame and use it to construct an extended written response.

General notes

Extension activities could include research into other aspects of black people's contribution to the World Wars, into individuals or into particular geographical or military areas. Students could also investigate recent efforts to record and highlight these contributions.

Case study 1: Walter Tull

Walter Tull was born in 1888 in England. His father had come from the West Indies ten years earlier. Walter's grandfather had been a slave. By the time he was nine, both his parents had died and he was brought up in an orphanage.

In 1908, he began playing for Clapton FC. He won winner's medals in the FA Amateur Cup, London County Amateur Cup and London Senior Cup. He played for Tottenham Hotspur and then for Northampton Town. He was the first outfield black professional footballer in Britain.

He was just about to join Glasgow Rangers when World War I broke out in 1914. He joined the army and was promoted to sergeant. In 1917, he became the first black officer in the British army. He was recommended for this despite military regulations forbidding 'any negro or person of colour' to be an officer.

He served in France at the Battle of the Somme and in Italy before he was killed in France in 1918. Tull's men risked heavy machine-gun fire in their efforts to retrieve his body but were unable to do so. He was awarded the British War and Victory Medal and recommended for a Military Cross.

His story was then largely forgotten, but recently there have been articles about him in newspapers and on the radio. His old club, Northampton Town, made him the centre of their anti-racism campaign and this has been followed by several other clubs.

Walter Tull.

Case study 2: The Tuskegee Airmen

When the USA entered World War II in 1941, its armed forces were segregated and the opportunities for black people were very limited. Pressure on Congress led to the formation of a black fighter squadron, against the wishes of the military.

This was set up at the Tuskegee Institute in Alabama, a famous college for black students founded by Booker T. Washington. As well as training pilots, the Institute trained members for all other military occupations, including mechanics, radio operators and policemen. The pilots were trained by Captain Benjamin O. Davis Jr and went on to fight in all the main theatres of war. Davis went on to become the first African-American general in the US Air Force.

As well as fighting the enemy, they had to fight racism at home and abroad. They were treated as inferior and denied access to the officers' clubs and other facilities. They were not on equal terms with white pilots.

In all, 992 pilots were trained in Tuskegee from 1940 to 1946. One hundred and fifty lost their lives in training or combat. Many received medals. When the war ended, they returned to an America of segregation and discrimination.

In 1948, President Truman ended segregation in the military forces. This was the first step toward racial integration in the USA. Shortly afterwards, the Civil Rights Movement began to successfully challenge other areas of segregation in the United States.

A film was made about the Tuskegee Airmen in 1995.

What can we learn from the stories of Walter Tull and the Tuskegee Airmen?

Case study	Achievements	Impact	Importance
Walter Tull			
The Tuskegee Airmen			

Black soldiers in the World Wars

World War I Community pressure led to the formation of two major all-black units – the 92nd and the 93rd – in the USA.	**World War I** One thousand of the over 10 000 soldiers who left Jamaica never returned.	**World War II** The US Marines ended their 167-year ban and finally enlisted their first black Marines in 1942.
World War I The French awarded the Croix de guerre for 'gallantry in action' to 171 men from the all-black units of the USA.	**World War II** Black soldiers were still in segregated units within the US army.	**World War I** Over 370 000 black soldiers represented the USA in World War I but only 10 per cent were assigned to combat.
World War II Over 150 000 black seamen served in the US Navy during World War II.	**World Wars I and II** There are memorials to the Caribbean's World War veterans in Jamaica and on the other islands in the West Indies, but not in Britain.	**World War II** In the USA, African American women served in the Women's Army Corps and the women's division of the US Navy.

Fighting for Freedom

Freedom is Never Given; it is Won

World War I The men of the British West Indian Regiment were generally restricted to carrying out hard labour, digging trenches and carrying supplies to men at the fronts.	**World War II** The all-black 92nd division and the 761st tank battalion were among the few exceptional divisions to participate in full combat during the war.	**World War II** Black British servicemen received racist abuse from white US servicemen.
World War I Many black people came to Britain to volunteer. Some men successfully enlisted, whereas others were turned down by recruiting officers on the grounds of their colour.	**World War II** 50 000 people from the West Indies volunteered for the British armed forces. Many more came as nurses.	**World War I** In 1919 and 1920, racially motivated riots and attacks took place in many seaports in Britain and the victims were usually black seamen and ex-servicemen.
World War I In 1916, the Miners', the Railwaymen and the Transport Workers' Unions passed a resolution opposing 'the sinister movement to import coloured labour into this country'.	**World War II** British units were not segregated. Black Britons, male and female, served in all of the armed forces at home and abroad.	**World War I** In Britain, black men were allowed to become privates in the army, but military regulations barred black men from becoming commissioned officers.

What similarities and differences were there for black soldiers in World War I and World War II?

Similarities	Differences

How did black soldiers contribute to the two World Wars?

Use your record sheets and notes from discussions to complete the writing frame. Then use the frame to construct an extended written response to the question above.

Introduction
Black soldiers contributed to both World Wars in many ways. They...

Particular heroes were...

Other important contributions were made by...

They faced many difficulties, including...

After the wars, their contribution was largely forgotten...

It is important to write them into history because...

Equal Before the Law
Strange Fruit

Runaways

Aims and objectives

These activities are designed to enable students to consider the types of decision that runaway or fugitive slaves had to make. They have to consider the advantages and disadvantages of each decision and support their choice. They then have to evaluate the significance of the Underground Railroad.

Background

The Underground Railroad was the name given to the system for helping slaves to escape from the South. It involved large numbers of people working in secret and in great danger. The Railroad has attracted great interest in recent years because it demonstrates how slaves resisted slavery and how abolitionists were prepared to break the law to help them.

Activity 1: *Taking the Underground Railroad*

- Initial preparation: provide copies of the 'Underground Railroad fact sheet' (page 52), the 'Underground Railroad decision cards' (pages 53–55) and the 'Underground Railroad decision record sheet' (page 56) for students to use in small groups.
- Introduce the tasks, explain the objectives and go through the 'Underground Railroad fact sheet' with the students.
- Students should take each card and discuss the advantages and disadvantages before making their decision.
- Each decision should be recorded with reasons for making it on the 'Underground Railroad decision record sheet'.
- Discuss the findings with the class and allow them to modify their record sheets accordingly.

Activity 2: *What was the Underground Railroad?*

- Initial preparation: photocopy the writing frame entitled 'What was the Underground Railroad?' (page 57) for all students.
- Students should complete the writing frame and use it to construct an extended written response.

Equal Before the Law

Strange Fruit

General notes

Students can also use the activity to write narratives from the point of view of the runaway slaves or of those who helped them to explore the range of dangers and difficulties on the journey. They could also research further the importance of Harriet Tubman, Levi Coffin and Frederick Douglass as individuals. They could consider the roles of the Quakers or of female abolitionists.

Underground Railroad fact sheet

- It was called the Underground Railroad from the 1830s but the system had already existed for about 50 years.
- It is estimated that up to 100 000 slaves used the Underground Railroad to escape from slavery in the southern states of the USA.
- Slaves went to the northern states were there was no slavery or to Mexico or Canada.
- The Railroad was secret and did not involve trains.
- Thousands of people worked on the Railroad.
- Slaves were moved from safe houses or stations by conductors.
- They would travel by foot or by covered wagon.
- Each move would be about 20 miles.
- Conductors were ex-slaves or people who wanted to abolish slavery.
- A journey could take up to three months.
- To protect the Railroad, the conductors usually knew a small part rather than the whole route.
- Runaways or fugitives were often captured and taken back in return for a reward.
- Messages between conductors were written in code for secrecy.
- Religious groups such as the Quakers were very important in the running of the Railroad.
- Levi Coffin was a Quaker who helped 3000 slaves to escape.
- As well as food, money was collected and given to runaway slaves for clothes.
- Harriet Tubman was an ex-slave who helped 300 slaves to escape.
- Some operators were killed and others imprisoned for their work on the Railroad.

Underground Railroad decision cards

Decision 1 Should you learn to read and write before you escape? **Advantage** It will help you to read road signs should you escape. **Disadvantage** It will take time and might lead to punishment from the plantation owner.	**Decision 2** Some slaves from the plantation talk about the Underground Railroad. Will you use it to escape? **Advantage** You will be getting away from the misery of slavery. **Disadvantage** It will be difficult and dangerous. If caught, you will be severely punished by being whipped or branded.
Decision 3 Will you take your family with you? **Advantage** You will have care and support along the way. **Disadvantage** It will be easier to look after yourself.	**Decision 4** Should you save up food to take with you? **Advantage** Food might be difficult to get along the way. **Disadvantage** It will be more to carry and may slow you down.

Equal Before the Law

Strange Fruit

Decision 5 Should you leave in summer or winter? **Advantages** Summer is warmer. Winter allows you to cross ice-covered lakes. **Disadvantages** Summer days are longer and there are more people about. Winter is cold and there is less food in the woods and fields.	**Decision 6** You have left the plantation and you are following the riverbank north. Should you travel at night? **Advantage** You will be able to follow the North Star to help you get to the North. **Disadvantage** It will be difficult to find the signs written on trees to help runaway slaves.
Decision 7 Should you steal food from people's houses? **Advantage** It will give you strength to travel. **Disadvantage** It is a crime and you risk being caught.	**Decision 8** Underground Railroad 'stations' are marked by lanterns burning at night. Should you use them? **Advantage** The people will feed you and help you to the next station. **Disadvantage** The stations may be watched by slave catchers.

Equal Before the Law

Strange Fruit

Decision 9 Should you stay in churches? **Advantage** Many religious groups are against slavery and help runaways. **Disadvantage** Churches are the centre of every community and someone might report you.	**Decision 10** There are 'conductors' to help you to get from station to station. Should you use them? **Advantage** They know the area and those who can help you. **Disadvantage** You have to trust people you do not know.
Decision 11 You have reached a northern state where there is no slavery. Should you stay? **Advantage** People who want to abolish slavery will look after you. **Disadvantage** There are people who kidnap slaves and rewards are offered to those who give information about runaway slaves.	**Decision 12** Should you travel to Canada? **Advantage** You cannot be captured and returned to the United States so you will be free. **Disadvantage** You have to cross the wide waters of Lake Erie.

Underground Railroad decision record sheet

Decision	What did you decide?	Reasons
1		
2		
3		
4		
5		
6		
7		
8		
9		
10		
11		
12		

What was the Underground Railroad?

Use your record sheets and notes from discussions to complete the writing frame. Then use the frame to construct an extended written response to the question above.

Introduction
The Underground Railroad was...

'Stations' and 'conductors' were...

The journey was very difficult because...

Slaves used the Railroad because...

The Railroad was very successful because...

Overall, I would say that...

Equal Before the Law
Strange Fruit

Aims and objectives

These activities look at the ways in which US law was used to control and limit the everyday life of black people and keep them in an inferior position. Students will be able to consider the impact of the laws on people's attitudes and how difficult it was to challenge them.

Background

Following the end of the Civil War and the liberation of slaves, 35 out of the 50 states in the USA passed laws that segregated black and white people. They were called 'Jim Crow Laws'. 'Jim Crow' was a term of racial abuse for black people used by white people. There were hundreds of laws that affected all aspects of life for black people. Anyone who broke the laws risked punishment, either by the police or by mobs of white people. These laws lasted until the 1960s in many states.

Activity 1: *What were Jim Crow Laws?*

- Initial preparation: photocopy the 'Jim Crow cards' (pages 60–61) and the 'Jim Crow worksheet' (page 62) for students to use in pairs or small groups.
- Introduce the task and explain the objectives.
- Students should then group similar cards together and record their findings on the worksheet.
- Discuss with the class what these laws tell us about the attitudes of white people and how they would affect the behaviour of black people.

Activity 2: *Living with Jim Crow*

- Initial preparation: photocopy the handout entitled 'Living with Jim Crow' (page 63) and 'Living with Jim Crow worksheet' (page 64) for each student.
- Introduce the task and explain the objectives.
- Students, working in pairs or groups, should put the cards in the appropriate place on the worksheet and jot down key points.
- Following this, they should discuss the reasons behind the different approaches and then jot down their reasons on the worksheet.

Equal Before the Law
Strange Fruit

Activity 3: *Using sources for Jim Crow*

- Initial preparation: photocopy and give out the sheets entitled 'Sources about Jim Crow' (pages 65–66) and 'Jim Crow: analysing sources' (page 67) to the students.
- Emphasise the difference between using sources for information and using sources as evidence, for example, to prove something or to show attitudes.
- Students should then use the sources to complete the worksheet.

Activity 4: *Consolidation into a written response*

- Initial preparation: photocopy the writing frame entitled 'How did black people live with Jim Crow Laws?' (page 68) for all students.
- Students should complete the writing frame and use it to construct an extended written response.

General notes

Students can compare and contrast the laws in different states and at different times and can also investigate, in greater depth, the legal and other challenges made to these laws.

Jim Crow cards

Marriages between white and black people were declared illegal and punished with up to ten years in prison.	Black children could not attend 'white' schools.	Railway and bus companies had separate seating and waiting areas for black people. Passengers and companies could be fined if they disobeyed the laws.
All horseracing tracks were segregated.	Black voters had to pay a poll tax.	Sexual relations between white and black people were punished with a fine or imprisonment.
Teaching mixed classes was punished by a fine or imprisonment.	Companies that did not provide 'For White' and 'For Colored' signs were fined.	White teachers were fined or imprisoned for teaching in black schools.
Black people could not serve on juries.	Black and white people could not play any game or sport together.	Parks, swimming pools and beaches were segregated.

Equal Before the Law

Strange Fruit

Black athletic and sporting teams could not compete against white teams.	Newspapers that encouraged inter-racial marriages could be fined.	Hospitals were segregated.
Hotels and restaurants could refuse to serve black customers.	Prison governors were fined if they mixed black and white prisoners in any way.	Black people could not stay in or rent accommodation in houses or hotels where white people lived.
White nurses could not attend black patients in hospitals.	Toilet facilities were segregated in public buildings.	Voters had to pass literacy tests.
Employers had to provide separate eating and toilet facilities for their workers.	Blood used in transfusions had to be labelled ‘white’ or ‘coloured’.	Any black soldiers had to be commanded by a white officer and kept separate from white soldiers.

Jim Crow worksheet

Education	Work
Voting	Social Life
Leisure	Other

Living with Jim Crow

Many black people would avoid any interaction with white people.	Black people developed their own music, including ragtime, jazz and blues.	Black teachers set up black schools.
Booker T. Washington set up the Tuskegee Institute to train black teachers and lawyers as well as educating students in business and agriculture.	4000 black people were lynched by white mobs.	Black people set up their own social clubs and self-help societies.
Organisations were set up to help black people in towns and the countryside.	Church leaders and civil rights activists spoke out against Jim Crow Laws.	W.E.B. Du Bois set up the National Association for the Advancement of Colored People (NAACP) to change the law and help to take cases to court.
Kansas Exodus – many black people left to live in new and undeveloped states, like Kansas.	In 1954, the NAACP persuaded the Supreme Court to declare segregated schools unconstitutional in the case of Brown v Topeka Board of Education	Millions of black people left the South to go to cities in the North.
Black people set up their own businesses.	A proposed march on Washington led to the ending of segregation in the arms industry during World War II.	The Civil Rights Movement of the 1950s and 1960s successfully challenged Jim Crow Laws.
Black people defended themselves in race riots.	Black people set up their own sporting leagues.	Newspapers campaigned against lynching and Jim Crow Laws.

Living with Jim Crow worksheet

Escaping	Challenging
Resistance	Developing

Sources about Jim Crow

A

7 August 1930: a crowd gathering to witness the killing of Tom Shipp and Abe Smith, two victims of lynch law in Indiana.

B Strange Fruit

Southern trees bear strange fruit,
Blood on the leaves and blood at the root,
Black bodies swinging in the southern breeze,
Strange fruit hanging from the poplar trees.

Pastoral scene of the gallant south,
The bulging eyes and the twisted mouth,
Scent of magnolias, sweet and fresh,
Then the sudden smell of burning flesh.

Here is the fruit for the crows to pluck,
For the rain to gather, for the wind to suck,
For the sun to rot, for the trees to drop,
Here is a strange and bitter crop.

Equal Before the Law

Strange Fruit

C Clifford Boxley remembers growing up in the South

'We had to walk to school, so you're talking about being able to survive in this Jim Crow jungle as a very young child. Skillful, skillful. If you had any money, you could catch the bus to a certain distance. You had to get in the back. You go in, and you put your little three cents or penny, whatever it is, and if the bus is full of whites, because up front whites are sitting on the bus. Your seats are all the way in the back. If it's full of whites all the way down the aisle, you put your penny or three cents in and get off the bus and go to the back door. You go to the back of the bus. If the seats are full of blacks and there are empty seats up there in the white section, you don't go, you just stand up and hold on and what have you. You don't challenge it. You know what type of communities to go right through. You know when you're interfacing with a white male what psychology to use – depending on the situation – whether to get the hell out of there or to stand and engage in a submissive form. You knew that the black girls going back and forth to school never should be going home alone. There always was a need for a boy to be with a girl. You knew that, as soon as a white man who might have his eyes on a young black girl came along in an automobile, you were to detain him in some kind of questioning way, while the girls hurried along. All of you stayed together and then, chances are, that you are not going to be bothered.'

Jim Crow: analysing sources

Source	What information can we get from the source?	Why is the source useful to us as evidence?
A		
B		
C		

How did black people live with Jim Crow Laws?

Use your record sheets and notes from discussions to complete the writing frame. Then use the frame to construct an extended written response to the question above.

Introduction
Jim Crow Laws were introduced to...

The laws forced black people...

This meant that black people had to...

The laws were resisted and challenged in many ways...

The laws encouraged white people to...

The laws lasted so long because...

Equal Before the Law

Strange Fruit

The Ku Klux Klan

Aims and objectives

These activities are designed to allow students to consider the history of the Ku Klux Klan and its impact on the black people of the USA. They also allow students to identify the factors that helped the KKK to operate outside the law. The tasks encourage students to organise information in response to a specific question.

Background

The defeat of the southern states in the American Civil War ended slavery in the USA. Soon after this, secret societies began to form. The largest and most important was the Ku Klux Klan. For over a hundred years, the Ku Klux Klan terrorised the black population in the South.

Activity 1: *What were Jim Crow Laws?*

- Initial preparation: photocopy 'A time line of the Ku Klux Klan' (page 71), 'The Ku Klux Klan: visual sources' (page 72) and 'The Ku Klux Klan: written sources' (pages 73–74).
- Students should be divided into small groups, with each group focusing on one or two pieces of evidence.
- Introduce the task and explain the objectives.
- Students should study the evidence and identify what can be learnt about the Ku Klux Klan from it.
- Groups should then feed back to the rest of the class so that all of the evidence has been considered.
- Distribute the record sheets entitled 'What can we learn about the Ku Klux Klan from written and visual sources?' (page 75) and 'What factors helped the Ku Klux Klan?' (page 76) to all students. Discuss what the headings mean and model the sort of points that could be included under them.
- Students should then record their findings.
- Discuss the findings with the class and allow them to modify their record sheets accordingly.

Activity 2: *How important was the Ku Klux Klan?*

- Initial preparation: photocopy the writing frame entitled 'How important was the Ku Klux Klan?' (page 77) for all students.
- Students should complete the writing frame and use it to construct an extended written response.

General notes

Students may come to different conclusions as to which factors helped the Ku Klux Klan the most and also as to how significant the Ku Klux Klan was at particular times. Students can be encouraged to investigate further by looking at opposition to the Ku Klux Klan and by looking at particular outrages in more detail, such as the bombing of the Baptist Church in Birmingham, Alabama in 1963.

A time line of the Ku Klux Klan

1865	Ku Klux Klan was founded by Confederate soldiers. Politicians who had helped black people were assassinated. Homes and churches of black people were attacked. Many black people were whipped and lynched (hanged). Schoolteachers who taught the freed slaves were also terrorised and new schools were burned down.
1871	Congress passed an Act that banned the Ku Klux Klan. Lynching continued, as did other forms of violence.
1915	The second Ku Klux Klan was founded, which was also anti-immigrant, anti-Catholic and anti-Semitic.
1920	There were four million Ku Klux Klan members across the country. The uniform of white cloaks and pointed hats, along with burning crosses, became their symbols. Black soldiers returning from World War I were attacked and killed. The Ku Klux Klan controlled the government of some states.
1930s	The number of members declined as the Ku Klux Klan was seen as similar to the Nazis.
1950s and **1960s**	Members of the Ku Klux Klan killed civil rights activists and bombed churches and schools. Black people were prevented from voting by the Ku Klux Klan.
1980s	Ku Klux Klan members were found guilty of killing activists and bombing churches 20 years earlier. The Ku Klux Klan was successfully sued for millions of dollars after a lynching in 1981.
2005	The Ku Klux Klan had 3000 members.

The Ku Klux Klan: visual sources

A

19 August 1925: members of the American white supremacist movement, the Ku Klux Klan, marching down Pennsylvania Avenue in Washington DC.

B

Un nègre pendu et flambe achève de se consumer
(Ce document nous a été aimablement communiqué par notre excellent confrère « Vu »)

A black person is hanged, then burned in front of a large crowd.

The Ku Klux Klan: written sources

A R. A. Patton, *Current History* (1929)
'A lad whipped with branches until his back was ribboned flesh: a Negress beaten and left helpless to contract pneumonia from exposure and dies; a white girl, divorcee beaten into unconsciousness in her home; a naturalized foreigner flogged until his back was pulp because he married an American woman; a Negro lashed until he sold his land to a white man for a fraction of its value.'

B Robert Coughlan *Konklave in Kokomo* (1949)
'Literally half the town belonged to the Klan when I was a boy. At its peak, which was from 1923 through 1925, the Nathan Hale Den had about five thousand members, out of an able-bodied adult population of ten thousand. With this strength the Klan was able to dominate local politics. It packed the police and fire departments with its own people, with the result that on parade nights the traffic patrolmen disappeared and traffic control was taken over by sheeted figures whose size and shape resembled those of the vanished patrolmen.'

C Robert F. Williams, *Liberation Magazine* (September, 1959)
'In 1957, the Klan moved into Monroe and Union County (N.C.). Their numbers steadily increased to the point wherein the local press reported 7500 at one rally. They became so brazen that mile-long motorcades started invading the Negro community.

These hooded thugs fired pistols from car windows. On one occasion they caught a Negro woman on the street and tried to force her to dance for them at gunpoint. Drivers of cars tried to run Negroes down. Lawlessness was rampant. Instead of cowing, we organized an armed guard. On one occasion, we had to exchange gunfire with the Klan.

Each time the Klan came on a raid they were led by police cars. We appealed to the President of the United States to have the Justice Department investigate the police. We appealed to Governor Luther Hodges. All our appeals to constituted law were in vain.'

Equal Before the Law

Strange Fruit

D Duncan Campbell, *The Guardian* (23rd May, 2002)

'A former Ku Klux Klansman was convicted yesterday of the murder of four black girls in the 1963 church bombing in Alabama that acted as a catalyst for the civil rights movement.

Bobby Frank Cherry, 71, was convicted of first-degree murder after the jury of nine whites and three blacks had deliberated for less than a day. He will spend the rest of his life in prison.

The court found that Cherry had been one of a group of Klansmen who plotted to bomb the Sixteenth Street Baptist Church in Birmingham, which was at the centre of local civil rights protests. Two other former Klansmen have been convicted and a fourth died before facing trial.

The bomb killed Denise McNair, 11, and Addie Mae Collins, Carole Robertson and Cynthia Wesley, all 14. Their deaths came days after local schools were desegregated.

During the week-long trial, relatives of the dead girls listened as some members of Cherry's own family gave evidence against him.

The former truck driver became a suspect immediately after the bombing but until 1995, when the case was reopened, it had seemed that he would escape trial. But members of Cherry's family, with whom he had fallen out, came forward to tell investigators that he had boasted of taking part in the bombing.

During the trial, his granddaughter, Teresa Stacy, told the court: "He said he helped blow up a bunch of niggers back in Birmingham." His ex-wife, Willadean Brogdon, told the court that he had confessed to her that he had lit the fuse to the dynamite that caused the explosion. During the early 60s in Birmingham, black people were attacked by whites with little danger of facing punishment, and Cherry was active in violent attacks against civil rights activists.

He had boasted of punching the civil rights leader Rev Fred Shuttlesworth with knuckle dusters, saying that he had "bopped ol' Shuttlesworth in the head". He also boasted of splitting open a black man's head with a pistol.

The case had been closed more than three decades ago after the FBI director at the time, J Edgar Hoover, had said it would be impossible to get a guilty verdict because of the existing climate of racism.'

What can we learn about the Ku Klux Klan from written and visual sources?

Membership	Methods
Attitudes	**Impact**

What factors helped the Ku Klux Klan?

Support	Methods
Attitudes	Impact

How important was the Ku Klux Klan?

Use your record sheets and notes from discussions to complete the writing frame. Then use the frame to construct an extended written response to the question above.

Introduction
The Ku Klux Klan was set up to...

The Klan's activities included...

The Klan was not stopped because...

Other reasons included...

Recently, the Klan has...

Triangles and Pyramids
Masters and Slaves

The slave trade

Aims and objectives

These activities are designed to allow students to understand how the triangular trade worked between Britain, Africa and the Americas. They will also explore how different people and places benefited, regardless of the human cost.

Background

As Britain grew into the first industrial nation, it developed an empire that stretched across the world. There was a complex inter-relationship between its industries, trade, transport and Empire. During the 18th century, when the slave trade accounted for the transport of six million Africans, Britain was responsible for almost 2.5 million of these. Other countries were also involved: Portugal was responsible for transporting over 4.5 million Africans (40 per cent of the total).

Activity 1: *What was the trade triangle?*

- Initial preparation: photocopy 'The triangular trade map' (page 80) for each student.
- Students should answer the questions to ensure they understand the workings of the trade triangle.

Activity 2: *Who supported the trade triangle?*

- Initial preparation: photocopy 'Supporters of the trade triangle (1)' and '(2)' (pages 81 and 82) for all students.
- Students should match the cards to the character and prioritise the reasons for each character.
- Lead a discussion on the similarities and differences between each character and also on how this would make the trade difficult to abolish.

Activity 3: *Consolidation into a written response*

- Initial preparation: photocopy the writing frame entitled 'What was the triangular trade?' (page 83) for all students.
- Students should complete the writing frame and use it to construct an extended written response.

General notes

Students could research further the impact and importance of the slave trade in towns in Britain and in particular areas of Africa. They could identify particular families that became very wealthy and consider how these people influenced Parliament to maintain the slave trade.

The triangular trade map

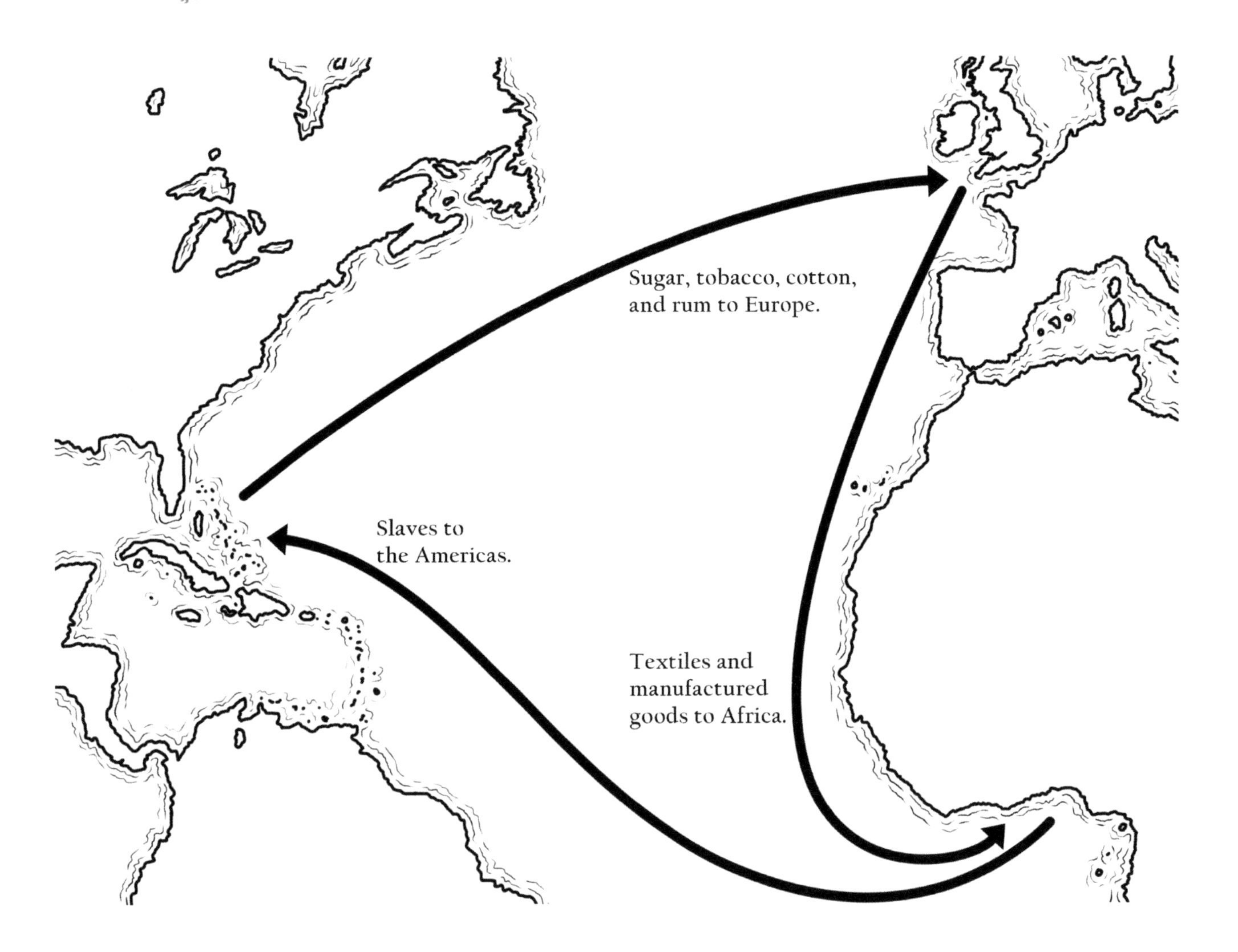

Tasks

Using the map, answer these questions:

- Why was it called the triangular trade?
- What would a ship carry on its voyages?
- Why would a ship be away from its home port for 10–12 months?
- Why were merchants able to make so much money from a single voyage?
- What would happen to slaves who died on-board ship?

Supporters of the trade triangle (1)

Towns like Bristol and Liverpool have become very wealthy.	Ship captains often fire cannons at us to try to keep the price of slaves down.	I invest money in the voyage and provide the ships.
We capture Africans from tribes and put them in forts by the coast. We then sell them to the ship captains.	The trade provides lots of work for dockers, ship builders, sail makers and warehousemen.	I buy the slaves at auctions at the ports.
I increase the price of slaves by playing the different European traders off against each other.	I pay an agent to manage the ship and do all the buying and selling.	I can speak different African and European languages.
Large plantations need a large workforce.	Africans are used to the heat and the work. More goods can be produced and sold.	I have become very wealthy from this trade.
The ship is never empty. There is always a different cargo.	I buy guns which are very useful against tribes.	People in Europe want more coffee, sugar and tobacco. Production needs to be increased.

Supporters of the trade triangle (2)

Merchant in Bristol

I support the trade triangle because...

I support the trade triangle because...

Planter in the West Indies

Slave trader in Africa

I support the trade triangle because...

What was the triangular trade?

Use your record sheets and notes from discussions to complete the writing frame. Then use the frame to construct an extended written response to the question above.

Introduction
The triangular trade was the name given to...

The main stages were...

The trade was supported by different people for different reasons...

The trade made many people very wealthy because...

As a result, opposition to the slave trade was made more difficult because...

Triangles and Pyramids
Masters and Slaves

Plantation life

Aims and objectives

These activities allow students to investigate what life was like for slaves on the plantations of the Americas. They should learn about different aspects of life through the writings of ex-slaves and illustrations from the time. This will allow them to consider the usefulness and value of different sources.

Background

Plantations in the USA, the West Indies and South America involved large-scale farming of single crops, including cotton, sugar, coffee and tobacco. They used large numbers of slaves brought from Africa and made vast profits for their owners. The abolition of the slave trade did not end plantation farming or slavery.

Ex-slaves wrote books about their life and illustrations of plantations appeared in newspapers in the USA and Great Britain.

Activity 1: *Constructing a pyramid of plantation society*

- Initial preparation: photocopy 'Constructing a pyramid of plantation society cards' (page 86) and the worksheet entitled 'Constructing a pyramid of plantation society diagram' (page 87) for students to work in pairs.
- Students should place and join cards to the diagram or jot down key points on their own copy.
- Students should feed back to the class.
- Initiate discussion as to how society operated and on different aspects of economic, social and political power.

Activity 2: *Using sources to discover what life on a plantation was like*

- Initial preparation: photocopy 'Plantation life: sources sheet' (pages 88–90) and 'Plantation life: sources record sheet' (page 91).
- Students should use the sources to jot down key points on the record sheet.
- Initiate discussion on the information taken from the sources and any deductions made.
- Continue with further discussion on the use and value of different types of sources, for example, written, pictorial, connections between the two, typicality of what is shown, small number of written sources, representativeness and value.
- Students should modify their record sheets in the light of the discussion.

Activity 3: *Consolidation into a written response*

- Initial preparation: photocopy the writing frame entitled 'What was life on a plantation like?' (page 92) for all students.
- Students should use the writing frame to note down key points from the activity and discussion and then use the writing frame to construct an extended piece of writing.

General notes

The activities focus on categorising information and assessing the usefulness of sources. Extension work could focus on researching further the individuals named in the source activities and finding out about the other aspects of plantation life that they illustrate.

onstructing a pyramid of plantation society cards

Mulattoes They had white fathers and slave mothers. Many continued to be slaves and were often sold. Some were given an education. They went on to work in offices or workshops. A few went on to write books about slavery and campaigned to abolish it (for example, Frederick Douglass, Booker T. Washington and Harriet Jacobs).	**Slaves** They were owned by the planter. They worked in the fields picking the crops. The hours were very long and the work was very hard. Their living conditions were terrible and they were often punished.	**The planters** They were white. They were very wealthy. They owned plantations that produced sugar, cotton, coffee or tobacco. They owned the slaves who worked on the plantations. They owned servants who worked in their houses.
Household slaves They were owned by the planter. They worked in 'the big house'. They would work in the kitchen or as servants. Some looked after children. They often had better food and living conditions than the field hands.	**Clerical workers** They were white. They worked in offices for planters and traders. They lived in their own houses.	**Overseers** They were white. They lived on the plantation. They were paid to supervise the field hands. They worked the slaves very hard. They handed out punishments, especially the whip, to get the slaves to work harder.
Shopkeepers They were white. They lived in the town. They owned shops that sold food, clothes, guns and other products.	**Merchants** They were white. They lived in the town. They made money from the trade in plantation crops and from the slaves themselves. They became rich, employed servants and owned slaves.	**Professionals** They were white. They lived in the town. They had servants and owned slaves. They worked for the government or were doctors or lawyers.

Constructing a pyramid of plantation society diagram

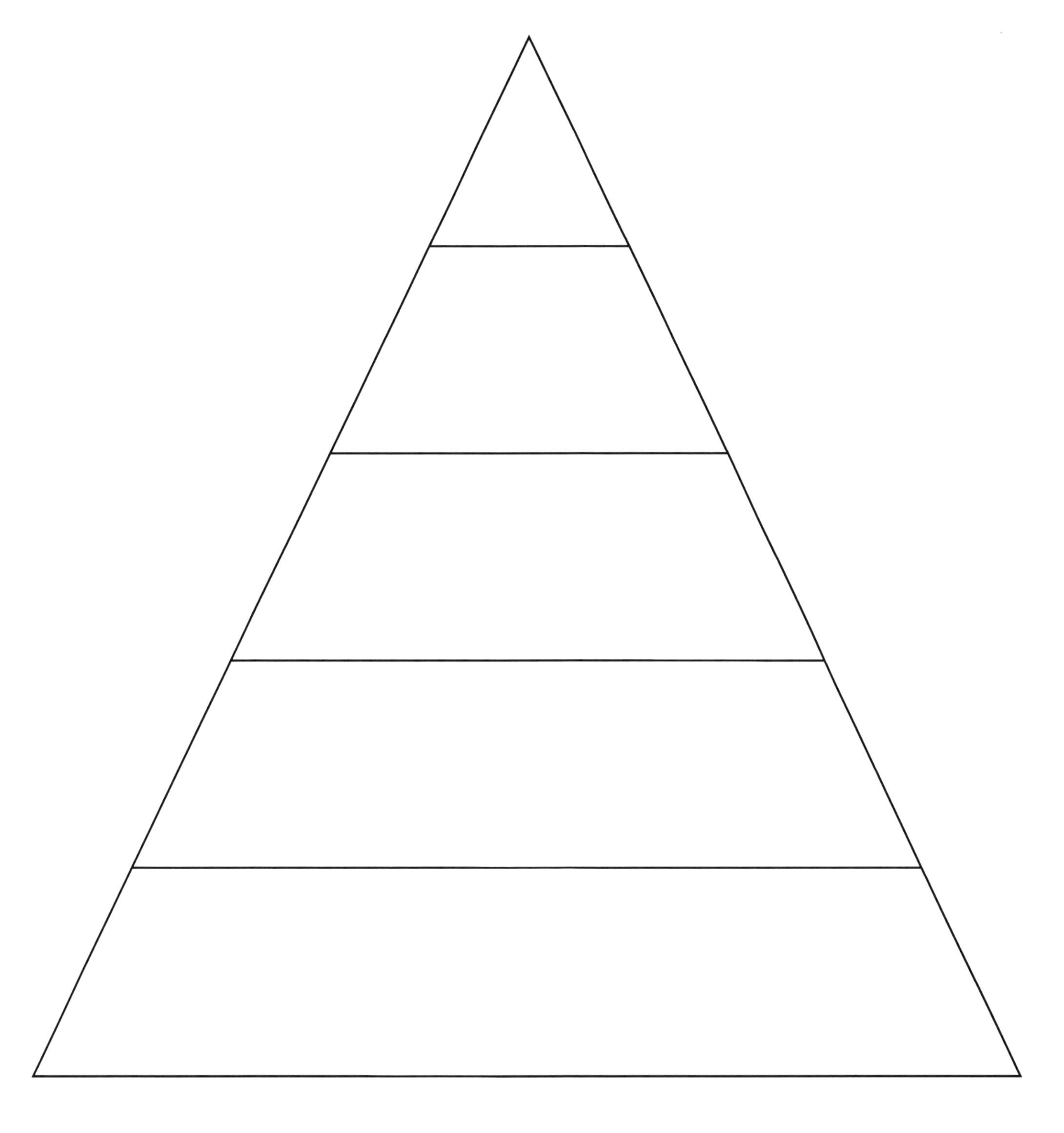

Plantation life: sources sheet

A Austin Steward, *Twenty-Two Years a Slave* (1857)

'It was the rule for the slaves to rise and be ready for their task by sun-rise, on the blowing of a horn or conch-shell. Hence, they were usually found in the field where they worked until nine o'clock. They were then allowed thirty minutes to eat their morning meal, which consisted of a little bread. At a given signal, all hands were compelled to return to their work. They toiled until noon, when they were permitted to take their breakfast, which corresponds to our dinner.

On our plantation, it was the usual practice to have one of the old slaves set apart to do the cooking. All the field hands were required to give into the hands of the cook a certain portion of their weekly allowance, either in dough or meal. The overseer was always on hand to attend to all delinquents, who never failed to feel the blows of his heavy whip.'

B Lewis Clarke, *Narrative of the Sufferings of Lewis Clark* (1845)

'There were four house-slaves in this family, including myself, and though we had not, in all respects, so hard work as the field hands, yet in many things our condition was much worse. We were constantly exposed to the whims and passions of every member of the family; from the least to the greatest their anger was wreaked upon us. Nor was our life an easy one, in the hours of our toil or in the amount of labor performed. We were always required to sit up until all the family had retired; then we must be up at early dawn in summer, and before day in winter. If we failed, through weariness or for any other reason, to appear at the first morning summons, we were sure to have our hearing quickened by a severe chastisement.'

C Josiah Henson, *The Life of Josiah Henson* (1849)

'We lodged in log huts, and on the bare ground. Wooden floors were an unknown luxury. In a single room were huddled, like cattle, ten or a dozen persons, men, women, and children. All ideas of refinement and decency were, of course, out of the question. We had neither bedsteads, nor furniture of any description. Our beds were collections of straw and old rags, thrown down in the corners and boxed in with boards; a single blanket the only covering. Our favourite way of sleeping, however, was on a plank, our heads raised on an old jacket and our feet toasting before the smouldering fire. The wind whistled and the rain and snow blew in through the cracks, and the damp earth soaked in the moisture till the floor was miry as a pig- sty. Such were our houses. In these wretched hovels were we penned at night, and fed by day; here were the children born and the sick- -neglected.'

D Henry Bibb, *The Life and Adventures of an American Slave* (1851)

'Slaves were not allowed books, pen, ink, nor paper, to improve their minds. There was a Miss Davies, a poor white girl, who offered to teach a Sabbath School for the slaves. Books were supplied and she started the school; but the news got to our owners that she was teaching us to read. This caused quite an excitement in the neighbourhood. Patrols were appointed to go and break it up at the next Sabbath.'

Triangles and Pyramids

Masters and Slaves

E

Triangles and Pyramids

Masters and Slaves

F

(Châtiment des quatre piquets, dans les colonies, par M. Marcel Verdier.)

G

SLAVE AUCTION AT RICHMOND, VIRGINIA.

Plantation life: sources record sheet

Work	
Housing	
Punishment	
Family life	

List the effects on slaves.

____

____

____

____

What was life on a plantation like?

Use your record sheets and notes from discussions to complete the writing frame. Then use the frame to construct an extended written response to the question above.

Introduction
It is important to study life on a plantation by...

Plantation society was...

Work on the plantations...

Living conditions were...

Slaves were treated...

We know a lot about plantations through using...

This evidence is useful and valuable because...

The Promised Land?
Free at Last

Empire

Aims and objectives

These activities are designed to allow students to investigate the size of the British Empire and the reasons why it grew in size. Students will be able to group reasons together and identify the relative importance of different types of reason.

Background

The British Empire was the biggest empire the world had ever seen. It included territories in every continent as well as thousands of islands around the globe. The Empire had a great impact on the Americas. Britain controlled Canada and the West Indies as well as parts of Central and South America. In North America, 13 colonies defeated Britain and set up the United States of America.

Activity 1: *How big was the British Empire?*

- Initial preparation: photocopy the maps on the sheet entitled 'Empire' (page 105) for students to work with in pairs or small groups.
- Introduce the task and explain the objectives.
- Students should compare the maps and identify the key features that they show.
- Discuss the findings with the class, moving towards some conclusions about the extent and importance of the Empire.

Activity 2: *Why did Britain have such a large Empire?*

- Initial preparation: photocopy the handout entitled 'Reasons for Empire' (page 106) and 'Reasons for Empire record sheet' (page 107) for each student.
- Introduce the task and explain the objectives.
- Students should read the reasons and consider how each one may have helped or encouraged Britain to have such a large empire.
- Discuss what the different terms on the record sheet mean and why there is a need to separate reasons into different types.
- Students should jot down on the record sheet the different reasons.
- Follow with a discussion on what connections there are between the different reasons and which type is most important.
- Students should modify their record sheets in the light of the discussion.

Activity 3: *Consolidation into a written response*

- Initial preparation: photocopy the writing frame entitled 'What was the British Empire?' (page 108) for all students.
- Students should complete the writing frame and use it to write an essay.

General notes

The activities focus on the extent of the British Empire with little room for each particular territory. Students could choose, or be allocated, a territory and feed back on it in the following lesson. Students should be encouraged to identify points about the economy, government, society and culture of the territory.

GOVERNMENT

The Promised Land?

Free at Last

Empire

Map 1: The British Empire

Key: ■ areas owned by Britian

Map 2: The world today

Reasons for Empire

Plantations could produce large amounts of coffee, tobacco, sugar, tea and cotton.	Islands and ports on the coast provided places for ships to stop.	Large numbers of slaves from Africa were transported to the Americas to work on plantations.
Explorers moved inland from the coast and gave information to the government.	Britain fought wars against Holland, France and Spain and took colonies from them.	The 13 colonies of North America defeated Britain and set up the USA.
Factories in Britain needed raw materials such as cotton and rubber.	There was a big demand for coffee, tea, sugar and tobacco in Britain.	Britain already had some colonies around the world.
Britain took over more colonies to defend its Empire more effectively.	Britain had the most powerful navy in the world.	Many people emigrated from Britain to work in the colonies.
Factories in Britain needed places to which they could export their products.	Britain wanted to spread the Christian religion.	Britain built faster and stronger ships than any other countries.
Britain sent convicted criminals to the colonies.	The British government encouraged private companies to take over and rule large colonies.	Protestant Britain wanted to be stronger than Catholic France and Spain.
Britain was the wealthiest country in the world.	Britain was the first industrial country in the world.	Britain wanted naval bases for its warships.

Reasons for Empire record sheet

INDUSTRY AND TECHNOLOGY	GOVERNMENT AND POLITICS
SOCIAL AND RELIGION	**WAR AND DEFENCE**

What was the British Empire?

Use your record sheets and notes from discussions to complete the writing frame. Then use the frame to construct an extended written response to the question above.

Introduction
The British Empire was the largest empire the world had ever seen. It included...

The main reason for the British Empire's size was...

The next most important reason was...

Other reasons included...

As a result, the British Empire was important because...

The Promised Land?
Free at Last

Aims and objectives

These activities allow students to consider what freedom means and what barriers exist to freedom. They then consider the role of government in enabling freedom to exist.

Background

In the 18th century, slavery and the slave trade flourished throughout the world. Britain became the dominant power in the slave trade as millions of Africans were transported to the Americas to work on plantations. In the 19th century, governments acted to end slavery due to public pressure, slave resistance and other economic and political factors. However, segregation, discrimination and prejudice continued into the 20th century.

Activity 1: *What is freedom?*

- Initial preparation: photocopy the sheets 'What prevents freedom? (1)', '(2)' and '(3)' (pages 111–113) for all students.
- Students should match the cards on 'What prevents freedom? (1)' to the barriers on 'What prevents freedom? (2)'.
- Students need to consider the meaning of freedom and to discuss how the different barriers prevent freedom.
- Finally, they can use 'What prevents freedom? (3)' to come up with a working definition of freedom and the types of law necessary to achieve different types of freedom.

Activity 2: *Emancipation time line*

- Initial preparation: photocopy the 'Emancipation time line' (page 114) and 'Emancipation time line cards' (page 115) for students to work with in pairs or small groups.
- Introduce the task and explain the objectives.
- Students should place the cards on the time line.
- Lead a discussion on the rate of change and the impact of government removing barriers to freedom.

Activity 3: *Consolidation into a written response*

- Initial preparation: photocopy the writing frame entitled 'When did black people become free?' (page 116) for all students.
- Students should complete the writing frame and use it to construct an extended written response.

General notes

Students may like to consider what barriers to freedom exist today and what governments can do to counteract these barriers. They may also wish to look beyond the Americas and consider how people in other continents are being prevented from realising freedom.

What prevents freedom? (1)

Being owned by someone else.

Being forced to travel against your will.

Not being able to go to the same school as everyone else.

Being punished without a fair trial.

Not being able to vote.

Not being able to go into any hotel or restaurant.

Being governed by another country.

Not being treated the same as everyone else.

Not standing the same chance of employment or promotion as everyone else.

Being sold to someone else.

Not being forced to work without being paid.

Being split up from your family.

Being paid less than others for the same job.

Having to use separate toilet and washing facilities.

Being unable to stand for election.

What prevents freedom? (2)

SLAVERY

DISCRIMINATION

PREJUDICE

SEGREGATION

What prevents freedom? (3)

My definition of freedom is...

To ensure freedom, governments have to...

Emancipation time line

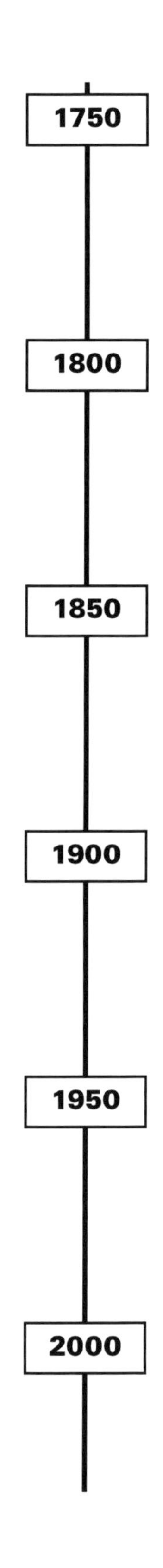

Emancipation time line cards

1770s Some northern states abolish slavery.	1848 France abolishes slavery.	1886 Slavery abolished in Cuba.
1960s Islands of the West Indies achieve independence.	1858 Portugal abolishes slavery in its colonies.	1948 Segregation ends in the US armed forces.
1776 USA declares independence from the British Empire.	1888 Slavery abolished in Brazil.	1965 USA passes law ending obstacles to voting and holding office.
1833 Britain abolishes slavery in its colonies.	1865 USA abolishes slavery.	1807 Britain abolishes the slave trade.
1896 US Supreme Court allows segregation.	1964 USA passes a law ending discrimination in public places.	1861 Dutch abolish slavery in Caribbean.
1954 US Supreme Court ends segregated schools.	1815 Britain forces Holland, France, Spain and Portugal to end the slave trade.	1902 Cuba becomes independent from Spain.
1840s + Ex-slaves continue to work on plantations in the Caribbean.	1890s + Lynching reaches a peak in USA. Government takes no action.	1870s + Ex-slaves continue to work on plantations in the USA.

When did black people become free?

Use your record sheets and notes from discussions to complete the writing frame. Then use the frame to construct an extended written response to the question above.

Introduction
Freedom means...

To make people free, governments had to...

Slavery and the slave trade were abolished by different countries at different times...

Segregation continued in the USA until...

Governments acted to stop discrimination in...

Overall, I would say that...

The Promised Land?
Free at Last

Aims and objectives

These activities are designed to allow students to consider the reasons for and the consequences of independence for the Caribbean islands and to select relevant information and organise it in response to a specific question.

Background

The end of World War II led to the end of the Empire and the growth of the Commonwealth. The Caribbean islands achieved independence at different times and in different ways. As well as having to deal with problems inherited from the days of Empire, they also had to decide whether to face the future as independent states or as a collective group in order to deal with the issues of development and security.

Activity 1: *Interpretations of independence*

- Initial preparation: photocopy 'Interpretations of independence' (pages 119–120) and 'Independence record sheet' (page 121) for students to work with in small groups.
- Introduce the task and explain the objectives.
- Students should read the interpretations and identify any similarities and differences.
- They should jot down key points on the record sheet.
- Students should note which points are from **A** and/or **B**.
- Discuss the findings with the class, considering the importance and priority of points and the reasons for differences.

Activity 2: *Consolidation into a written response*

- Initial preparation: photocopy the writing frame entitled 'When did the West Indies achieve independence?' (page 122) for all students.
- Students should complete the writing frame and use it to construct an extended written response.

The Promised Land?
Free at Last

General notes

Students may come to different conclusions as to the most significant points and their overall evaluation. This is to be encouraged as long as the points are effectively supported. They should come to a balanced answer and be able to select criteria for their judgements. Extension activities could include research into individual islands, which could lead to a discussion on how similar/different their experiences were.

Interpretations of independence

A A historian explaining the reasons for the end of the British Empire.

'The Second World War was the major turning point for the British Empire. The war cost Britain a lot of money and the government wanted to spend money on improving the lives of the people in Britain through the National Health Service as well as replacing housing destroyed by bombing.

The colonies were spread all over the world and had become too expensive to maintain. They had been vital in winning the war by providing human and material resources. This demonstrated the loyalty of people in the colonies towards the 'mother country' but it also increased demands for independence, particularly in India.

Britain was no longer as powerful after World War II and was faced with armed resistance in some colonies and passive resistance in others. Britain's main trade was also increasingly with Europe and the USA. There was also a domino effect with the success of one country's move to independence encouraging others.

By the 1960s, much of Britain's Empire in Africa and Asia had disappeared and been replaced by the Commonwealth. Given the size of the Empire, there was remarkably little bloodshed.'

The Promised Land?

Free at Last

B A historian explains the causes and consequences of independence in the Caribbean.

'There was a growing movement for independence from the 1930s. New political parties and trade unions saw independence as a way of solving the problems of unemployment, low pay, bad housing and a poor education system. Although some people had become independent farmers, many were still dependent on working on large farms that produced one crop such as sugar. When demand fell, as in the Depression of the 1930s, there were huge problems of unemployment and poverty.

Many people from the Caribbean had fought for Britain in World War II and many of Britain's colonies in Africa and Asia had achieved independence by the 1960s. This fed feelings of nationalism and discontent with the system of government.

An attempt to join the islands together in the Federation of the West Indies in 1958 lasted only four years. Then the larger islands of Jamaica, Trinidad and Barbados became independent in the 1960s. The other islands became independent in the 1970s and 1980s. There was investment from the USA and the development of industry and tourism. There were still problems of poverty and unemployment however, along with the issue of whether the different islands should try to develop independently or together.'

Independence record sheet

War

Economy

When did the West Indies achieve independence?

Use your record sheets and notes from discussions to complete the writing frame. Then use the frame to construct an extended written response to the question above.

Introduction
The West Indies are made up of many different islands...

They achieved independence over a long period of time...

The main reason for this was...

Another importance reason was...

Other reasons include...

The consequences of independence have been...